A MATTER OF TRUST AND HONOR

"Tex," LBJ said. "What you know about certain events, son, should never be told to anyone. And I mean anyone. What you know about that young communist SOB should never be mentioned. You've got a good future if you can do what I'm telling you. My people tell me you're a bounty hunter. I believe we can find plenty of work for a fellow in that business. And you're going to learn a whole lot more about it in the years to come. Son, what you're doing for your country is a service not many people get the opportunity to perform. And you're going to do it right.

"Remember one thing," he said, donning his hat. "What you know must stay between you and me. It's a matter of trust and honor."

"I'll remember, sir."

He slid into his white Continental and drove away. Then the realization slammed into me like a Mack truck. Was my silence going to help someone get away with murder, while the blame was piled on a dead man? I had agreed to live a lie. I wondered how long it would take for the guilty feeling to go away.

Or if it ever would.

BROKEN SILENCE

Ray "Tex" Brown
and
Don Lasseter

Pinnacle Books
Kensington Publishing Corp.

PINNACLE BOOKS are published by

Kensington Publishing Corp.
850 Third Avenue
New York, NY 10022

First Printing: October, 1996
10 9 8 7 6 5 4 3 2 1

Printed in the United States of America

Prologue

My name is Ray "Tex" Brown, cowboy, bounty hunter, and weary keeper of a tormenting secret for thirty-three years. I'd give anything if the story I have to tell, about my involvement in the murder of President John Fitzgerald Kennedy, had never happened. Regretfully, it did, and every detail of it is etched into my memory with torturing clarity.

In the late summer of 1963, a chance encounter pulled me into a series of events that sent my life tumbling into a living hell and probably cost the lives of several people I loved. A young president died in a sudden, gory halo of blood, leading to the shootings of a police officer, a suspected assassin, and eventually, a parade of victims whose lives ended in savage violence and mystery.

Few events in history have generated so much controversy as those tragic murders in Dallas, Texas, beginning on November 22, 1963. More than 2,000 books have been written analyzing them from all conceivable points of view. Television documentaries have dredged out every foot of film remotely related to the people involved, and a major motion picture poured new fuel on the polemic fires. In the year following the assassination, the Warren Commission, after an intensive investigation, concluded that one man, acting alone, fired the deadly shots from the sixth floor of the Texas Book Depository Building. Immediately, investigative journalists began punching holes in the commission's conclusions. Since then, a torrent of dispute has cascaded through the years charging conspiracy, fraud, treason, cover-up, and incompetence.

The American public has begged for and demanded the truth, yet the keepers of government secrets still maintain the veils of secrecy. If the truth is to be known, then ordinary people who have been afraid to reveal their personal knowledge must step forward.

That is what I am now ready to do.

The personal experiences I'm revealing in this book have never before been told; not to the Warren Commission, not to Oliver Stone, not to the press, not to anyone. With controversy still raging and shrouds of mystery still in place, I hope that what I tell you in the following chapters will shed a little light into the dark, dusty corners.

Perhaps I should have told this story three decades ago. There are a number of reasons I didn't. Fear. Honor. A misguided sense of loyalty. I promised a man I respected and trusted with my own life that I wouldn't divulge what I knew. And I wanted to protect innocent loved ones whose lives were threatened.

With the passage of time and the deaths of so many people, I can no longer keep silent.

Lee Harvey Oswald, according to what I saw, could not have fired the shots that killed President Kennedy! I knew Oswald. I met him through Jack Ruby!

I was a young Fort Worth cowboy when these events began to unfold. I worked for a bounty hunter called Big John Marshall who earned my undying respect and affection. He taught me about guns and about life. His untimely death still haunts me. Some of my other exploits following those tragic days have been chronicled elsewhere. But in those accounts, some mysterious gaps in time and events exist. What I reveal here should clarify why that was necessary. I'm going to tell you a little bit about some of my personal life, loves, and adventures with Big John, with the hope that it will help you understand the forces that kept my secret sealed.

The bizarre murder of Lee Harvey Oswald by Jack Ruby, shown live on television two days after the assassination, stunned a grieving nation. What you are about to read may help you understand why Ruby charged into that police headquarters basement and shot Oswald to death, preventing him forever from revealing the truth. You'll be able to see the link to a powerful underworld kingpin from Louisiana who made a trip to the Dallas area just prior to Kennedy's journey.

Perhaps the most astonishing experience I will share with you relates to the man who replaced Kennedy at the helm of the most powerful nation in the world. Why did President Lyndon Baines Johnson summon a young cowboy to his ranch in Texas and swear him to absolute secrecy?

I've paid for my long silence for over thirty years. I walk with a painful limp, still feel the effects of multiple broken bones, and have struggled with internal conflict for what seems like an eternity. Now it's time that the people of Texas, and the whole country, know the truth.

I was there.

Ray "Tex" Brown

One

December, 1963

Four days after I'd watched from a distance as Lee Harvey Oswald was laid in his grave, I sat at a well-worn table in my usual haunt, the Rodeo Cafe. From the jukebox, a Patsy Cline song moaned of lost love, making me wish that my churning stomach and jumbled thoughts were tied to something as trivial as a broken romance.

"Hey, Tommy, when are you gonna' hire some pretty girls to wait on your customers? Maybe it'd improve business around here," I teased the cafe owner and chief cook, trying to hide my misery.

"Aw, most of you guys are too tight to tip 'em right anyway," he shot back, with a big grin that was nearly hidden by his full beard. He shoved a fat hamburger at me, refilled my iced tea glass, and wiped his hands on the stained white apron covering his skinny midsection.

I lifted the glass to wash down the first bite and caught sight of two men striding through the entry door. One wore a blue pinstriped suit, the other a solid dark suit along with black-rimmed sunglasses. Each of them sported a button-down collar, narrow tie, well-shined wingtip shoes, and a short haircut. In an eatery full of faded blue jeans, pearl-button shirts, and dusty cowboy boots, they stood out like two thoroughbred horses in a herd of mules. I felt my gut tighten when they headed directly to my table.

"Mind if we join you?" Pinstripe tonelessly asked, while pulling out a chair and plopping down, as did his buddy.

"What good would it do me to mind? Looks to me like you're already sittin'," I replied, deliberately rude.

"We have a message for you," Sunglasses said, with no trace of a Texas drawl. "Tomorrow morning, at eleven-thirty, be at the pay phone in front of the Texaco station up the block. Park your pickup next to the restrooms at the station, and walk to the phone booth with both of your hands out at your sides so it will be obvious that you're not carrying anything with you."

Their arrogant attitudes immediately rubbed me raw. "I'm not in the habit of takin' orders from strangers," I growled. "And I don't know you two from Adam's cat."

"Someone wants to talk to you," said Pinstripe, "and it will be worth your while to be in front of that Texaco station when the phone rings. Remember—Twenty-eighth and Main, at eleven-thirty." They rose together, grimly nodded, turned, and strolled out the door. The whole episode didn't last five minutes. I stared after them and watched through the plate glass window as they climbed into an unmarked white car, the kind plainclothes cops drive, and sped away. When I turned around, I saw Tommy's puzzled stare.

"What was that about?" he asked, the grin long gone.

"I think they mistook me for somebody else," I lied, probably not very convincingly. "I never saw them before in my life." That part was the truth. I knew a lot of people around Fort Worth, but not these two. They sure didn't look or sound much like locals.

* * *

Given the events of the last few days, my already uneasy feelings grew even worse. Who on earth would go to all this trouble just to have a phone conversation with me? And why all the drama? It reminded me of something that might happen in a spy movie. I had no intention of going to that station, but I couldn't keep my mind off the strange request, if you could call it that. I was young and stupid, and my curiosity kept nagging at me. I guess there's a sense of adventure in most people, a drive to do things logic tells you not to. A young cowboy just a few weeks from his nineteenth birthday might be especially vulnerable to that urge.

The next morning, after I'd fed and watered my horses, I hopped into my pickup and headed toward Twenty-eighth and Main.

Feeling a little apprehensive, I drove past the Texaco station once, and then again. I didn't know exactly what I'd expected, but the place didn't look any different, just the same ordinary gas pumps, greasy maintenance bay, and a guard rail made of four-inch white metal pipes stuck in the pavement to keep cars from banging the pumps. No suspicious characters hung around. The phone booth stood empty, and the unmarked white sedan was nowhere in sight.

Finally, I decided to see what was going on. I parked on the side of the station described by Sunglasses, and took one last look around before getting out of my truck. As instructed, I walked toward the phone booth with my hands out to my sides, feeling ridiculous. At exactly eleven-thirty, the pay phone rang, and I nearly jumped out of my boots. I let the bell jangle three times, then picked up the handset.

"Hello?"

"Who am I speaking to?" asked a deep male voice in a disturbingly familiar Texas drawl.

"Who were you expecting?"

"This is no time to play games," replied the voice. "Tell me your name."

"Ray Tex Brown," I said, trying to sound confident and tough.

"Do you know who this is?" asked the voice.

It hit me like a mule kick in the stomach. All my instincts rejected the notion, but I knew who it was——Lyndon Baines Johnson, the new president of the United States!

"Yessir, I do."

"Some of your friends have had a little trouble lately, haven't they?"

"If you mean who I think you mean, they're not my friends. I just did some business with them."

"Son, I'm calling to ask you to do something for the nation. There are some things you know about that you should keep to yourself, and it would be a good idea for you to take a little vacation from that part of the state—to make yourself scarce. Move down to South Texas—you'll find plenty of work down there. Will you do it?"

I don't know if I stammered. I sure tried not to, and finally answered, "Since you're the President, sir, I don't guess I have much choice."

"You'll always have a job, and you'll always have a way to make a living. And remember, you'll be doing a service to your country."

With that he hung up. No good-bye, no kiss my butt, or anything. Just a click in my ear, and the lonesome silence of a dead line.

I was stunned. The President of the United States, calling me? Asking me to lose myself in South Texas? That was his territory—was he planning to have me watched? I walked back to my pickup in a daze.

As soon as I opened the door and started to climb in, I saw it. A thick white envelope lay on the leather seat.

Perspiring despite the December cool, I picked it up and peeled it open with shaking hands. My eyes must have looked like headlights on high beam when the money came into view. A rubber band held together a half-inch stack of greenbacks. I riffled through them while my heart pounded. Every one of them had a picture of Benjamin Franklin. It took a couple of minutes to count all fifty. Five thousand dollars! A small fortune in those days. At a hundred and fifty bucks a week, I was already making what was then good money, in the days when you could buy hamburger for thirty-five cents a pound, and a good pair of boots cost twenty-five dollars.

What was I going to do with five thousand dollars? Who had left it there? Whoever they were, they were pretty slippery—I hadn't seen a soul around my truck.

I stuffed the bills back into the envelope and crammed it in the glove box. I didn't even want to think about what I'd gotten myself into now, or about how it had all started just a few months earlier. It seemed like years.

Two

I'm a loyal Texan—always have been, always will be. I love the wide-open plains, the countryside, the rivers, the cities, and the people. True Texans stick together, and I wouldn't do anything to betray that fellowship. My biggest worry is that my fellow Texans will think that what I did in 1963, and subsequently, was disloyal to them and to the state. It shattered and embarrassed nearly all of us, knowing that President Kennedy was murdered in "Big D," our beautiful Dallas. And my role in that tragedy, plus my silence for so long, has torn my guts out.

Each person's life is a series of crossroads where small decisions make for big changes. And when you look back, the hand of fate that guides you along that trail sure seems strange, sometimes.

One hour before midnight, on Christmas Eve in 1944, I was born in Fort Worth, Texas. To tell the truth, I don't remember much about my parents. I have no doubt they were decent people, but I've heard they could never settle down and apparently had some troubles they just couldn't sort out. None of the sordid details have ever been explained to me, but I know they split up when I was just two years old and left me to be raised by my mother's sister and her husband.

My aunt and uncle were different from Mom and Dad, solid citizens and fairly prosperous. They provided a home for me in a nice middle-class neighborhood with safe surroundings and good schools. Unfortunately, most of what I heard in school bored me silly. Grammar and math problems excited me about as much as watching the grass grow. One of the few things I paid attention to was local history—not stuff about Napoleon, or Egypt, or ancient Greece, but about Fort Worth and the Texas Rangers. Now, *that* was interesting.

Fort Worth, I found out, really was a fort in the mid-1800s, a military outpost housing soldiers whose job it was to protect ranchers from Indians. When the War between the States was over, the big cattle herds of longhorns being driven up north stopped for a rest in Fort Worth. The trailhands could let off a little steam, get falling-down drunk, dally with some painted ladies, gamble away everything they had, then go back to the drive, broke and hungover. When the railroad came along, the place boomed. But Fort Worth folks hadn't seen anything until those funny lookin' little cars started replacing horses and somebody discovered oil underneath the surrounding prairie. Boomtown. Extravagant riches. Money. Adventure. Why hadn't I been born in those days?

Maybe my problem was that my foster parents' house was an easy bus ride to and from Northside, the section of town close to the Fort Worth stockyards and Rodeo Park. The old Western-style boardfront buildings made me think I was strutting down a dusty main street at high noon, ready to use my lightning draw to drop a villain in his tracks. My domain was the old West, where cowboys hung out and adventure waited.

As soon as I learned how to play hookie, I'd grab a bus, or hitchhike over to Twenty-fifth Street, then spend all my time hanging out at the livestock exchange, following cowboys around. I watched them handle horses, admired the way they spoke and dressed, and tried to imitate them. Somehow, I felt comfortable with their easygoing ways, good humor, and toughness when it counted. I found it easy to strike up conversations with them and loved exchanging tall tales. I insisted on being called "Tex," and the cowboys humored me.

On weekends, my foster parents hoped I'd follow the routine of other neighborhood kids. Nothing would have pleased them more than to see me laboring over school homework, or mowing the lawn and raking leaves, or attending Sunday school. But not little Ray "Tex" Brown. No, sir. When I was eleven or twelve, I'd spend those days in Cowtown, or skipping out and heading to the country, where I could practice shooting at prairie dogs with my single-shot .22-caliber rifle. One Saturday, I ran into a group of oil prospecting wildcatters, followed them thirty miles out of town, and figured I might as well stay with them. After three days of feeling like a real maverick on his own, someone found me sleeping inside a discarded wooden crate and called the sheriff. There was hell to pay back at home that night.

I can't say my aunt and uncle didn't try. They worked really hard at it, but I just wasn't wired to be the academic they'd hoped for. I know they wanted a foster son who would grow up to be doctor, lawyer, or suit-wearing professional, but I just couldn't squeeze myself into that mold. Disciplinary measures didn't change me, nor did promised rewards. I felt bad for them, but I just couldn't conform to the future they had in mind for me.

Finally, one warm humid night in July 1958, before the sun came up, I pulled an old burlap sack from under my bed where I'd hidden it and stuffed it with a clean shirt, some Levis, socks, and a few other things. I poked my rifle into the bag, slipped out into the predawn darkness, and said good-bye to my childhood. I had no idea where I was going or how I was going to make a living.

As I understand it, my aunt and uncle finally realized their dreams for me were hopeless, so they accepted the inevitable.

On the afternoon of my second day of independence, feeling lonesome and isolated from the world, and hungry, I trudged along a dusty prairie road that seemed like a hundred miles from Fort Worth, even though I'm sure it was far closer. As I approached a couple of old-timers lounging around a beat-up rusting truck, I saw them squinting in my direction. I'd slung the burlap sack over my back and I carried the rifle in my right hand.

"Know how to use that rifle, son?" one of them called to me, spitting a wad of brown juice into the dust.

Glad for some human contact, I shot back, "Fair to middlin'."

They glanced at each other and grinned, deepening the creases in their brown, wrinkled leather faces. The speaker raised a skinny arm, pointed past some rocks and brush, and cackled, "I'll give you a dollar if you can bring down that coyote settin' out there."

I followed the direction of his gaunt finger and saw the animal squatting on its haunches, eyeing us with a suspicious look. Nodding toward the men, I eased my sack onto the ground, raised my rifle, and took aim. One of the men clapped his hands and yelled, "That shot's too easy, boy. Let's see if you can get him on the run." The coyote sprang to the alert and began trotting across the horizon.

For some miraculous reason, the animal halted again to take a last look at us. I squeezed off a shot that would have missed by a mile if the critter had kept moving. But he dropped with a lifeless thud.

"Dad blame," the old-timer shouted. "That was some fine shootin'." We trotted together to the dead coyote, where the cowboy produced a big knife and sliced off the tail. "Oh, yeah," he remembered, and fished a folded dollar bill from his watch pocket.

"How'd you like to go to work, bounty huntin' coyotes?" the old man asked me. He explained that members of the stockman's association were troubled by a spate of coyote attacks on lambs and calves, and were offering five dollars for each tail brought in. This sounded like the real bigtime to me, getting paid for hunting. My beaming face announced my agreement before I could stammer out the words.

They hauled me in the old truck to a ranch where they worked and introduced me to a well-dressed man. I didn't know if he was the owner or a foreman, but he said I could bunk in a shed and eat beef and beans with the hired hands for a couple of dollars a day, to be paid out of my bounty profits. He even agreed to lend me a horse to search for my prey.

I'll always remember that old horse. They called him "Lefty," for a very sound reason. He was blind in his right eye, so he refused ever to make a right turn. No matter how hard I tugged on the reins, Lefty would go straight ahead or to the left. To turn right, I had to accept his way; that is, to make three left turns. You have to learn to adapt in all walks of life.

I couldn't have been happier. Each day, my aim got better and my horsemanship astraddle old Lefty improved by leaps and bounds. By the end of August, I'd brought in seventy-nine tails and felt rich.

Now and then, the hands would let me ride in the truck bed on trips into Fort Worth. In wandering around Cowtown, I found two restaurants that served barbecued rabbit. Always talkative and inquisitive, I learned that they bought dressed jackrabbits, paying fifty cents each. That sounded like easy money to me, because I flushed out hundreds of rabbits during my coyote hunts.

Back at the ranch, I made a deal with the boss to store skinned and cleaned jackrabbits in his underground icehouse to keep them fresh during the day before various hired hands would truck them into town each evening on their way to the saloon. On weekends, I personally delivered boxes filled with ice and rabbit by hitching a ride with the ranch workers. Sometimes, when the cowboys had a snootfull, they'd let me drive the truck back out to the ranch late at night.

With my burgeoning profits, I bought my first black Stetson, even though it was used, and a bone-handled hunting knife. One of the evenings in town gave me my first sex experience, too . . . well, almost. A drunken woman lured me over to her car, exposed her breasts, and made an offer she thought I couldn't refuse. She was wrong. It scared the hell out of me, and I scuttled back to my compadres like a spooked colt being chased by a hungry cougar.

The most searing experience in Cowtown occurred one Saturday night when a giant of a man roared out of a saloon waving a Bowie knife around, threatening to kill the man he thought had dallied with his wife. Trouble was, he thought half the men on the street were guilty. Finally, a tough, grizzled old deputy sheriff had no choice but to drop the enraged knife wielder with three .45-caliber shots to the chest, within about five feet of where I stood. On the way back to the ranch, under a big full moon, the cowboy driver pulled the truck over, stopped, and poured each of us a drink into paper cups from his bottle of Jack Daniels. We drank a toast to the dead man, who the cowboy had known for years. He explained to me that his old pal had reacted to a mixture of booze and drugs that had made him crazy as a wild horse on loco weed. That moment made a deep impression on me. It instilled in me a hatred of drugs, a feeling that would last for the rest of my life.

On the next trip to town, with the help of a thirsty wino, I bought my first handgun, a .38 Colt revolver, from a pawnshop.

During the year and a half living in the shed and hunting coyotes, I spent hundreds of hours on horseback and became even more proficient with guns. I nearly wiped out the coyote and jackrabbit population within fifty miles of the ranch, causing me to range so far that I often had to camp out several nights at a time in search of my bounty. Out there on the endless prairie at night, under a sky full of stars, I grew to an early maturity. My goal, I decided, was to become a rancher. I would breed horses and sell them at the stock shows where wealthy men dealt in such matters. I would become like them, respected and secure.

With my quarry nearly depleted by January of 1961, I said good-bye to old Lefty with a lump in my throat, shook hands with the rancher, the foreman, and some of the men, and hitched a ride into town. At the Fort Worth stock show, I landed part-time work exercising horses and shoveling out stalls. In my spare time, I snatched rides on champion horses and circulated among movie stars, politicians, tycoons, oil barons, and ranchers. This was my kind of life. I also met two budding teenaged girls who apparently thought I was a young Clint Eastwood, maybe because I was trying to imitate Rowdy Yates in the *Rawhide* television series. The skinny little blonde took my virginity in a haystack, but I fell in love with the auburn-haired girl who had eighteen-year-old curves on her sixteen-year-old body. She gifted me with passionate fireworks in the cab-over bed of her parents' luxury camper.

When the horse show ended, I'd apparently impressed a wealthy oil company executive who offered me a job on his ranch about an hour's drive from the city. I had no car, so most of my evenings were spent reading a few books, playing poker with the ranch hands, and watching some television, mostly westerns. My favorite show was *Cheyenne,* starring Clint Walker.

After the first few weeks, one of the hands taught me auto mechanics on his old Ford pickup. I kept it maintained in return for borrowing it every other weekend to visit my honey in Fort Worth. But she slammed the door on our romance in March, causing me to understand why country western songs about lost love hurt so much.

The next January, back at the stock show, I met the most influential man of my life. Actually, when I saw him from behind, I thought it was Cheyenne himself, the actor Clint Walker. He stood about six foot six, weighed 260 pounds, had big, broad shoulders, wore a buckskin coat, and walked with the easy, muscular grace and the confidence of a star. A little later, when I had the opportunity to engage him in conversation, I could see that Big John Marshall was a little older than Walker, but he did have the same deep, booming voice, only with more of a Texas drawl. He wore a white Stetson over his thick, graying hair, a well-cut Western shirt, and expensive hand-tooled boots.

After several contacts, I learned that Big John owned a small ranch a few miles north of Fort Worth, but spent a lot of time on the road hauling loads in his eighteen-wheel Mack truck and trailer. Maybe because of the obvious hero worship he could see in my face, or because he liked the way I handled horses, or for whatever reason, he offered me a job. It took me about three seconds to accept. I would be a general ranch hand, in addition to learning how to drive the big rig. The third part of the job would turn out to be the most important, but that would come later.

I had never even been close to the cab of an eighteen-wheeler. Big John demonstrated the complex gear-shifting ranges, showed me how to start the diesel engine, took me to a big vacant parking lot, and put me behind the wheel. Within a few hours, I was truckin' on down the road.

John Marshall, I learned, was an expert at making money as a wildcat trucker and in a few other enterprises. He knew every technique for intimidating or cajoling trucking brokers into assigning him a payload, getting it hustled aboard first, and hitting the road ahead of company or union drivers. Almost always running overweight, he also knew the complex web of alternate routes, dirt roads, or back trails to avoid the weigh stations and state line crossings. He hauled produce from farms of the Rio Grande Valley to major cities, plus livestock, machinery, and a good number of loads that he didn't want to identify. I learned the highways and byways extending north, east, and west from Texas.

A natural chemistry took hold between me and John Marshall. He became sort of a godfather to me, and a role model. The feeling seemed to be mutual. One thing I didn't have to learn from him was hunger. I was always hungry and could eat twice as much as most fellas my age and size. John could put away a pound of barbecued beef, along with some beans, corn, and biscuits. I could keep up with him and have two slices of apple pie afterward. He got a kick out of my giant-sized appetite and obsession with food.

Big John passed on to me things he had learned over a lifetime, in many ways treating me like a son. In my spare time he showed me how to use guns. I thought I had learned a lot while hunting coyotes and rabbits, but I knew virtually nothing. Big John took me under his wing and taught me, like a rodeo champion teaching a tenderfoot on a dude ranch. The man had talents few people could imagine.

Within a few weeks, I also learned of John's third trade. I'd been a bounty hunter for desert critters. He was a bounty hunter for the biggest game—human beings. Well, some of them didn't deserve that honor; their crimes should demote them to something less than human.

Most people have a misconception about bounty hunters. Very few are mercenaries, and they are not interested in killing the people they hunt. Some prefer to call themselves bail enforcement agents, or special agents, or fugitive recovery agents, and work legally with an arrest warrant and a letter of assignment from a bonding company. The fugitives they chase are felons, or suspected fel-

ons, who have posted bail through a bondsman, then failed
to appear in court as promised. A bondsman can lose many
thousands of dollars if the fugitive remains at large, so he
is willing to pay well for the capture and return of the run-
away. There are active bounty hunters in every state, and
some work internationally. It's a dangerous game that can
get into your blood. Big John Marshall was one of the best.

Over the next few months, we chased down several
dozen bail jumpers: a murderer, some bigtime burglars, a
few dope dealers, and even a couple of women who'd operated houses of ill repute.

The danger hit home early in my tutorship. It became
known in the shadowy alleys of the hunted that I was John
Marshall's partner. One night at a truck stop, while John
was inside the mart, three thugs grabbed me near the rig,
drug me behind a garage kicking, biting, and flailing, and
pounded on me with what felt like baseball bats. When I
finally collapsed under the beating, one attacker delivered
a kick that broke my rib. They'd already scurried into the
darkness like sewer rats when John showed up and took
me to a doctor he knew. From then on, I started wearing
that old .38 tucked in my belt when we traveled. John had
an M-16, a .12-gauge shotgun, and a .30-.30 scoped rifle
in the truck, and he usually had his beautiful pearl-handled
.45 Colt revolver somewhere on his person.

My interest in learning about guns was renewed. He
showed me how to disassemble each one, properly clean
it, and snap it back together, just as fast as any soldier in
boot camp. He taught me the fast draw, the "Texas Shuffle,"
and the art and philosophy of gun handling. One exercise
was especially fun—placing a coin on the back of my hand
shoulder-high, dropping the hand and drawing, then firing
off three shots before the coin hit the ground. I practiced

with a vengeance, hoping someday to be half as good with the weapons as Big John was.

Bounty hunting provided excitement, trucking filled my need to see more of the country, and working with horses gave us both deep personal satisfaction. Nearly a year after I went to work with Big John, we launched a project that saw us wrangling more horses than I ever could have imagined. A sudden demand for Appaloosas hit the horse crowds, giving John an enterprising idea. We headed north to Wyoming, Montana, and Idaho, where we caught every wild horse that remotely bore the speckled and spotted markings of an Appaloosa.

The name Appaloosa comes from the Palouse country in eastern Washington, where Nez Perce Indians bred them from original Spanish stock, refining their strength for working and speed for racing over a period of one hundred years. So people talked of "a Palouse" horse, slurred the words as we Westerners tend to do, and it eventually became "Appaloosa." Good ones have strong backs, big bones, and thin manes and tails, and stand about fourteen hands high. They're calm horses, but they're alert and responsive when you work or race them.

Hustling night and day, we halfway saddle-broke our wild captives, hauled the herds to various Western ranches, and put them up for sale. I'm still not sure how John presented the credentials of the horses, but we got top dollar for them at fairs and stock shows. My share came to seven thousand dollars, which I used to buy some property John owned near Fort Worth, not far from his ranch. He gave me a bill of sale with the commitment to transfer a deed to my name when I reached twenty-one. As a bonus, he let me lease some attached acreage to use as pasture. The deal included a small two-bedroom house with a screened-in front porch, a barn, a corral, and plenty of water from a stream and a well. I took a couple of the wild horses we caught and bought four more. It would be, I thought, the start of my dream.

Three

Big John Marshall and I rumbled along Lancaster Street in his red '62 Ford pickup, leaving Forth Worth behind us, heading toward Dallas through midday traffic. A bail jumper we planned to bring back had skipped out after being accused of multiple burglaries. Hauling this punk in would be a special pleasure for both of us, since we'd heard that he made a hobby of beating up women. Gripping the steering wheel with those massive hands, which reduced it to the size of a toy, John peered into the shimmering distance far beyond the bends in the highway. His intense stare and tight jaws made it obvious to me that he had a burr under his saddle; something other than our fugitive on his mind. Never what I'd call talkative, John seemed unusually silent, and that bothered me. Generally, if he had something to say, he'd say it. He hadn't spoken a dozen words during the entire trip, and I dared not ask why. I knew better.

After we'd passed Rose Hill Burial Park and driven through Grand Prairie, during which Lancaster changed to Division Street, then Main Street, and finally Fort Worth Avenue, we stopped at a red signal, where John finally spoke.

"Tex, I've really tried hard to teach you how to handle a gun, and I'm proud of the way you've picked it up. I . . . you might be working a little too hard at it. You've gotten pretty fast."

I couldn't argue. The endless hours practicing with handguns, perfecting my fast draw, and refining my skill with the "Texas Shuffle," that is, tossing a big six-shooter from hand to hand without losing control of it, had resulted in a certain proficiency.

Not quite sure how to reply, I muttered, "I just want to be able to do it right, that's all."

"You're damn good, all right. Just don't let it go to your head, Tex."

I guess he felt he'd said his piece so I tried to take it to heart, even though I really had no idea what he was driving at. His advice had always been exactly on target, and I'd never rejected it. Sometimes he had the uncanny ability to see what was going to happen about twenty miles down the road. I'd learned long ago to pay attention when he got in that kind of mood.

We rolled into a seedy section on the edge of Dallas and stopped close to a little hole-in-the-wall bar. Directions we'd received from a bruised and furious prostitute had made it easy to find. The fugitive's girlfriend, after enduring a severe beating from him, had provided information that our escapee hung out in the dive, and she'd described the battered old blue Chevy he drove. We spotted it parked at the curb.

After circling the place twice to survey the layout, we made brief and simple plans. John took the front door and asked me to cover the back exit. I trotted to the alley, waited outside for about a minute until I heard some grunting, thumping, and yelling inside, then charged in through a pall of cigarette smoke and stale beer odor. Big John had wrestled a sweating, tattooed man to the floor, drawn the black-handled Colt .45, and started to snap the chains on him.

A blurred movement caught the corner of my eye. I twisted to my left and ducked low just in time to see a pockmarked, ponytailed thug raise a pool cue in an arc aimed directly at the back of John's head. With probably the quickest draw I'd ever executed, I slipped my right hand under the black vest I wore, to the left waistband of my jeans, and jerked out my own Colt .45. Tough Guy's head swiveled toward the cannon barrel leveled at his chest, freezing him where he stood. Making a sick, wilted expression, he followed the gestures of my left hand to cautiously and gently place the cue on the pool table. John looked up, saw that everything was under control, and nodded. "I appreciate your watching my back," he said.

"No problem. The sonofabitch thought he was going to cave your skull in, but I reckon he's changed his mind." I couldn't suppress a little smile.

With our grumbling prisoner in tow, we headed toward the front door, when a thickly built dapper man in a tailored dark suit and a gray hat with the brim flipped down over his left eye stepped into our path. In his early fifties and soft spoken, he apologized and said he'd like to talk to us.

"Sure, I'll talk to you in just a minute," John said. "Just let me get this fella into the truck so he cain't go nowhere." The stranger followed us outside, and stood by while we secured our captive. After we'd trussed him, padlocked him to a couple of steel rings welded to each side of John's pickup bed, and thrown a light tarp over him, the observer introduced himself.

"My name is Jack Ruby," he said, and offered his hand

to John, while I stood over to one side, keeping my eye on
the unhappy prisoner.

The dapper dude stood about my height, five-nine, but
probably outweighed me by forty pounds. In a voice like
a muted trumpet, with clipped words and very little trace
of a drawl, Ruby said he owned a couple of businesses in
Dallas.

"You own some clubs, don't you?" John asked, showing
little expression. I didn't have any idea how he knew that.
He seemed to have an inexhaustible source of information
about everything and everyone.

"Yeah, I do," Ruby agreed, and handed John a business
card. "Let me get to the point. That was pretty impressive
work in there. I'd sure like someone to show me how to
handle a gun like you and that kid just did. Be willing to
pay well for it. Sometimes I carry a lot of money on me,
and I need to know how to use a gun."

"I'm not in the business of teaching everyone I meet,"
John said.

"I'll make it worth your while," Ruby offered.

"Well, I'll give it some thought and let you know."

"Where can I get hold of you?"

"You can probably find us at the Rodeo Cafe in Fort
Worth from time to time. Give me a day or two to think it
over." I admired the way Big John could talk to people
firmly without being offensive. Ruby thanked him and
headed back into the bar.

In the truck again, John commented, "You never know
what or who you're going to run into."

"Who is he?" My curiosity had grown when John
wouldn't divulge our addresses or phone numbers.

"I hear he's got some shady clubs here in Dallas. Booze

and women. Nothing you'd be interested in." He gave me
a sidelong glance, a downturned smile, and a wink.

Despite the clear signals, I couldn't resist prying.
"Women?" That topic always interested me.

"He runs some stripper bars." Compressing his lips before continuing, John's voice took on a serious tone.
"That's really no big deal. But I've heard that he supposedly
has some ties with the Mafia out of New Orleans and some
connections up in Chicago." John never revealed to me
where he'd heard this, but I knew that his contacts in the
world of bounty hunting gave him ready access to a full
pipeline of underworld gossip. I had no reason to doubt his
information.

"Well, what do you want to do?" I felt a tingle in my
spine, a slight rush of excitement.

"First thing we do is get our man here back in jail, where
he belongs, and then we'll go up to the cafe and eat." It
was clear that John didn't want to discuss Mr. Ruby anymore.

"Let's go," I said.

All the way back to Fort Worth I thought of the man
we'd met and what John had told me about him. When we
reached Tarrant County Jail, John escorted our bail jumper
inside and turned him over to the desk sergeant. Half an
hour later, we headed over to the Rodeo Cafe.

"Tommy," John bellowed to our owner-manager friend,
"how about some lunch? Just bring us the usual." My usual,
for lunch, was a thick, well-done hamburger with mustard,
mayo, pickles, onions, the works, plus a double order of
fries and a tall glass of iced tea. John teased that one day

all that grease would put a paunch on me, but it hadn't happened yet.

In the midst of our meal, while I fiddled with my burger and fries, John said, "Okay, come on back to earth and finish eating before whatever's on your mind sprouts legs and walks. What are you thinking about, anyway?"

"Why would a man like Jack Ruby want us to teach him how to shoot a gun?" I asked. My mind couldn't leave our odd meeting with the man in a suit. In some peculiar way, he kindled my interest.

"That's a good question, Tex," John said, but dropped the subject there. I took his hint and avoided bringing it up again the rest of the day. But it gnawed at my mind that whole evening while I watched a rodeo with some friends, even though we had a great time cheering for the bull riders and the ropers we knew. In bed that night, I kept waking up and mulling over the idea of teaching a stripjoint owner how to shoot. Sleep brought dreams of women gyrating on bales of hay, wearing very little and firing pistols into the air.

John had agreed to meet me for breakfast, and I hoped he might open up a little about our encounter. Tommy had just delivered two platters of bacon and eggs, over easy, with mugs of steaming coffee, when John said, "Tex, we need to talk."

"Okay, what's up?" I knew I'd be disappointed if the subject wasn't Jack Ruby.

"Look, I know you could use some extra money. I don't have time to teach Ruby how to use a gun, but if you want to, I won't stand in your way. I told you that he might be associated with some shady people, so you know what you're getting into."

"Well, you're right, John. I do need a few things, maybe a new Stetson, and some good boots. And I've got to admit, I'm curious as hell about that guy. If the pay is right, I might be willing to teach him to shoot."

Mulling over my answer, John took a sip of coffee. "The main thing I want is for you to be careful. Watch yourself real close. Don't get sucked up into his life or his friends. If you keep it entirely on a professional level and restrict it to shooting lessons, I guess not too much can go wrong. Just try to remember some of the things I've tried to pass on to you."

One of the main lessons Big John had tried to impress on me was to listen. Early on, he'd pounded that into me repeatedly, advising me that the person who does most of the talking is the one who is doing the least amount of learning. One of the key ingredients for success in the bounty hunting business is to prime the other guy's talking machine and keep it running. You had to use caution, though: avoid too many direct questions that sound like interrogation. Better to drop short comments that inspire the talker to continue blabbering about his experiences and impress you with his vast knowledge. Of course, a great deal of what you hear is trivial chatter, but a careful listener will sift through it and find the useful nuggets. Jack Ruby lived in a world foreign and fascinating to me, and if I could beat him at the pumping game, I could learn a lot from his colorful experiences.

"Don't worry," I nodded to John. "I won't turn my back on him."

We attacked the breakfast platters and had nearly finished when Jack Ruby pushed the glass door open, scanned the diners, and marched over to us. He greeted John, then turned to me and asked, "What do I call you? Billy the Kid?"

That was a damn poor start, and I could feel the heat rising to my face. I may have been young, but I was no idiot, and I didn't like smart-mouth comments about me. "My name is Ray 'Tex' Brown, Mr. Ruby and you can call me Tex. Yes, I can handle a gun, but I'm not anything like Billy the Kid. I don't draw on anyone unless it's absolutely necessary——that way it's not murder."

Ruby turned to John. "Is he always like that?"

"Yeah, and I wouldn't have it any other way." John's voice was even and deadly serious.

Ruby sat down, pushed his hat back, and smiled. "Well, John, can you work with me? Teach me how to handle a gun?"

John shook his head. " 'Fraid not. I don't have the time, but Tex here does. I taught him most of what I know about firearms, so you'd be getting the benefit of my experience and his enthusiasm. Now and then, I might drop by and see how things are coming along. If you really want to learn, it'll have to be from Tex."

A scowl darkened Ruby's face. "I'll think about it and let you know." He stood, grabbed the check off our table, tipped his hat brim, walked to the cash register, and paid for our meals. My impression was that he didn't like the idea of a man half his age teaching him how to shoot.

After Ruby had left, John reached for a toothpick and said, "He wants something real bad, but hell if I know what it is."

"I hope we don't end up regretting meeting him."

"Why do you say that?"

"I don't know." I wanted to express my curiosity without sounding like a fence straddler. "If he is tied up with the mob, what's he want with a couple of cowboys like us? Seems like there ought to be any number of people he knows who could teach him what he needs. I know horses and guns, and not much else. He must have contacts who know a hell of a lot more. It doesn't add up."

Tommy interrupted to tell John there was a phone call for him. While I finished my coffee, I watched as John cradled the phone between his cheek and shoulder and scribbled furiously on a scrap of paper. The one-sided conversation lasted about fifteen minutes. I heard him tell the caller that we were on our way out of town today. When he hung up, he told Tommy that if anyone asked about us, we'd be gone for a week or two. Back at the table, he asked, "Tex, how long will it take you to get ready to hit the road?"

Within an hour, I'd loaded two horses into a trailer and rejoined John. We headed south on Highway 35 toward Waco, going after a killer who'd crossed the border into Mexico after skipping bail provided by a bondsman friend of John's. Legal extradition can strangle you in red tape and take forever. For a healthy cut of the recovered bail money, John and I would deliver the fugitive safely back into the custody of Texas authorities.

Four

Pulling a trailer with two horses inside, I followed John's red pickup south on Highway 35. Before leaving, we'd split our road money between us, one thousand dollars, just in case we got separated and one of us found himself in a tight spot. That way, the free partner could come galloping to the rescue, so to speak.

On our trips, I usually pulled the horse trailer, and John drove his faster Ford to do the scouting ahead. My horse, named Chief, and Marshall's, Booger, both dependable Appaloosas, rode contentedly behind me. I'd heard that Booger, easily identifiable by his white blanket and spots on the rump, was a descendant of a great Appaloosa named Double Six Domino, who stood over fifteen hands and had sired nearly a hundred stallions and even more mares in the early fifties. I know Big John wouldn't have sold that horse for any amount of money. I felt the same way about Chief.

We rolled into Ed's truck stop at the traffic circle in Waco. The restaurant there wouldn't earn any four-star ratings in the tourist books, but they served up their food with down home hospitality. Their specialty was a huge, mouthwatering chicken-fried steak that covered the entire plate. While we ate, John kept turning to the window to scan the parking lot outside, and halfway through our meal, he caught sight of the man he'd been expecting. "Here comes Paul now," he announced. I watched the new arrival, who stood ramrod straight despite his age, probably around sixty. He wore a finely tailored hound's tooth sportcoat over a silk shirt, expensive black slacks, and saddle oxfords. The word "Yankee" formed in my mind. He quickened his stride when he located us and thrust his open hand toward Marshall. "John, it's been a very long time."

"Yes, it has, Paul. Damn good to see you." Pointing a thumb toward me, John said, "I'd like you to meet Tex, my right-hand man." Proud to be called that, I shook hands with the elegant arrival, impressed with his tight grip. "Tex, this is a good buddy from way back, Paul Butler."

Butler raised his dark eyebrows. "So you're the Tex John told me about on the phone. Too bad you don't live up my way. I could put you to work."

John laughed. "There aren't enough horses around Chicago for Tex. He'd feel out of place. Probably die without the smell of a barn to wake him up every morning."

Butler took a chair and pulled an envelope from his jacket. It bulged open, and I could see a thick stack of greenbacks. John had told me very little about the task ahead, and my curiosity was giving me a headache. From another coat pocket, Butler withdrew some color photos and handed them to John. His voice grew tense. "Two of my men have been on this guy's trail for three weeks."

Studying the pictures, John asked, "So this is the guy we're after?"

"His name is Jim Cochrane, and he's killed four people. He started out with small stuff—burglary, penny-ante robberies. Then he graduated to knocking over a jewelry store. Police in a small town outside Chicago nailed him three months ago. Cochrane's father came to me for the bond to get his kid out of jail. Put up his house for collateral. The ungrateful jerk betrayed his father and skipped out. And then the killing started four days later. He's a suspect in a gas station murder, two dead customers in a sleazy bar, and a motorist found dead on a highway shoulder. The poor victim on the road had just bought a new Chevy Impala, which is missing. Apparently Cochrane drove it to Mexico. We got a tip he's been seen in Reynosa, but my guys don't want to cross the border. John, I know you've got the right contacts down there to find Cochrane and bring him back."

I tried to resist, but a smile forced its way across my face, as I remembered a painted lady in a bordello down there who had fallen hard for Big John and given him information that might have taken months to dig out elsewhere. Paul noticed my expression, frowned, and asked, "What are you smiling about? Did I say something funny?"

"No, sir," I apologized. "I was just thinking, we've been there a time or two before. No offense."

"Of course not," Butler said, his face softening. "I have two men standing by in Pharr, about fifteen miles north of Reynosa. They're staying in the Texas Motel, ready to provide whatever assistance they can, this side of the Rio Grande."

John and I had stayed in Pharr on another job, and my mouth started salivating. There was a little Chinese restaurant there with the best chow mein I'd ever tasted. John's thoughts were a little more to the point. Thinking aloud, he recalled that a ranch owner he knew would stable our horses on his spread near Hidalgo, on the north side of the Rio Grande. Paul wondered why we'd need mounts, and John explained we could use them to ford the river when we brought Cochrane back, away from nosy officials at border stations. Wanting to help, Paul volunteered to stand by in

Pharr, with his men, ready to supply any logistical help or provisions. At John's suggestion, Paul agreed to ride the first leg of the trip with me. All together, we faced a four hundred-mile drive.

We worked out some preliminary plans and finished our meals.

As they sipped coffee, and I drained my iced tea glass, John shifted the subject. "Paul, you know a lot of people around Chicago. Ever heard of a man by the name of Jack Ruby?"

"I've heard the name. Runs some joints in Dallas now, doesn't he?"

"Yeah. We bumped into him the other day. Tex can fill you in during the trip." Looking at me, he hitched his head in the direction of the counter. "See that lady over there, Tex? Her name is Betty Lou, and she's the manager. Why don't you go over and ask if she has a safe place to keep Paul's car while we're gone." It wasn't a question. He nodded toward a buxom woman in her forties with flame red hair who wore a half tube of lipstick and eyelashes stolen from a black Angus calf.

I waited at the end of the counter, staring to catch her attention. She shimmied over to me, all flirtatious smiles, bosom, and willingness.

"Ma'am, John Marshall asked if you could find a safe place for our friend's car for a few days."

"Honey," she bubbled, "You tell that big handsome rascal that I'll do anything he wants, and I mean anything." She raised her voice to make sure John, and a dozen other customers, could hear. "And tell him if he made his way to Waco more often, he'd find that out." She followed with an impish laugh that had kept her customers coming back for years. John nodded his appreciation to her, then yelled back with mock temptation, "I'll remember that."

Paul threw his gear into my truck bed, and we headed south. When I drive, I like to keep the two-way radio on, listening for traffic tips, hoping to hear where any police vehicles are hiding on the lookout for speeders, and trucker gossip. But Paul was a talker, so much that I finally flipped the switch off. It took him nearly an hour to get around to the subject of Jack Ruby. I filled him in with details of our meeting him and Ruby's request to learn how to use guns.

"There's not a whole lot I can tell you about him," Paul said. "I've heard he's in thick with some mob types in Chicago, but as far as I know, he's never served any time. Seems like there was some talk about him associating with the top guy in Mafia circles down in New Orleans. If Ruby really *is* connected to him, I'd say watch your behind."

We drifted on to other topics, including Paul's concern for the fugitive's father. He really didn't want to foreclose on the house or lose the bond money. I promised him we'd do everything we could to bring Cochrane back. More general chatter followed, ninety-nine percent of it one-way. I don't think I heard more than ten consecutive seconds of silence. I needed a break.

When we reached San Antonio, and a stop at the Gas 'n' Eat truck stop, John and I took the horses out to stretch their legs and feed them. John's eyes sparkled with mischief. "Did Paul talk your leg off?" he smirked.

"So that's why you stuck me with him. You knew he liked to blabber, didn't you?"

"Yeah," he laughed outright. "But he's a good man. I knew his father and thought the world of him, too. He wore a badge for thirty years and got killed wearing it. I don't think Paul's grief over it has ever healed up." John paused, then asked, "So what'd he tell you about Ruby?"

"Not a whole lot. Pretty much what you'd already told me. But he did mention a Mafia type in New Orleans Ruby might know. I still don't understand why he wants us. We're usually trying to arrest his kind, not work with 'em."

"Your guess is as good as mine, for now. I've asked a fellow over in Dallas to work up some information on Ruby. When we get back, I might be able to get a better handle on him." While we gassed up, I gave John a pleading look, and he invited his old pal to ride with him the rest of the trip. I exhaled a whole lot of relief.

All of us were exhausted by the time we reached the ranch at Hidalgo. While I unloaded the horses, Paul offered to help, and said, "John tells me you've learned to draw a gun almost as fast as he can. My dad was a pretty fast hand, too, but he didn't stand much of a chance. He was shot in the back. If you're anything like John, you've got eyes in the back of your head and the nine lives of a cat. Or you've both made a pact with the devil. John says you've listened well and learned how to handle yourself. He paid you a compliment and said you're a lot like him."

"Well, I sure appreciate him saying that. I don't know about eyes in the back of the head or any deals with the devil, though. I think I've been lucky a few times, or maybe stupid for getting myself in a position to get killed. I'd prefer to think that it's luck."

"I hope your luck continues, Tex. I've been worrying about your contact with Jack Ruby. I don't know for sure who he's mixed up with, but watch yourself. It happened to my dad, and he was one of the best at dealing with hard-case criminals. If there are Mafia connections, you'll need all the luck you can get."

"I'll keep a sharp lookout, Mr. Butler, and try to keep from getting bushwhacked. I appreciate your concern."

Well rested after a good night's sleep, we loaded up John's pickup for the trip into Mexico. I hid some guns in a concealed compartment John had designed and built. Butler would stay at the motel. His two cohorts, without much enthusiasm, had finally agreed to accompany us into Mexico, but one of them broke out in a nervous sweat at the idea of carrying guns in. He'd heard that the *Federales* took a dim view of that, and he feared getting busted and tossed into a Mexican jail. "Jesus," he moaned, "we'd never get out." John gave him a scornful look and we crossed the bridge into Reynosa.

I drove southeast along the river, called the Rio Bravo on that side of the border, noting that it was wide but shallow in spots. We found a place just beyond a bend where horses could easily cross, concealed by bluffs and brush.

Back in Reynosa, we hit a few cantinas, hung out in the central plaza, and walked the streets, hoping we might strike it lucky and run into Cochrane. But it didn't work out, so John reluctantly said he'd use his contact in the *casa de prostitutas.* An hour later he came out reeking of cheap perfume and *cigarro* smoke. Oh, the sacrifices we have to make sometimes.

At John's directions, I drove to a row of shacks on the east side of town, where we waited in the shadows of a *mercado* close to a hotel. John's cooperative *señorita piruja* had informed him that our fugitive was staying there in *cuarto veinte,* room twenty. She knew because Cochrane had required her to pay a call several times to make her services available. After almost an hour of waiting, Cochrane strolled out shortly after noon as if he didn't have a care in the world. We ducked our heads to keep him from seeing us.

Once again on the U.S. side, we worked out our plan. John would drive his pickup to the hotel that night, pick the lock on Cochrane's door, and stagger inside like a drunk who'd wandered into the wrong room. There was no doubt in any of our minds about John being able to subdue the fugitive and bring him to the river shallows. I'd wait on the other side with two horses. When John flashed his headlights twice, I'd ford the river and bring Cochrane across on horseback like a sack of potatoes.

At 10 PM, I waved to John and pulled the trailer to the riverside to wait.

Something went wrong. I'd begun to worry when John didn't show by midnight. Finally, at two in the morning, I heard a burst of gunshots on the other side and saw the double flash of headlights. I leaped on Chief's saddled back, grabbed the rope tied to Booger's bridle, and rushed into the water, splashing in a wild run across the river. I reached John's red pickup and crouched close to him where he kneeled beside a fender, aiming his .45 into the darkness. Neither of us ever knew if the gun-toting hombre, who had followed and taken some potshots, had hightailed it back to town for help, or if John's return fire had drilled him out there in the dark desert. In any case, the shooting had stopped, so we strapped a grunting, hogtied, gagged Jim Cochrane onto Booger's back.

Before I remounted, I asked John if he wanted me to tie our captive in the trailer and come back across to ride shotgun on his return trip to the bridge. "Don't worry about that," he said. "You just get our man into Texas. He made a lot of racket back there at the hotel and all hell broke loose. Somebody followed us. Whoever it was probably ran for help, so if I get going right now, before he can round up a posse, I'll make it okay."

I hated to leave him alone, but he'd always been right, so I couldn't argue. "Okay, John. I'm gone. Take care of yourself." I hit the water at a gallop, hoping that the lurching horse was rattling the hell out of Cochrane. With a streak of orneriness, I led Booger into deeper water close to the U.S. side, just to give our captive a scare.

When I reached my truck and trailer, I was surprised to find Paul Butler and his two sidekicks waiting for me. I thought they'd be at the hotel. Paul had convinced them that John and I might need some help. Cochrane, still furious and struggling, saw Butler and his eyes went wide. Paul gave him a grin and a little jab. "You thought you'd never see me again, didn't you?"

"You can't come after me in Mexico," Cochrane protested, after we'd removed the gag.

"Too late, we already did," said Paul.

Cochrane shot daggers at me with his eyes and grunted, "That big buddy of yours ain't going to get out of Mexico. I've got friends there. They'll take care of him for me."

"I wouldn't underestimate him if I were you," I said, hoping Cochrane was wrong. "He'll be back."

We lifted him off the horse and snapped chains on his legs and wrists in the back of my truck. Cochrane complained about the rough treatment. "You damn near drowned me out there in the river."

"You might have been better off if I had, instead of

spending the rest of your life in prison, or sweating it out on death row 'til they execute you."

Paul, his two men, and I waited nervously back at the motel, pacing and drinking coffee until well after dawn. Groggy and worried, we dreaded the idea of crossing the border again to search for John, or to find that he'd been killed. The minutes crawled by. Then we heard tires crunching gravel around the corner. We couldn't restrain ourselves from cheering when that red pickup rolled into sight in the motel parking lot. After welcoming him back, we examined the truck's tailgate and found six big ragged bullet holes.

We decided to keep the captive in my truck because no one associated with Cochrane had seen it. John instructed Paul and his men to meet us at the Waco truck stop, where they could take custody of Cochrane and deliver him to Chicago. I would closely follow John's pickup to keep anyone off his tail. As we drove, I noticed two cars following close behind me for fifty miles, but they finally made a U-turn across the median and headed south.

In Waco, I suggested to Paul they rent a truck and put their prisoner in the back. No one trying to rescue Cochrane would think about a rental truck being used. They liked the idea, and thanked us. We shook hands all around and said good-bye.

Back at my place, John and I were exhausted, dirty, unshaven, and hungry. Before he headed home, he pulled out a wad of money and paid me for the completed job. "I've got a little something extra here for you," he said. "Paul asked me to give you this." He handed me a Colt .45, model 1911, the kind produced for the U.S. Army. "I think Paul's dad used to carry the gun. He wanted you to have it. I guess he thought you could make some use of it."

"That's really generous of him, John. I'll write to him

and give him my thanks." I couldn't think of anything else to say, and if I had, the lump in my throat would have prevented me from saying it.

Five

On the third day following our return from Mexico, John Marshall had agreed to meet me for lunch at the Rodeo Cafe. He had a few chores to run, which generally made him late, and since I was early, Tommy delivered my usual. Halfway through the juicy hamburger, Jack Ruby pushed the front door open, spotted me, and marched straight to my table. He wore a dark suit, white shirt, blue tie, and a hat, just the same as the other times we'd seen him.

"Been looking for you," Ruby announced, in that clipped tone. "You and Mr. Marshall been out of town?" He stood across from me and took his hat off, revealing thin slicked-back strands of black hair plastered to his scalp. He mopped it with a handkerchief.

"Yeah. We've been out making a living. John'll be here a little later. We ain't used to punching a time card or explaining our coming or going." I wasn't sure why I felt the need to be curt; maybe just to assert my extreme independence, or maybe to let him know I was no kid to be pushed around.

Ignoring my bluntness, Ruby said, "I thought we were going to work together. Are we still on, or not? Because if not, I can probably find someone else." His jaw muscle flexed noticeably.

Not wanting to kill the deal, I eased off. "Sure. We're still on. Care to sit down?"

"Thanks." Ruby nodded and pulled up a chair opposite me. I sensed that he was no pushover or soft executive type. There was a toughness about him suggesting a hair-trigger temper. The oval face was strong with dark, piercing eyes, a broad forehead, a prominent nose, a tight-lipped, firm-set mouth, and a distinctive cleft in the center of his chin. My first impression had been of a somewhat pudgy man, but on second thought, he seemed pretty solid. I didn't know much about the Mafia or organized crime figures, but to me, he perfectly fit the stereotype of movie mobsters.

"How's the club business doing?" I asked, trying to make conversation.

"Business is okay. Sometimes it's a tough grind. Good times and bad times. You ever been over at the Carousel or Vegas Club in Dallas?"

"No, I haven't." I couldn't tell if he was being cute or if he really didn't know that I wasn't yet twenty-one and couldn't buy alcohol legally. His bouncers probably wouldn't even let me past the front door, even though I looked older than I was. I really had no interest in sitting in a smoke-filled joint hours on end, anyway. Never could understand why anyone wanted to waste time like that. "You're not from Dallas originally, are you?" I wanted to shift the subject.

"Nah. I'm a Chicago native. Tough town. Had to start supporting myself while I was still a kid, hustling on the streets. I learned to hold my own among some pretty rough company. They called me 'Sparky' up there. Used to make me mad as hell. I knocked more than one kid on his rump for that." I thought I could see the trace of a smile. "How about you, Tex? I take it from your nickname you're from around here?"

"Yup. Right here in Fort Worth."

"How long you been working with guns? I was impressed with your speed."

"Oh, I don't know. I've been interested in guns most of my life. I'm still not as good as I'd like to be."

"You're not old enough to have been at it very long. Nevertheless, you looked really good, and I'd like to learn how to do it." I knew he wouldn't be able to resist making a sideways reference to my age.

"I've been around long enough to know that guns are serious business and to respect them. I look at 'em as tools. Just like a good pickup truck. If you know how to drive it and take care of it properly, you can always rely on it. Keep it clean and well maintained, and it'll be there when you need it. But if you misuse a truck or a gun, it can get you killed." I was impressed with my own speech, and I meant every word of it.

"That's an intelligent outlook," Ruby nodded. "Kind of like women. Treat 'em right, and they'll be good to you."

"Yeah, I guess so. But my guns are a lot more predictable than any women I've ever known."

Ruby finally let out a real laugh. "You're right about that, son."

Damn. That put my teeth on edge. I hated anyone to call me "son." The only person I allowed to be that personal was John Marshall, and even then, not very often. "I don't mean no disrespect, Mr. Ruby, but don't call me 'son.' I'm not your son."

A shadow passed quickly over his face, but if I'd made him angry, he recovered instantly. "Sure, Tex. It's a habit. The only way I can find out about people is talking to them.

I'm usually pretty good at getting people to talk and tell me what I want to know." It was almost like he'd read my mind about using the advice Big John had given me to make the other guy do the talking.

"I don't doubt that. If you can shoot as good as you can talk, you'll probably be able to outshoot me someday."

"Maybe I will," he said. "Maybe I will. Anyway, Tex, like I mentioned before, sometimes I carry a lot of money around with me. Can't be helped in my business. I think it would be a good idea to improve my ability with a gun."

The front door swung open and Big John Marshall strode through. He covered the fifteen feet to us in about four steps and asked, "Hey, have y'all eaten yet?" I looked down at my half-consumed hamburger, now cold and soggy. I'd been so busy talking to Ruby that I'd forgotten about my meal. John had the solution. "Let's go on over to Little John's Bar-B-Que for lunch. I'm in the mood for some of those great ribs."

I pushed my plate away, always ready for a spicy rack of messy pork ribs.

"Why don't you guys ride with me?" Ruby volunteered.

"Are you sure there's enough room in that Oldsmobile?" John asked, having seen the white car parked out front. He never missed anything.

South of the city center, we barged into the tiny restaurant, a whitewashed cinderblock building in a section of town occupied mostly by African Americans. The owner met us with a toothy grin that lit up the room. "Big John Marshall. And Tex. Where've y'all been? Haven't seen you around here in a lo-o-ong time." Ruby glanced around, frowning.

John and I ordered the house specialty, full racks of barbecued baby-backs with extra sauce. I strongly recommended them to Jack Ruby, while Big John stared out the window with a little knowing smile. Ruby studied the chalkboard menu. "I'll just have a salad and a glass of water."

A tiny ball of anger fused inside me. Just who the hell did he think he was, looking down his big nose at our friend's cooking? Maybe he was racially prejudiced. John and I had been here eating here for a long time, usually the only white people in the place, and there'd never been even a hint of disharmony.

"Don't get the wrong idea," Ruby said, evidently noticing my flushing face. He winked at John, who was trying to keep from laughing out loud. "Maybe you didn't know it, Tex, but I'm of the Jewish faith. There are some things we don't eat. Besides that, I really watch my diet. Gotta' keep trim, you know."

"Oh," I muttered, quickly wilting with embarrassment. How the hell was I supposed to know? I knew horses and guns. A man's religion, to me, was his own business. Of course, I'd heard snide jokes exchanged by drunk rednecks about Jews, plus every other religion and race. It all seemed goofy to me. I sure couldn't tell by looking at a person which church he went to. No, I hadn't realized that Ruby was Jewish, kosher all the way. It wouldn't have made any difference anyway. With all that in mind, my embarrassment washed away. I had no reason to feel guilty or uncomfortable. We ate in silence.

On the way back to the Rodeo Cafe, Ruby asked me where we'd go to work with the guns. I told him about a site next to a small bay on Lake Worth where I liked to set up targets and practice. "Could we go out there today and get started?" he asked.

I turned to John. "What about it? You want to do some shooting?"

"You go ahead, if you want to. I've got a few other things to take care of. Don't let him shoot himself."

At the Rodeo Cafe, Ruby suggested we go together in his Oldsmobile, but I preferred to have my own transportation. He agreed to ride with me in my pickup. We stepped over to his car, where he unlocked the trunk and retrieved a .38-caliber revolver.

On the Jacksboro Highway, we passed used car lots, trailer parks, and weathered auto courts through Sansom Park and Lake Worth. After crossing the long, low bridge spanning a narrow neck of the shimmering blue water, I swung left at Casino Park, hugged the shore for a couple of miles, and halted near the bay. I picked up a few empty cans near a trash barrel to use as targets.

We paced about ten yards away from a line of six cans I'd placed on the ground, and Ruby pointed his revolver in their direction. He snapped off six shots, and missed every can. "All right," he growled, upset with himself, "What am I doing wrong?"

"You're not relaxed, you're jerking the trigger, and you're not honing in with a good aim."

"I think it's the gun," he muttered.

"Let me give it a try. Maybe something is wrong with the sights," I humored him. After reloading it, I slipped the barrel into my belt, and stood still for a moment. I know that my next move could be considered showing off, but I couldn't resist. In one easy motion, I drew the weapon, leveled it in the direction of the targets, and popped holes in five of the six cans in quick succession. In a deliberately slow mock examination of the gun, I drawled, "Well, if it ain't the airplane, it's gotta' be the pilot."

"Yeah, I can see that," he replied. I don't think he appreciated the humor in my comment. "That's good shooting. Now, show me how to do it."

"I'll do my best, but you've got to realize, it's going to take some time."

"Whatever it takes, I've gotta learn."

I felt strange lecturing a man old enough to be my father, and he seemed so out of place dressed in that suit. Patiently, I demonstrated how to hold the piece, showed him where to place his feet while relaxing and aiming, and instructed him about the hand and eye working together. As soon as he'd taken a couple of dry runs, he wanted to blast away with more live ammunition.

This time, he did smash a hole in one of the cans, causing him to beam with pride.

For the first time, I noticed two things about my middle-aged student. First, he couldn't keep his left arm still while firing. He bent it at the elbow and pumped the whole arm back and forth. I'm sure it threw him off balance enough to make accurate firing impossible. Second, while I studied that arm, I saw that the tip of his left index finger was missing. It would probably be very difficult for him to shift the gun into that hand and fire quickly.

I pointed out the swinging arm problem to Ruby, which totally surprised him. He'd been completely unaware of it and promised to try to work on keeping it still.

We fired a few more rounds and practiced what I'd shown him, working for another half hour before we decided to call it a day. I'd nearly forgotten my other commitment. "I've got a date tonight," I told Ruby, "and she's a hell of a lot better looking than you, Jack." He didn't object to my addressing him by his first name.

"I can understand that. I'm ready to leave when you are."

On the way back to town, Ruby seemed lost in deep thought for several miles. Finally he asked, "How long have you been running with John Marshall?"

I hesitated a couple of minutes before answering, reluctant to go into a lot of private details about myself. John's warning about not getting tangled up personally with this guy sat heavy on my mind. But I figured there was no harm in some general conversation. "I'll tell you. John Marshall has been like a father to me. He's taught me most of what I know. If it hadn't been for him, I probably would have gotten myself killed by now." I had no intention of revealing anything about our bounty hunting activities, or any of our other business.

I knew he wanted to ask more. A creepy premonition nagged at the inner reaches of my thoughts but wouldn't materialize into specifics. I vaguely wondered just what Ruby had up his sleeve. My suspicions were interrupted when we pulled into the Rodeo Cafe parking lot and John Marshall's wife rushed out. "Tex, have you seen John?"

"Not since we ate together a couple of hours ago. We've been at the lake."

"Well, if you see him, tell him there was a telephone call from Oklahoma City. By the way, if you're keeping that date tonight, you'd better get in early and get some sleep. I have a feeling you and John are going on a little trip out of town real soon."

Ruby hadn't missed a word. "John Marshall's always got something going on, doesn't he?"

"We stay busy," I said, hoping he got the hint that I wasn't going to reveal any details.

"Sure, Tex." He patted his hip to make sure the .38 was there, and turned toward his car. "Thanks. It's been fun. I'll get in touch with you and we'll do it again."

The phone rang in my bedroom that evening just as I stepped out of the shower. A soft, feminine voice said, "Hi. It's me. Are you still going to pick me up at seven?"

"I'll be a little late," I told Ann. "Some business today took longer than I'd expected." Her long pause should have alerted me that I'd said the wrong thing.

We danced that night at a country-Western barn, then had dinner. Ann wanted to know just what kind of business I'd meant during our phone conversation earlier. She had some vague idea about my adventures with John Marshall, about which I'd revealed few details. I'm sure her imagination ran wild about what we did, but she probably had a pretty good grasp of the danger involved. Ann's mother had tried to discourage the relationship, suggesting to her that I was probably an outlaw. I told Ann that I was teaching a man how to use guns and that I'd be out of town for a few days with John. She shook her head, compressing those gorgeous lips until her dimples showed. Despite her curiosity, she reluctantly dropped the subject and enjoyed the rest of the evening. Much later than I'd planned, she smothered me with soft, warm goodnight kisses that jolted me all the way to my toes. She begged me to be careful.

"Get up, boy," Big John yelled outside my front door, just before the sun spilled a thin layer of coral across the dark horizon. I grabbed my pants, rubbed the sleep from my heavy eyelids, and stumbled to the door, where John stood with a big grin and a welcome mug of steaming coffee from his thermos. "Here. Get this down your gullet, and let's feed the horses. We're headed up to Colorado after a man who kidnaped his daughter."

Had I known who the child in question was, the sleepiness would have melted away a lot quicker.

Six

While we prepared the horses for travel, Big John filled in some details. "The courts gave custody of the little girl to her mother, but the father, a man named John Cove, snatched the kid from a babysitter. The family thinks he's holed up on a ranch he owns in Colorado. You and I both know the tangled mess with trying to get her back through the courts and the red tape of law enforcement. It could take forever. The kid would be grown before anything happened. Besides, the grandfather is worried that Cove might skip across the border to Canada rather than give her up. I think we can work our way onto his place on horses, acting like lost hunters, and get her back."

"Sounds interesting."

"Well, it may be more interesting than you think. You already know the child's mother."

That grabbed my attention, but John let me dangle for a few minutes. Finally, he said, "You remember that little girl who had you all aflutter the year before we met, the one you raved about for so long? Girl named Judy?"

My Lord! Did I remember her? That wonderful auburn-haired beauty, my first serious romance, when the teenage sap had started to rise. The girl who had shattered my heart. My stomach did a little flip, and memories of pain flooded back. "She has a little girl? How old?"

"Just turned three." A quick calculation wrenched my emotions again. Judy must have been pregnant when she broke up with me that sad March, when she was only sixteen. No wonder she'd completely disappeared out of my life. Right out of the blue, she'd told me that we couldn't see each other any more, and not to call her again. I had moped around for weeks like a sick dog. I just couldn't believe my sweet Judy had meant it, but her parents turned away my desperate calls, telling me that she wasn't home. It took all the strength I could muster to finally give up. My friends on the ranch had tried in vain to console me. Months later, when I'd shared the lingering heartbreak with John and his wife, they'd helped me get over it.

"Judy and her father are on their way over here," John announced.

I tried to concentrate on packing for the trip, but I had no idea what I was stuffing into my bag. Twenty minutes later, a small pickup halted in the driveway and Judy emerged from the driver's side. It almost knocked me over to look at her. She was no longer the teenager I'd known. She'd blossomed into gorgeous womanhood, a shapely young mother with shoulder-length hair the color of a chestnut colt running in the sun.

"Hey, cowboy," she sang out. "It's been a long time. I heard you were working with Mr. Marshall now. It's good to see you."

I felt tongue tied, but managed to croak, "It's good to see you, too." Her father moved alongside her. I'd only met him a couple of times, but he looked much older than I remembered, and his shoulders stooped. "Tex," he said, "I know that you got hurt, and maybe you don't like us very much. But Judy believes that you and John Marshall can get my granddaughter back."

"Sir, I always admired you, but I figured you didn't think much of me back then."

"I'm sorry. I think I made every boy Judy dated feel that way. And then, there were circumstances . . ."

"Daddy, you know you liked Tex," Judy chimed in, trying to ease the strain.

"Well, if you had only listened to me about John . . ."

"Please don't, Daddy." Tears welled, and she struggled to keep them from spilling. Her father apologized and turned to Big John.

"Don't worry, we'll get your little girl back," John promised, his deep voice having a soothing effect. I nodded my agreement.

Judy's father extended his hand to John, then to me, and said, "We'll sure appreciate any help you can give us."

While he and John chatted about the mission, Judy motioned by tilting her head toward the corral and led me several yards away. "Tex, I'm sorry the way things worked out. I think you might understand a little more now. I do need your help."

"Hey, it's done and forgotten and in the past. Like John said, we'll get your daughter back." I tried not to let any bitterness show. Her father, I had always believed, had something to do with the breakup. Somehow, it had never occurred to me that another man was involved. Not wanting to rehash the past, I switched the subject. "I didn't know your family knew John Marshall. He's the right person to get this job done."

"There's something I think I should tell you. Take a walk with me out to the corral for a minute or two." She took both of my hands and pulled me in that direction. An electric shock tingled through me at her touch, making it seem for an instant as if we were two teenagers in love again.

"Tex, my little girl's name is Rae. Some people think you are her father. I really don't mind if it stays that way."

My mind reeled as I froze in my tracks. "I couldn't be—I mean—I just—" No sensible words would come to my lips, so I just stammered like an idiot.

"Think about it, Tex. Count the months and years. It's awful close to the time we were together. Isn't it possible that she could be yours?"

"If that's anywhere near the truth, then why—?"

She put her forefinger up to my lips, hushing me. "It's a long and complicated story. Right now, my dear old friend, we have urgent business." She turned to lead me back to the house. I wanted to grab her and make her say just what she meant. But she was right; other problems needed ironing out.

Before we rejoined John and her father, I reached the conclusion that the little girl really couldn't have been mine, but if that's what people wanted to believe, then so be it.

John brought us back to the task facing us. "Okay, let's get everything we need loaded up. Tex, I'll drive my truck and you pull the horse trailer with yours." Turning to Judy and her father, he added, "If you plan on coming along, pack something warm to wear. It can get chilly up there at night."

"I'm definitely going," Judy said. Her father would stay home by the phones, to field any emergency calls. As I headed toward the horses, he followed me.

"Tex, it would be less than honest if I didn't own up to my part in what happened with you and Judy. I pushed for the breakup. I'm sorry, but I just couldn't see her with a gun-toting young cowboy whose prospects didn't look very promising. Now, John has told me some things about you and I'm afraid I had the wrong impression. I wish to apologize."

I wanted to be noble, but it was difficult. "Well, I was awfully young. I'm sure you desired the best for Judy."

"Take care of my girl out there, Tex. Since my wife passed away, Judy and Rae are about all I have left."

"We'll do our best," I assured him.

Four hours into the trip we halted at a rest stop. Judy stepped out of John's truck, stretched, and asked if she could ride with me for a while. I opened my door for her, bringing a sunshine smile to her lips and a comment from her that gentlemen still existed. As we pulled out into traffic, she asked, "Why haven't you gotten married?"

"I will someday. I haven't found the right one yet."

"You don't sound too happy about it. In fact, you sound a little lonely." I felt the warmth of her presence but avoided looking into her face.

Dusk dimmed the sky after another couple of hours, and Judy had been silent for some time. I risked a glance in her direction. She was sound asleep. Even in the fading light, I could see dark circles under her eyes. The strain of worrying about her kidnaped daughter had drained her.

At Amarillo, I followed John into a truck stop, climbed out of the pickup, and gently closed the door. Inside the station, he asked, "How y'all getting along?"

"About as well as can be expected."

"You've never really gotten over her, have you? Do you still love her?"

"Yeah, I guess there's a part of me that will always love her. She was real special to me then. Seeing her now brought it all back." We walked into the cafe and slid into a booth just as Judy walked in, needing a bathroom break. We ordered hamburgers and coffee.

John spread a map on the table to point out the route we would take from Amarillo. "We'll head north from here and cut across the corner of the Oklahoma panhandle," he said, running his finger along the red road markers. "Then, we'll take 160 west from Springfield, up to Branson, right on the state line with New Mexico."

"I've been there several times," Judy piped up. "I can show you the way in."

"Good," John agreed. "We'll set up camp for a couple of days to scout the layout and observe John's routine. We should be able to find a place out there. Some of the country looks pretty remote."

Judy nodded. "It is. It's going to be hard for me to be that close and not be able to see my baby or do anything right away."

"That's the way it's gotta be," John warned. "I don't see much point in continuing on tonight. It's dark, we're tired, and there's a motel right next door. Let's get a good night's sleep and start fresh tomorrow."

After we checked in, I walked Judy to the door of her room and kissed her on the cheek.

"Tex," she said, with a hesitating softness, "would you like to—?"

"I think I'd better keep my mind on business. I want to see Rae safe in your arms as soon as possible. Sweet dreams."

After a quick breakfast and attending to our horses, we headed for Colorado. By mid-afternoon, we'd found a hidden spot to set up camp, in a small meadow by a stream of clean, fresh water, two miles from the Cove's ranch house and barn. Before saddling up the two horses, John and I convinced Judy to stay and mind the camp during scouting missions. I gave her a little snub-nosed .38 revolver in case of emergencies.

On horseback, we made our way to a high point where we could watch Cove's activities from behind an outcropping of boulders. We spotted the little girl playing in a front yard enclosure. With powerful binoculars, John learned that the gate had a latch Rae couldn't reach, but it was unlocked. "Okay, Tex," he said. "We'll just stake it out for a couple of days, keep track of his every move, and figure just how we're going to take the child." The plan was nothing new to me. It's standard procedure on most bounty hunts.

During our long hours of observation, John made some suggestions. "When we've safely got the girl, you take her and Judy south to New Mexico and I'll make sure anyone who's thinking of coming after us sees me heading north. Think you can handle it?" He gave me that knowing grin.

"Yeah, boss, I can handle it."

When the mountain shadow crept over the ranch, we returned to camp, where Judy had heated some Spam and beans for supper. "Did you see my daughter?" she begged. I felt a sense of relief that she didn't say "our daughter."

John swung his long leg over the saddle and stepped down in one graceful motion. "We sure did. And as soon as we know what kind of schedule her daddy keeps, we'll get her back for you."

By the time the sun reached its zenith on the third day, after we'd seen Cove leave the child in the play area and head to the barn, where he spent at least two hours each afternoon, we moved in. Judy doubled up with Big John on his horse, and they rode directly to the gate, where she jumped down, unlatched it, and raced to her little girl. "Be quiet, baby," she soothed, "We're going home." She scooped up the happy child, handed her up to John, and remounted behind him. They trotted easily back to camp, where I had everything ready to skedaddle. While Judy hugged Rae, I loaded John's horse, then herded Judy and Rae into the truck. We figured we had at least two hours before Cove would notice the child was missing.

"Get going, Tex," John ordered. "I'll meet you back at your place in a couple of days. Meanwhile, I'll get Cove and anyone with him headed north."

Rattling along and bumping in the potholes of the rutted road, we bounced and laughed in the truck cab. "Rae, this is Tex," Judy said to her daughter. "He's our friend from a long time ago." The tiny duplicate of her mother gave me a shy smile.

"Pleased to meet you, Miss Rae," I said, looking into her dark hazel eyes, the exact shade of my own.

"I be your fwend," she whispered.

"I'd be honored, little lady." A rush of emotion and a sudden need to blink a lot forced me to face straight ahead.

After a two-day detour through New Mexico and a couple of fun nights with the beautiful pair, I drove them into the driveway of a sprawling upscale home where Judy's father lived. "Come on in and celebrate with us, Tex," the delighted grandfather urged.

"Thanks anyway, sir. I've got to get these horses back on solid ground and fed. Maybe another time."

"We hope you mean that, my boy." I didn't feel anger. He was doing his best to make amends. "I can't thank you enough for what you and John have done." He grasped my right hand in both of his, and pumped incessantly.

"It was truly my pleasure." I looked over at Judy and Rae, both beaming. "I'll be seeing you two ladies. Take care of yourselves."

"You'd better make that a promise, Tex," Judy said.

Two days later, John and I sat again in the Rodeo Cafe and were startled when Judy walked in, leading little Rae. "Ray," she said, making it clear the name change was deliberate, "Your namesake wants to say something to you."

I looked at the child's sparkling eyes, and she carefully recited her memorized message. "I like you. And Momma likes you, too." She looked at Judy for approval, then quickly added, "And good-bye."

"Well, I don't like saying good-bye," I said, directly to the child. "That sounds like we won't see each other again." I bent down and gave her a hug. "I hope we see each other again real soon."

Judy took her hand. "C'mon, sweetheart. We have to be going. 'Bye, Ray. I hope you meant what you just said." I watched as they walked out through the door and waved back at Rae.

Big John took a sip of coffee and muttered, "I got the feeling she wanted you to ask her to stay."

"I kinda got the same feeling, but it wouldn't work out. I couldn't settle down with anyone right now. I'd be coming and going and it would just make their lives miserable." I had no sooner finished than John's wife walked in.

"Tex, a Mr. Jack Ruby called looking for you. He said he would like to meet you for lunch tomorrow at the Lone Star Drive-In at twelve-thirty."

"Wouldn't you know it? We haven't been back in town long enough to settle down, and he's calling already." I had mixed feelings. On one hand, I wouldn't really have minded if Ruby had decided to put an end to the shooting lessons. On the other, there was still a sense of mystery and excitement, plus I could use the money.

Seven

Running a little late, I pounded the steering wheel and leaned on the horn several times, trying to convince a creeping left-lane hog into passing a convoy of smoke-belching trucks on the Jacksboro Highway. I nearly got broadsided making a wild left turn into the Lone Star Drive-In. Sliding out of my truck, still boiling and muttering about other drivers' questionable ancestry, I saw Jack Ruby pull leisurely in at 12:45. I don't know why I always gave myself stress trying to be punctual.

The drive-in offered carhop service, but Ruby and I went inside, where I let my tension drain away. "Tex," he said, as we sat, "here's the deal I'm going to offer you. I'll pay you fifty dollars for every day you teach me to use a gun. One hour, or all day, makes no difference, it'll be fifty dollars."

"Can't complain about that. Seems more than fair."

"All right. Then I might want you to ride with me to check on some money, now and then."

Slapping the menu shut, I jerked the reins on that real quick. "Wait a minute! I'm not going to work for you as some kind of a bodyguard or something." A couple of heads snapped around at other tables.

"Hold on, hold on." Ruby raised both palms toward me, motioning for me to lower my voice. "Just give yourself a chance to get to know me before you start judging or making rash decisions." He reached into the breast pocket of his coat and pulled out a billfold. Peeling off four fifties, he handed them to me. "This is to start with. It's for that first lesson the other day, and an advance for the next three. Now, I plan to raise it another twenty-five each day when a friend I'm expecting gets back from New Orleans."

"What's the extra twenty-five for?" Tiny alarms buzzed deep inside me again.

"I want you to teach him how to handle a gun, right along with me."

"Who is this guy? What's his name?"

"Lee. He's just a guy I know and he needs a job. I'm thinking about putting him to work for me, and I want him to learn how to handle a gun." Ruby picked up his menu and casually scanned it as if the deal was all set.

At first, my gut feeling told me to reject adding another person to our agreement. But I couldn't think of any logical objection. It would be just as easy to teach two people, and would take very little extra time. Also, the money certainly sounded good. "Okay," I said, without much enthusiasm. "You got a deal."

"Good. I hope you're as skilled with long guns as you are with revolvers, because I also want you to teach us how to use a rifle. Think you can work that in as well?"

"I reckon so."

Over lunch, Ruby continued to ask questions about various types of guns and told me how he had been involved in some import and export business dealing in weapons. He had a better-than-average knowledge about the subject and spoke animatedly, with excitement in his voice.

I interrupted. "You know, I like guns, but there are other things in life that interest me, too. There's women, and rodeos, and music, and . . ."

"Sure," he cut me off, "but when you hold a gun, can't you just feel the power in it? It's a damn good feeling. Don't you think so?" He lifted his right hand from the table, closed it around the imaginary handgrip of a pistol, then mimed squeezing the trigger. I realized that I was dealing with a grandmaster in the game of revealing little about himself and getting the other guy to tell it all.

Trying to keep the score even, I chose to be vague. "I never really thought of it that way," I hedged.

"I want you to show us, Lee and me, how to hit a target that's moving," Ruby said, stressing the last word.

"Why a moving target?"

"In case I get robbed and want to plug the thief on the run." His answer sounded rehearsed.

I tried to think how to word my next question tactfully, but couldn't, so I just spit it out. "You're not making any special plans to shoot someone, are you?"

"Ah, don't worry." Ruby reached across the table and patted me on the shoulder. "You're all right, Tex. You're an all right kid."

Brilliant. He avoided answering my direct question, then threw in the "kid" part to get my goat. And it worked. I didn't like being called a "kid" any more than I liked anyone to call me "son." I'd left home at thirteen and made my way in a rough-and-tumble world among some hard-bitten hombres. Seemed to me like I'd earned the right to be considered a man. But I bit my lip and refused to give him the satisfaction of losing my temper.

He eased off "What do you say we go out in the morning and start to work?"

"Well, you've paid for a teacher, so I'm ready to earn my money whenever you're ready. I'll meet you here about eight-thirty."

"Whoa," Ruby groaned. "You're kidding, aren't you? I probably won't go to bed until after three in the morning, or thereabouts."

"Oh. What time would be convenient for you, then?"

"How about eleven-thirty? Or make it noon?"

"That would kill half a day. But, hey, it's your money." He smiled. "That's right. It is."

Heading to our cars outside, Ruby's mood changed suddenly. He stopped for a moment and watched a man sharply jerking the leash attached to a small dog's collar. Something had triggered his anger. In quick, giant strides, Ruby moved toward the dog walker, shouting furiously. I couldn't make out exactly what he said, but his face and waving arms made his rage very clear. I thought for a minute he was going to clobber the guy right there, but the confrontation ended without any blows.

Back at his car, he still fumed. "I can't stand to see dumb bastards abuse dogs. The little fellows have to trust people to take care of them and really have no way of fighting back. I should have kicked that guy's ass." When his anger cooled, Ruby said that a couple of his dogs, dachshunds, were his best friends. "I've thought about bringing them out to the lake with us, but I imagine the gunfire would scare the hell out of them, so I guess they're better off back in the apartment." I like dogs, too, but I agreed with his decision to leave them at home.

* * *

I watched as he aimed the white Oldsmobile into Dallas bound traffic. Each time I met with this guy, the uneasy feeling grew, but I couldn't pin down anything specific.

Back on my place, I'd finished some chores in the barn and with the horses, when John Marshall sauntered in. "How'd your meeting with Jack Ruby go?"

"He's going to pay me fifty dollars a day to teach him, even if it's only an hour or two."

"That's not bad, Tex. Seems like just a short time ago you were a scrawny pup who cleaned barns and built a fence on my place for room and board. Now, here you are, pulling down the big bucks." A broad grin accompanied his teasing.

"Yeah, that seems a lifetime ago. You were a hard old man, but I think that's what I needed then. I appreciate what you've done for me."

"You've done most of it yourself, Tex, and just fine. I reckon Jack Ruby can see that you're a capable guy, or he wouldn't be asking you to teach him. I still think he bears watching, though. He didn't just fall off the turnip truck. I hope you don't mind if I nose around once in a while."

"C'mon, John. You know very well that any part you want to play is okay with me. By the way, Jack's going to be bringing some other feller along to learn, too. Guy named Lee. He just kind of sprung it on me, and I'm not sure what to think about it. I shouldn't worry. I don't have anything they can cheat me out of."

"Did he tell you anything about this other guy?" John's face registered concern.

"Just that he's coming in from New Orleans and Jack's thinking about putting him to work."

"That's not a whole lot of information. When's he bringing him in?"

"He didn't say. I guess it could be any time. Anyway, Jack wants both him and Lee to learn to shoot a rifle, too, along with the handguns."

John studied the ground for a few moments, rubbing his chin before he spoke again. "Well, use your own good judgment, Tex, but I wouldn't show them everything I know. Never can tell. There might come a time when they turn on you and you want to have a couple of tricks in reserve they don't know about."

The warm Texas sun had rolled down to the horizon, streaking some high clouds with fiery colors by the time Big John left. I tried to watch a John Wayne movie that night on television but couldn't keep my mind on it.

Before driving to the Rodeo Cafe, I put a couple of .22-caliber revolvers in the cab of my pickup. The ammunition would be cheaper, and it might help Ruby to work with the smaller-bore weapons, then move up to .38s and .45s. I also tossed a sack of empty cans into the bed, along with a four-foot-square piece of plywood.

This time, Ruby was at the cafe promptly at noon. He chose to follow me in his car to the lake. When I pulled out the .22 pistols, he looked disappointed. "What's this?" he demanded. "These are kid's guns."

"Jack, you've got to learn how to shoot first, and then we can move up to bigger guns."

With some reluctance, he agreed. I placed the plywood on top of a discarded fifty-gallon drum, lined up the cans in a row on the wood, and paced off ten yards. I handed a loaded handgun to Ruby. "Okay, start with the ones on the left and work your way to the right, one at a time."

He quickly fired off two shots, missing with both of

them, pumping his left arm with the usual vigor. Looking at me with dismay written all over his face, he asked, "Now, what am I doing wrong?"

I reminded him of the active arm, then decided to take a new tack. "Jack, it's like a woman. You don't squeeze her too tight, or she can't breathe. When you dance, you do the leading with a light, delicate touch. It's pretty much the same way with guns. Take it slow and easy, and *gently* squeeze the trigger. It's like making love. If you get in a hurry, it's not any good at all."

The tension left Ruby's face, and he broke into laughter. "Where'd you learn something like that?"

"Big John Marshall taught it to me just that way. It's pretty accurate."

We worked for three hours, repeatedly setting up the cans after my demonstrations. Gradually, Ruby improved to the level of hitting one can out of four shots, which pleased him immensely. He was like a kid with a new toy. But he couldn't completely stop that wild left arm from gyrating back and forth. He promised again to work on it.

"I'm looking forward to the next time, Tex. I'll leave word for you at the Rodeo Cafe when I can work it in my schedule." He waved and rolled out in cloud of dust.

I was glad we had quit early enough to allow me plenty of time to get ready for my date with Ann. I pulled up in front of her house twenty minutes early to avoid making her angry again. When she'd climbed into my truck, she wanted to talk. "Tex, my mom saw you leaving the cafe with some guy in a suit who she thought looked like a gangster. Someone told her he's the guy you're teaching to use guns. She's worried about it and putting pressure on me to stop seeing you. Would you be willing to stop seeing that guy for me?

"Ann, he's paying me well to teach him, and I don't see anything wrong with it."

"But Tex, she thinks you're probably making more money with your guns than she does at a legitimate job. Mom said you might as well be a hired killer."

The words hit me like a slap on the face. I had to wait a few seconds so I wouldn't explode in anger. When I'd simmered down and felt more composed, I answered. "Ann, that's ridiculous. I think your mom is drawing some unfair conclusions. I'm sorry she thinks that way, but the man paid me in advance, and I'm not going to back down."

She jumped out of the truck, slammed the door, and yelled, "You're so hardheaded."

"Maybe I am. But I'm not going to welch on a deal." I didn't voice my real thoughts, that it was none of the old lady's business what I did, and I sure as hell wasn't going to let her run my life.

"You're going to regret it," Ann shrieked, and stormed back into her house.

Since my reunion with Judy, and meeting her little girl, Rae, I probably hadn't been very good company for Ann, anyway. But I felt bad about our broken plans, and a little sorry for myself. I didn't want to spend the evening alone, and I didn't want to beg for a last-minute date from any of the other girls I knew. I stopped at a pay phone and called John Marshall.

"I thought you had a date tonight," he chuckled.

"I did. But I don't now."

"Why don't you come on over and have some supper with us? I'll throw another T-bone on the grill for you. We've got plenty of stuff."

When I arrived, John and his wife were in the backyard, cooking on an outdoor grill. I explained about Ann's mother thinking I was hanging around with gangsters and reckoned that Ann seemed ready to accept that judgment without even hearing my side of it. "I guess we're all washed up."

"That's too bad, Tex," John's wife sympathized. "I know it hurts."

John nodded agreement. "It's not easy, I know. But I admire your decision to stick with a job you've taken on." He lifted three thick steaks from the smoking grill, and handed me a plate. I loaded it from a pile of roasting ears, fresh tomato slices, and hot biscuits. We sat outside at a redwood picnic table, munched on the tasty meal, and talked the evening away. They were truly my family.

Near the end of the week, Ruby left word at the cafe, as he'd promised, and we arranged for another shooting session. I threw an old tire and some rope into the bed of my pickup, planning for a new exercise. At the lake again, he watched as I hung the tire from a tree, like a child's swing, and placed four cans in the groove. After giving the tire a push, we paced off the usual distance and took turns firing at the swinging target. Ruby loved it. His enthusiasm soared, and we used up four boxes of ammunition in two hours. I could see improvement in his skills, but that damned left arm just would not stay still.

"When can we start using some bigger guns again?" Ruby asked.

"Don't be in such a hurry. The fast movements we're starting to practice can get you killed with the higher-caliber weapons," I warned. I could see a stubborn streak forming in him. He insisted that we step up to the bigger bore guns and some rifles. "You're really getting wrapped up in this, aren't you?" I asked.

"I have to admit that I enjoy it, Tex, and I think it'll be useful to me. Plus, it's a nice break from the business routine at the clubs. Some problems there have been getting on my nerves." He asked if I had access to any rifles. I told him I had some, and could borrow more from John Marshall. We agreed that we would use them in our next session.

As we parted, Ruby's new enthusiasm reflected itself in his wanting to meet again in two days, at 9:30 in the morning.

I returned to the Rodeo Cafe for supper, where my eyes kept straying to a nearby booth while I ate. Three very attractive young women occupied it, and their chattering voices partially reached my hearing range. From their high-pitched giggles, I got the impression they were exchanging some hilarious jokes, sharing scandalous gossip, or talking about men. When some fellows who'd also been rather loud got up and left, the place was quiet enough for me to hear most of what the women were saying. I didn't make a habit of eavesdropping, but their words were easily heard. Several times, I caught them darting looks in my direction. One of them said, "I was told that his friend runs some clubs over in Dallas. The girls who work in his place make oodles of money in a single night. I tried to get a job dancing there, but I guess I don't have the boobs for it."

"That sounds exciting," a second girl chimed in. "I wonder if they would hire me. I'm a hot number when it comes to dancing." That brought another round of giggles.

The waitress came over to my table to make small talk and asked how my teaching job was coming along. I realized who had told the laughing trio about Jack Ruby's clubs. While she still stood there, one of the girls slid out of the booth and walked over to us. I hoped I didn't drool or look pop-eyed. A vision of lush beauty, she stood about five-six and wore a summery light blue skirt with a low-cut white blouse. Her bouncy blond hair, cut in a cute little flip style, and eyes the color of bluebonnet petals accentuated a face that belonged on magazine covers. Her legs reached all the way to heaven. Mentally, I nicknamed her "Angel."

Her smile increased my heartbeat. " 'Scuse me," she sang, "Is it true that the man you've been meeting here, the one in the suit, owns some nightclubs over in Dallas?"

"Yeah, I've heard that. I've been doing some work with him, but it doesn't involve his businesses." I tried to sound sophisticated, but I'm not sure I was successful.

"We'd sure like to meet him, if we could," she cooed.

"That shouldn't be too difficult. He'll be here about 9:30 tomorrow morning." She had such a wholesome look, I hated to think of her working in one of Ruby's strip joints. I wondered if she really knew what she was asking for. I had no doubt that Ruby would be very interested in her.

"Thanks," she said, and whirled around to return to her companions. They chattered about splitting their tab, then headed toward the cash register. The one who'd spoken to me turned around and said, "I'll see you tomorrow, cowboy." She was a real flirt and had the technique down to a fine art.

One of her pals glanced in my direction and said, "I'll

bet he can't even ride a horse." Her comment caused the third one to giggle hysterically.

Angel walked over to me again and asked, "Are you a real cowboy?" Another burst of snickering from the other two. I felt like they were playing with me, but I decided to go along with the gag.

"I ride and raise Appaloosa horses, not cattle. I've been around ranches all my life. Yeah, I guess I qualify to be a real cowboy."

With another smile, Angel returned to her giggling pals and demanded, "Okay, pay up. I told you he was a real cowboy." The other two, playing at pouting, handed her some folded bills. I didn't know whether to be flattered or insulted. I chose the former. As they departed, Angel turned again, and in that voice of pure music, said, "Thanks, Cowboy. See you in the morning. I'll be here to meet your friend."

Eight

When John Marshall dropped by that evening to help me with some barn chores, he still appeared concerned about the turn of events in my bargain with Jack Ruby. In contrast to John's agitation, I felt great. My meeting with the girl I thought of as "Angel" had lifted my spirits and eased the anxiety I'd been feeling about the mysterious Mr. Ruby and his desire to master the art of shooting.

"Y' know, John, believe it or not, I think there's some hope for Ruby's gunsmanship. I'm actually getting to like the man. He kind of grows on you, I guess."

After a period of thoughtful silence while chewing on a straw, John spoke. "I can see that he's a pretty slick dude, Tex, and persuasive as hell. He's made that his business his whole life, and he's good at it. I have a lot of trust in your ability to judge people and see through any con games. And I know you're curious, just like when you were a kid, poking a long stick at a rattlesnake to see how it would react. Don't get bit, Tex."

"I appreciate the advice, John, and I truly respect it. I can't remember you ever being wrong. I promise to watch my step." Filling a feed bucket with some oats, I shifted the subject. "You ought to see the honey I met at the cafe this afternoon. Wow! She's as pretty a woman as I've ever met, maybe even seen in person. I don't know her real name, but to me, she's 'Angel.' I'd like to take her out, even though I think she's a year or two older than me. Only one thing worries me."

"What's that?"

"She wants to meet Jack Ruby. Says she needs to make some money and wants to ask him for a job. I can't sit easy with the idea of her taking off her clothes in one of his sleazy clubs."

"Maybe she meant she wanted office work, or receptionist, or waitress."

"Nah. I overhead her telling the two women she was with that she'd like to dance. If she starts something like that, dancing around damn near naked, she'll get all used up and ruined. Probably thinks it's all fun and games."

John took a long look at my expression. "Boy, that girl really got to you, didn't she?"

"You should have seen her. She's the kind that makes you go weak in the knees."

He started laughing. I know he didn't mean to, but it made me feel foolish for going so goofy over a girl I knew nothing about. Maybe I was vulnerable to her charms because of my troubles with Ann and the recent emotional upset caused by seeing Judy again. Their faces tumbled around in my mind, blurred behind the sunny brilliance of Angel's perfect features. John recognized my discombobulation and laid a big paw on my back. "Don't worry, son. Everything'll come out in the wash."

I rolled out of the sack at 5:30 in the morning, eager to meet Angel again. With the horses fed and my four rooms as neat as they'd ever been, I showered and put on my favorite outfit: a red long-sleeved shirt with snap buttons, clean Levis belted with a silver buckle I'd won with a champion Appaloosa, the black leather vest, my best hand-tooled pointed boots. Topped by my silver-banded black Stetson, I examined the results in a mirror. The fellow staring back at me looked a lot more relaxed than I felt, with butterflies replaying the battle of the Alamo inside my stomach.

Too early, I took my usual table in the Rodeo, ignored Tommy's smart-aleck comments about being all slicked up, and sipped coffee until she came in. Angel looked just as gorgeous and feminine in tight jeans, high heels, and a blue checkered blouse as she had in the skirt. With the grace of a goddess she glided over to my table. "Hi, Cowboy. I'm glad you're here."

I stood, remembering the gallantry people had tried to instill in me for years, and pulled out a chair for her. "Why don't you call me Tex? All my friends do."

"Am I going to be your friend, Tex?" A coy smile lifted the corners of her full lips. The crusty array of old-timers sitting at the counter stools and booths, nearly got whiplash twisting their heads to watch her.

"Yeah, I think I'd like that," I squawked. I could hardly recognize my own voice, which sounded too loud and high-pitched. Trying to lower it to Clint Walker's masculine bass, like when he faced down the hostile Indians in the movie *Yellowstone Kelly*, I told her that I'd already decided what her name was.

With a delighted giggle, she coaxed me to tell her. "Well, it's not Hortense," I teased, "nor Petunia, and it's not Matilda." She shook her head, laughing, and wrinkled her nose.

"C'mon. What did you name me?"

"Gosh. This is kind of embarrassing. But to me, you

look like you just dropped down from heaven, so I've been thinking of you as Angel."

"Why, Tex, I think that's lovely. What a beautiful thing to say. I think I'll change my name permanently to Angel."

I regretted telling her, because now she might be reluctant to reveal her real name. But the curiosity in my eyes must have given me away. She said, "I'd be honored if you wanted to call me Angel anytime, but most of my friends call me Candy." I wanted to make some comment about that being just as sweet, but held my tongue. She turned to Tommy, whose eyes had also zeroed in on her, and ordered coffee with lots of cream, no sugar. I'd just started to open my mouth to learn more about her when Jack Ruby made his entrance. Damn!

He marched over to us, removed his hat while eyeing Candy, and asked, "Tex, who's your attractive companion?" Without waiting for an answer, he thrust an open hand toward her and said, "My name's Jack."

"Pleased to meet you," she said, putting dainty manicured fingers into his. "My name's Candy." She flashed me a conspiratorial smile. Ruby sat and signaled Tommy an order for coffee.

Never tearing his gaze from Candy, he said, "This time of the morning is a real struggle for me. I run a couple of nightclubs that keep me up until the wee hours. I haven't seen the sun rise for a long time."

"I've heard about your clubs, Jack," Candy purred. "Actually, that's why I'm here. I persuaded Tex to introduce us. My girlfriend and I arrived from Florida a few days ago, and we need jobs. We heard you're the man to talk to. We can put on a damn good floor show."

Now I wondered if she'd had experience dancing in a nightclub. Her innocent looks didn't seem consistent with that type of work, but maybe I'd been lulled into a false impression. Tommy came over with the coffee and a notepad to take our orders. "My place would be full all the time if I had a waitress who looked like you," he said. I got the impression he was offering her a job as a waitress to rescue her from Ruby's clutches. But she ignored it, probably having heard every kind of an offer a man could dream up. Tommy shrugged, and left without taking any breakfast orders.

Had I completely misread her? I sure didn't want to think so, but she acted too at ease with Ruby. A hint of depression clouded my good mood, threatening to rain all over it.

Ruby handed her a business card and suggested she drop by the Carousel Club on the corner of Commerce and Field, in Dallas, any evening after seven. He'd be very interested in finding a job for her, he hinted, and mentioned that he was thinking about opening up a new club. He finally turned to me. "Tex, this is just too early for my night-owl blood. Let's make it another day."

"You're calling the shots," I muttered.

Facing Candy, and grinning like a dog eating burrs, he asked, "Do you have a place to stay?"

"We're temporarily living with a friend of ours here in Fort Worth," she said, deftly avoiding the obvious bait.

"Tell you what," Ruby said, "why don't we get you and your friend settled into a place of your own, closer to the clubs in Dallas? We can take a run over there now, if you'd like, and have a look around. We'll drop by the club, and I can show you the layout." Without bothering to face me, he said, "Tex, let's make it Thursday."

"Thursday it is." I felt like a damn fool. Candy gave me a pouting "I'm sorry" look, then rose as Ruby pulled her chair out. He flipped a couple of dollars onto the table for the coffee and escorted her toward the door.

I looked over at Tommy, who was shaking his head and watching Candy's backside as she walked away.

The Thursday meeting with Jack Ruby turned out to involve more talking than shooting. We practiced with the guns, but his interest was halfhearted. The late-autumn sun was warm with strength-sapping humidity, so we drove back over to an air-conditioned cafe on the Jacksboro highway for a cold drink. He picked up a newspaper someone had left, and absent-mindedly scanned it. His interest perked up at one article. He commented, "Says here that all that conflict over in Vietnam will be over by the end of 1965. I hope so. We've been sending military people over there as advisers. Hell, if our government isn't careful, we'll wind up in a full-fledged war in that hellhole. The French found out you can't win in those jungles, got smart, and got out. I hope the president doesn't make the same mistake. Let the people over there fight their own battles. Who gives a damn if the communists take it over? There's nothing there for us."

I had heard about some kind of struggle in that part of the world, but didn't pay too much attention to it. It wouldn't effect me, anyway. When I'd registered at my draft board, I hobbled in on crutches with a broken ankle, courtesy of an Appaloosa who didn't take kindly to a saddle on his back. After the physical examination, they'd classified me 4-F, ineligible for induction into military services. I didn't have any trouble accepting their decision because my plans for the future certainly didn't include spending two years in some godforsaken army post.

Sipping his drink, Ruby asked about my school years and I told him that I'd left home early and had had to learn what I knew the hard way. "Is that right?" he responded, with a burst of enthusiasm. "I did the same thing. Like I told you before, my family lived up in Chicago. There were eight of us kids and we moved around a lot. School was the dumps. I got tired of it and dropped out for a while, then went back and finally quit again before I finished high school." He fell silent for a few moments, as if lost in the past, then asked, "How about your parents? You get along with them okay?"

"I was mostly raised by an aunt and uncle."

"My old man cut out on us when I was a little kid," he said. "My mom had a tough time and went a little batty. Made it rough on my brothers and sisters. I spent a lot of time on the streets and learned how to handle myself when guys tried to get tough. You ever hear of a boxer named Barney Ross?"

"No. 'Fraid not."

"Nah, you wouldn't have. He was before your time. Barney was a buddy of mine when we were kids, and we used to spar around, boxing together. He went pro and won the welterweight championship of the world. But I got tired hanging around Chicago and decided to give California a try. Spent some time in L.A. and San Francisco. There was a gal there I thought about marrying."

For the first time I wondered whether he'd ever been married and asked him about it. "Nah. I never found the right one." He seemed uncomfortable with the subject, so I let it drop. He stood and said, "I have to go. Got some telephone calls to make."

Ruby said he had to go to New Orleans over the weekend to scout out some new dancers for his club, and asked if we could meet again next Wednesday. That was fine with me. This time, Ruby wanted to meet at noon in the Clover Club restaurant, about two and a half miles east of the Rodeo Cafe. "I'll bring Lee with me," he said.

I returned to the Rodeo and found a message waiting for me. Candy had left a telephone number and asked me to call her. I didn't know what to expect as I dialed the pay phone.

"Oh, hi, Tex," she sang. "I just wanted to thank you again for introducing me to Jack Ruby. He hired me on a training basis, and it wouldn't have happened without you." Then she shocked me almost out of my boots. "I'm off tonight, and I was wondering if you'd like to get together."

"You bet," I replied, trying not to stammer. "A few of my friends are coming over to my place tonight for an outdoor barbecue. I'd like you to meet them. Especially John Marshall and his wife."

A fresh breeze cleared the warm air as I drove back into town late that afternoon to pick Candy up at the Rodeo. She chatted gaily all the way out to my little spread, but avoided mentioning Jack Ruby or her new job. John Marshall, his wife, Tommy, and four other pals welcomed Candy into the group with sincere Texas hospitality. Big John gave me a quiet nod of approval. The dropping sun colored the horizon in pastel shades of scarlet and gold, adding a nice touch to the outdoor meal.

After everyone pitched in to clean up the mess, said their goodbyes, and departed, I asked Candy if she'd like to go for a moonlight horseback ride. She clapped her hands like a child, saying she'd love to. I put her astride a gentle old mare, climbed up on Chief, my favorite Appaloosa, and we rode leisurely through the pasture and along a creek bed. The breeze had played out, but it had washed the air clear, leaving sparkling stars and soft moonlight. Candy sat that horse as gracefully as she moved on foot, and as well as she danced I'm sure. I was tempted to ask her if she was learning to dance in Ruby's club but didn't want to seem like I was prying or judging her.

We dismounted on a little knoll and sat on a stump. "Tex," she whispered, "how come you haven't tried to put the make on me?" The question caught me completely off guard, and I struggled for an answer.

"I think it's wise not to rush important things." I paused, not having a clue how to follow up. Finally, without looking her in the face, I asked, "So, how do you like working for Jack?"

"I don't know yet. It looks like an opportunity to earn a lot of money, counting tips." She stared off into the dark. The mood was romantic, but I felt a strong internal conflict. Because of my curiosity and concern for Candy, I itched to keep asking questions, but something held me back. Maybe I really didn't want to know if she was going to be a stripper.

We rode back to the barn, exchanging pleasant conversation, nothing too deep or personal. I drove her into town and we had coffee at the Rodeo, where her girlfriends had agreed to pick her up for a ride back to their apartment. I didn't know if she was being purposely secretive about the location, or if she was just being considerate, not asking me to drive the extra distance. When they arrived, Candy gave me a discreet peck on the cheek and said she'd really enjoyed the evening and hoped we could do it again soon.

I spent the night tossing and turning. I felt such a strong attraction to her, but had serious doubts about having a relationship with someone who might be taking off her clothes for a living. I'd really meant it when I'd said it's important not to rush things.

Nine

On Friday morning, I helped a neighbor round up a dozen stray cattle that had bolted through a fence, then tackled a long list of backed-up chores on my own place. Over the next few days, I resisted the urge to call Candy, even though romantic and biological urges tried to convince me otherwise.

When Wednesday rolled around, I headed into town to meet Ruby and the man he had mentioned, the one named Lee.

At the Clover Club restaurant, I waited an impatient, irritating twenty minutes before Ruby walked in. He apologized, and we sat near a window over coffee and iced tea. Ruby kept glancing at his watch, then finally looked through the window and said, "Here comes Lee now."

I don't know exactly what I expected Lee to look like, but he didn't fit any preconceived notions. Possibly, I thought he would wear a suit like Ruby and have the swarthy, menacing look of a movie gangster. Lee walked through the door, spotted Ruby, and marched confidently to the table. He did not look like a gangster. In his mid-twenties, he stood about five-nine and had short dark brown hair beginning to thin at the hairline and a high forehead. His most noticeable feature, on first impression, was his mouth, set between cherub cheeks over a little chin. With a razor-thin upper lip, and the lower lip slightly protruding, he held his mouth in a stiff smirk, which gave him an uptight, arrogant look. His gray eyes stared with intensity. A white, slightly wrinkled short-sleeved sport shirt hung over his narrow shoulders and covered a flat stomach. He probably didn't weigh more than 140 or 150 pounds.

"Lee, I'd like you to meet Tex Brown, the guy I've been telling you about," Ruby said, motioning him to sit. "Tex, this is Lee Oswald."

Without offering a handshake, Lee eased into a chair and spoke. "Mr. Ruby tells me you're very accomplished with guns. Are you as good as he says?" The softer accent sounded more like Louisiana than Texas.

Feeling my hackles rising, I waited a couple of seconds before answering. "I can hit a target when I need to."

"So, you're going to teach us how to do it and make us experts, too?" Without waiting for an answer, he continued, "I don't think you should have too much trouble. Mr. Ruby and I have both been in the military, and we qualified with M-1 rifles. I earned a sharpshooter badge in the Marine Corps and had some follow-up training when I did intelligence work in Japan. I'm also quite familiar with weapons used in the Soviet Union." He seemed to want to make a big impact regarding his personal importance and his international accomplishments, but it had the opposite effect on me.

"Well, that's pretty impressive, Lee," I lied. "Should make my work real easy." I hoped he could do as well as he boasted, because that would shorten the time I'd have to spend with him. A strong feeling overcame me, a realization that I wouldn't be able to tolerate spending a whole lot of time around him. The guy must have had very few friends, with his holier-than-thou attitude. To keep from saying anything more sarcastic to Oswald, I turned to Ruby to express surprise about his military experience, and asked him about it.

"No big deal," he said. "I got drafted into the Army during World War Two. Landed in the Army Air Corps. In basic training, I did okay on the shooting range with a .30-caliber carbine and what we called a grease gun, a .45-caliber submachine gun. It took me a coupla tries to get used to the M-1, but I finally made it, then had to requalify each year until they discharged me in early 'forty-six. They taught me how to do mechanic work on airplanes. Didn't even leave the States, missed out on combat, so I never had to shoot anyone," he laughed. "And I've probably forgotten what little bit I learned about shooting. Did you remember to bring some rifles to try out today?"

"Sure did." As soon as we finished eating a light lunch, we crowded into my pickup and drove to the lake. I lifted two small-caliber rifles from a locked compartment in the bed of my truck.

Oswald took one look and repeated the same complaint I'd heard from Ruby about small-caliber handguns. "I thought you said you had some guns. Those are nothing but twenty-twos."

"Well, Lee, if I was going to teach you to drive, I'd take you out in an old jalopy first, not a Mercedes-Benz racing car. If you wanted to learn to ride a horse, I'd put you on a gentle old mare, not a buckin' bronc. Lee, if you want to learn, we'll start with these, and move up to bigger-bore rifles and handguns later. Ammunition is cheaper, and these will give me an idea just how much teaching you'll need."

I handed him one of the guns, a semi-automatic loaded

with five long-rifle rounds. "Don't start shooting until I get some cans set up on that barrel over there."

When I returned to the firing line, after arranging a row of ten targets, I made clear to Oswald the importance of looking to his right, his left, and down range before firing. "Okay, start with the can on the left and work your way to the right."

As soon as he raised the rifle, I could see we had big problems. If he'd handled weapons in the Marines, he'd forgotten everything he'd learned, as Jack had said about himself. Oswald's stance was wrong, he had his right elbow too low, his grip was sloppy, and he jerked the trigger. It took him six shots to hit one can. I couldn't hold my tongue. "Marksman, huh?" He handed the gun back to me, mumbling something I couldn't understand. It sounded like a foreign language. I assumed he was making some lame excuse for his inept performance. Handing the other rifle to Ruby, I reloaded the one Oswald had used, and allowed myself to show off. I popped off five cans shooting right-handed, then switched to a left-handed stance and blew over the remaining four. In my mind, I could see the ghosts of those old coyotes and rabbits thumping down in the prairie dust.

Oswald's tight little smirk relaxed, and he forced a silly grin. I had to rub it in a little more. "Gee, I'm sorry I don't have the benefit of all that military training." Ruby covered his mouth to stifle a laugh, while Oswald just stared off into the distance. "Jack, do you want to take a few shots with a handgun and show Lee what you've learned?"

Ruby accepted the show-and-tell assignment, pointing a .22 revolver at the cans I'd reset. With four shots he whacked two cans. After a pause, he hit three of four. Lee congratulated him and I commented on his improvement, but reminded him of that damned left arm, crooked at the elbow, which kept swinging like he was sawing wood. Ruby suggested to Oswald that he needed to pay close attention to what I would show him, admitting that in our first couple of days together, his performance had been miserable.

We worked for about an hour, with me pointing out Oswald's errors to him, then pushing and pulling him into proper positions. He would stand correctly, with the right grip, for two or three shots, then revert back to his faulty ways. Seeming bored with the rifle, he kept asking questions about handguns. "What's the best size to use? Is an automatic better than a revolver?"

I guessed I owed him some answers, considering the money Ruby was paying. "The size of the weapon depends on who is using it and why," I explained. "For example, a lot of plainclothes cops stick with snub-nosed revolvers with two-inch barrels. Makes it easier to conceal under a coat, it's faster to draw, and it fits snugly in a shoulder holster. They also want the weapon to be equipped with a protected ejector rod, that little thing sticking out in front of the cylinder, under the barrel. It pushes the empty shell out of the cylinder. If it gets bent, it could cost a cop his life in a shootout. If you're hunting small game in the woods, a long barrel, up to eight inches, would probably give you more accuracy, but a slower draw. You gotta take balance into consideration, too. Some muzzles are heavier than others, changing the balance of different guns and various makes. So that's a matter of individual preference.

"My experience with automatics, or semi-automatic handguns, makes me shy away from them. They tend to jam, so I've always considered a revolver more reliable, especially in a prolonged shootout."

Lee wanted to know about "fanning" the hammer versus

just pulling the trigger, like he'd seen in wild west movies. I explained that revolvers are either single-action, in which you have to cock the hammer with your thumb for each shot, or double-action, where you can keep pulling the trigger repeatedly without manually cocking it. Fanning would involve holding a single-action trigger in the pull position and running your other palm backward over the hammer in fast sequence, letting it arc forward, striking the primer of the bullet, and firing it. I think it disappointed Lee when I told him that fanning was rarely used any more and could damage the gun's mechanism.

Ruby asked why some triggers seemed stiff and hard to pull, while others fired the gun with a feather touch.

"You have to adjust it to your own liking by using a trigger pull gauge. I generally keep my single-action guns set for a little less than a three-pound break, and my double action for about eight pounds."

I wound up the lecture by revealing a couple of little secrets about accuracy. "A person gets accustomed to his own revolver, the feel of it, the balance, the roll of the forefinger on the trigger, and can develop a high level of proficiency by practicing with the same weapon." Professionals, I advised, usually keep a second backup weapon identical to the first one, and practice with both. If someone else borrows your gun, they will invariably pull their shots to the right or the left until they get used to that particular piece. So, I told them, once we got past some of the basics, it'd be best to practice with their own weapons.

"The other important thing to remember," I said, "is the seven-yard rule. Which means that about ninety-nine percent of shootouts happen with people who are within twenty-one feet of each other. So the person who keeps cool and uses the gun with habits he's learned from long hours of practice will be the winner. The other guy, who gets excited and wild, will be lying on the ground, shot full of holes." I thought that was enough lecturing for one day.

Deciding to demonstrate his vast knowledge, Lee said guns were the easiest thing in the world to acquire. He informed us that you can get anything you want by mail order. "You can get the guns easy, and you can get them cheap." I knew there were far better ways to shop for guns that would allow you to select exactly the right one for your personal needs, but I chose not to enter into a head-butting contest with Oswald.

After we fired a few more rounds, Ruby decided to cut the day short. "Got some business back at the Carousel," he complained. "Some of the other club owners are giving me serious headaches by using amateur strippers in dance contests. Hell, the regular girls belong to a union, and it's not fair to put newcomers on at half pay unless we can all do it. I know customers flock to the joints because they have this fantasy about watching some housewife or secretary strip on so-called amateur nights, but it's not right. The other owners boost up their profits while legitimate operators, like me, pay full wages. I already complained to the Guild, but some of my competitors are still violating the rules. I travel all over trying to find good, professional dancers, and I think it's only fair that we all operate by the same rules. My colleagues in New Orleans feel the same way."

Curiosity nearly forced me to ask questions about Candy, but my commitment to John Marshall to avoid getting tangled up in Ruby's personal or business affairs won out.

On the way back to town, Oswald tried to probe for information about my political leanings, but I was in no mood to reveal anything about myself to him. We wheeled into the Clover Club parking lot, and I was surprised to see Candy standing near Ruby's Oldsmobile. As soon as I braked to a halt, Ruby and Oswald slid out and walked to the car, while she rushed around to my window, stuck her head inside, and gave me a quick hug and a kiss. I felt like sunshine had just broken through on a cloudy day. She said she just wanted to thank me again for helping her get the job and wanted to know if I was doing anything Sunday. I told her I didn't know yet.

"I'll get off about 3 AM. What would you do if I came out and woke you up and spent the day with you?"

"That sounds great, but won't you need to rest? You don't owe me anything for getting that job. Whatever little bit of help I gave, I was glad to do it." My words weren't completely honest because I still felt she didn't belong in Ruby's world.

"I know that, Tex. I enjoyed being with you before, and I'd like do it again."

"Well, I'm sure as heck not going to turn you down. I've been thinking about you ever since I first met you." I leaned toward her and returned the kiss, putting everything I had into it.

"It's a date, then?" she whispered.

"You bet. I'll see you when you get there." She waved at Ruby, blew me another kiss, climbed into a Volkswagen I hadn't seen before, and left.

Ruby walked over to my window. "Now that Candy's working for me, why don't you come on over to the club sometime?"

"No, thanks. Her work is one thing and her private life is another. Right now, I don't think it's a good idea to mix them up."

"Tex, you got some funny ways, but I like you. See you tomorrow, same time, same place." He smiled, shook his head, and returned to the Oldsmobile, where Oswald waited, drumming his fingers on the hood.

It had become standard practice for me to utilize the Rodeo Cafe as headquarters and message center. Tommy asked if Candy had found me, proudly informing me that he'd given her directions to the Clover Club. "I think she kinda likes you, cowboy."

"Thanks, pardner. She's sure an eyeful, and she has a great personality. Right now, though, I think I'll just proceed with caution. I don't think either of us is looking for a serious relationship."

Oswald and Ruby surprised me on Thursday morning by showing up at my place an hour before noon. They hadn't forewarned me. "Are you ready to do some shooting?" Ruby yelled apologetically.

"Sure. Just give me a few minutes to finish up a couple of things."

"How about you taking Lee out to the lake, and I'll meet you after awhile? I have some business in town first." I agreed despite my reservations.

En route to the lake, Oswald said he thought I had an ideal situation. "You work for yourself and not for some bureaucratic dictator where petty officials impose hardship on the workers. You don't have to tolerate imperialistic ideology."

I twisted my head to the right. "What the hell are you talking about?"

"I'm simply admiring your independence. I think there's a world struggle coming that will result in freedom for everyone, like you already have. Capitalism is dying. For a while, I thought the Communist system they have in the Soviet Union was the answer, but I realized that Marxism is probably the real solution. If a person makes a choice between capitalism and Communism, he's doing nothing but choosing between oppression and poverty. You're not really a capitalist, are you, Tex?"

"Lee, I'm a guy who wants nothing but to make an honest living raising horses. I'm teaching you and Jack how to use guns to earn a few extra bucks for some things I need. You might call it one of my side businesses. And I'm an American, through and through. I don't have any room in my life for any radical politics."

"But don't you realize the need in this country to eliminate racial segregation and oppression of the masses? Don't you think that capitalists hoard all the wealth at the expense of the proletariat? We have to end the struggle between extremist governments that enslave all of us."

"Where'd you get all of these ideas?"

"Didn't Mr. Ruby tell you? I spent two and a half years living in Russia. I met Marina, my wife, and brought her with me when I returned in April, last year. But I've been interested in Marxism since I was in grade school."

"No, Jack didn't tell me very much at all about you, except that he wants you to learn how to use guns. What the hell were you doing living in Russia?"

"I wanted to see how Communism worked. And I was greatly disappointed. Now, I'd like to know more about the revolution in Cuba, and maybe live there."

"So what have you been doing since you got back to the U.S.?"

"I started a chapter of the Fair Play for Cuba organization in New Orleans while I lived there last spring and summer. But I got arrested by the oppressive Nazi police for defending myself when I was attacked by hoodlums because I was passing out leaflets. The New York leader of the movement regards me now as a hero."

"Why'd you come back to Texas?"

"My wife, Marina, and my little daughter were staying in Irving with some friends because she's going to have another baby any day now. Some opportunities exist here that were not available in New Orleans."

"I hope those opportunities have nothing to do with using guns," I said, stating each word clearly. Oswald didn't answer as we braked to a stop near the lake. Our target practice, for the next hour, was with my .22 pistol. When Ruby arrived, we continued using handguns until about 1:30, when they left together.

I drove to a local market, picked up some Dr. Pepper and potato chips, and returned to the lake to sit by myself and try to settle the nagging worry, or maybe premonition, that something bad was about to happen. I sat there until the sun dropped low in the western sky, coloring the lake surface the same hues as leaves still dangling on nearly bare branches. The long, skeletal shadows from the trees lay on the thick autumn carpet covering the ground all around me, deepening my sense of dark foreboding.

Ten

At my request, John Marshall joined our target practice on Friday afternoon. I had asked him to come along to observe the abrasive, obnoxious personality of Lee Oswald with the hope that Big John could help me try to understand it and cope with it. Tommy wanted to tag along, too, so he left his Rodeo Cafe duties in the hands of a part-time cook.

True to form, Oswald, dressed in a black t-shirt, ill-fitting dark cotton pants, and shoes with well-worn heels, gave us that same arrogant smirk. As soon as he hopped out of Ruby's car and met Marshall, he began asking rude questions. He wanted to know if Big John had ever killed anyone with his guns, and how a bounty hunter could live with his conscience after chasing men as if they were hunted animals. For the most part Marshall ignored him, with that remarkable calm and dignity I hoped I could someday master. The only time I saw John's eyes glint, with a ripple of his jaw muscles, was when Oswald made some tactless remark about an over-the-hill soldier of fortune being lucky to survive so long.

We loaded the guns and Jack Ruby scored three hits along the row of tin cans out of six shots. He handed me the pistol and held both thumbs up with grinning pride. Oswald missed all six on his first try. Incredibly, he challenged Big John, suggesting that an old man probably couldn't do any better. Before the last word had left Lee's mouth, John drew his Colt .45 and decimated six cans in four seconds flat.

I knew what was coming next. John held a silver dollar on the back of his left hand and said he'd drop the hand, draw his gun, and fire three shots before it hit the ground. Both Oswald and Ruby shook their heads. "Impossible," Oswald said. "No one is that fast."

"I've got a hundred-dollar bill that says I can," John said.

Ruby covered the wager. I think he knew he was going to lose, because he was too experienced to be drawn into a sucker bet. But he still wanted something from us and thought the money might help grease the way and ingratiate him with both of us. He even forced Oswald to cover an additional gamble of ten dollars put up by Tommy.

Marshall extended his yard-long left arm, balancing a polished silver dollar on the back of his huge hand. He held it steady for ten seconds, then, with blinding speed, dropped it and filled the air with three explosions.

Lee and Jack whined that it had happened too fast, making it impossible to tell if the final shot had been fired before the coin had hit the ground. Big John winked at me, smiled, and repeated the performance, leaving no doubt this time. My pride in his skill nearly burst the buttons off my shirt. Jack paid off with the flair of a bigtime gambler, while Lee begrudgingly pulled a bill from his wallet. I think it was his last one. For the first time, I felt somewhat sorry for him, recognizing that he obviously had very little money.

I pulled my .30-.30 from the truck and handed it to Lee. At least, he assumed a reasonably good stance and grip this time, as I'd shown him, but he still failed to hit anything.

When Ruby took his turn with the rifle, he hit two cans with four shots.

John complimented him. "Not bad, for a big city boy."

"Coming from you," Ruby said, "that's very welcome praise." After another hour and several boxes of expended shells, we quit.

Back at the cafe, while preparing to depart, before John and Tommy had yet arrived, Lee said to Jack, "Well, I can see why you hired that old man and him," referring to me as if I wasn't standing right next to him.

I couldn't hold back any longer. "If I were you, Lee, I wouldn't call John Marshall an old man, at least where he, or anyone he knows, can hear you. He just might wallop you upside the head."

"Well, he *is* getting old."

"I don't know what you consider old, but he's probably got more good years left in him than you do." I felt like belting him one myself.

Oswald changed the subject, still addressing Ruby. "This coming weekend, I'm going to visit Marina over at the house where she's staying, so I won't be able to meet you. On Monday, I'm going to have to find a different rooming house. That bitch where I'm staying told me this morning that I'd have to get out. Hell, I've only been there five days. I don't know why she's mad at me."

I could guess.

Ruby patted him on the shoulder. "No problem. We'll look around in the Oak Cliff section where I live and find a new place for you. That would be a lot more convenient, anyway."

It didn't surprise me to learn that Oswald and his wife

were living separately. Of course, I had no inkling why, but with his personality, I doubted any woman would want to be with him for very long. Lee set up a howl about the transportation problems he'd encountered in Dallas. Since he didn't drive, he usually walked, rode buses, or hitched a ride with Jack. He said the woman with whom Marina was living had offered to teach him how to drive, and he looked forward to that.

Turning to me, Ruby said, "I might have to go out of town for a couple of days. Let's get together again next Tuesday afternoon." I nodded enthusiastic agreement, welcoming the three-day break. Ruby waved as he drove out, but Oswald stared straight ahead, completely oblivious of the need for any social amenities.

"See what I mean?" I said to Big John, when we were seated in the cafe.

"Yeah, I do, Tex. He's obnoxious, all right. But I think you can cut him a little slack. I've seen guys like him before. Their problem is, they feel so unimportant, they make fools of themselves trying to impress everyone with their great knowledge or achievements. Oswald probably has an ego the size of a peanut, so he has to boast and challenge other people in order to work up any good feelings about himself. The ironic thing is, all he's doing is making himself miserable and angry. My big worry about him is that he's going to do something really stupid one of these days and get himself in serious trouble. He's vulnerable to falling in with people who know how to take advantage of his weaknesses. Jack Ruby has the oily ways to make people like him, but he's connected with some real power brokers who just might have a need for a misguided dude like Lee. Something mighty fishy is going on. Seeing Ruby and Oswald cozying up together is like watching a weasel making friends with a chicken."

"So you think I ought to try to be more patient with him and ignore his annoying mouth?"

"It's up to you, Tex. The money's good. But I wouldn't make a career of dealing with these two guys. Maybe you can wrap it up pretty soon."

"Sounds good to me. Ruby's made some decent progress shooting, but I don't hold much hope for Lee. He thinks he knows everything already, and he doesn't listen. But I'll stick with it for a couple or three more lessons. I've already put down a deposit for a new saddle, and I can use the money."

"Do you recall me telling you that I asked someone I know in Dallas to get me some information about Jack Ruby?"

"Yes. Did you get any results?"

"He found some interesting stuff. I asked if Ruby had an arrest record. He does, but it's not for anything big. Some of it was for his women showing a little too much skin in the clubs. About ten years ago, he had a couple of beefs for carrying a concealed weapon and disturbing the peace. Then he got into some hot water for selling liquor after hours and letting his ladies keep dancing too long. Driving a car seems to be a real problem for Jack, 'cause he's had a whole string of traffic tickets and had to go to court for some of them. Way back in 1949 he got nailed by the Texas liquor control board for something about 'moral turpitude,' whatever the hell *that* means. Then, a couple of years later, they closed his place down for five days because he put on an obscene show. Happened again in 'fifty-four. He got another five-day suspension for an obscene strip-tease act at the Silver Spur club he was running then. He's had another couple of suspensions for bad checks and for another violation of liquor rules."

"Nothing there to connect him to the Mafia?"

"No. But he does run over to New Orleans now and then. Finds some of his strippers over there, sometimes in clubs owned by people who have been accused of having mob ties."

"How long has he been doing business in Dallas?"

"He first came here after World War Two, in 1947. The Carousel and the Vegas Clubs are only the latest joints he's operated. He's been involved in quite a few during the last sixteen years. Started out by helping his sister run the Singapore Supper Club, a little dinner and dance place. Then she moved away and he changed the club to a private dance hall called the Silver Spur. After that he bought into another place, the Bob Wills Ranch House, what we used to call an Okie stomp. You know, country music. He failed at both of them, sold out, and damn near had a nervous breakdown. Took off to Chicago, but came back after a couple of months. About ten years ago, he wangled a piece of the Vegas Club and started using strip-tease dancers. Another guy was involved in the business with Jack, but he landed in the pen over a sex rap.

"In 1955, Jack borrowed some money from a relative, got a business partner, and started another private club, called the Sovereign. He had to keep borrowing from other associates to keep the place running. Eventually, he changed it to the Carousel. They can't sell hard booze, just wine and beer, and the bubbly stuff. It pulls in about five grand a month, but very little profit. Our friend Jack is up to his armpits in debt. Pays the girls cash out of his pocket.

They say he's kind of tough on his people and has to use muscle now and then."

I remembered the time Ruby nearly beat up a stranger because he thought the guy's dog wasn't being treated right.

"From what I hear," John said, "Jack's got a quick temper and doesn't mind using his fists, or a blackjack, if he has to. He gets riled up if he hears someone criticizing Jews. Put one of his helpers in the hospital a couple years ago." Big John rubbed his chin like he was trying to be sure he'd covered everything. Then he added, "By the way, his name used to be Jacob Rubenstein. He legally changed it in 1947."

Ruby's reputation for having a short temper came as no surprise. I thought I'd detected a simmering anger in him, but he'd done a good job of keeping it bottled up around me, except for the incident with the dog.

Marshall continued, "I think there's very little doubt that he has mob ties in Chicago and New Orleans. Ruby's been friends for a long time with a couple of racketeers named Dave and Lennie from up north, and when he goes to New Orleans, he hangs around with some shady characters almost certainly tied to organized crime. He was supposedly seen in Cuba with Santos Trafficante, a Mafia bigwig."

I told John I appreciated the scuttlebutt, and that it would make me even more cautious. Playing around with Ruby, we agreed, could be hazardous to one's health.

I was sound asleep at 3:30 Sunday morning when I felt Candy's moist mouth pressing softly against my lips, deliciously rousing me. By the fresh scent of soap and shampoo and the taste of mint on her warm breath, I knew she'd stopped at her place to freshen up before driving over and slipping silently through my purposely unlocked door. I floated momentarily in paradise before letting my eyes open.

In that musical Southern drawl, from Florida, I think, Candy whispered close to my ear sweet, intimate words that sent tingling voltage all the way to my toes. Her soft curves conformed themselves to my body as she stretched on the bed beside me. The lamp I'd left on in the living room filtered enough light toward us to silhouette her golden hair and the pliant hills and valleys of her pure femininity. She wore something feathery and diaphanous, having dropped her coat on the floor. She'd used it as a discreet covering over her transparent nightie while she drove to my place. Her voice vibrated with an urgency. "Tex, I'm yours for the next thirty-six hours, if you want me."

If I wanted her? Does a dying man want life? Does a newborn colt want its momma's milk? "Only thirty-six hours? You reckon that'll give us enough time to do what we want to do?" I panted.

Candy gave a throaty little laugh, then a tiny groan. "Love me, Tex. I need you so bad it hurts." We curled into a tight embrace and tried to consume each other with kisses. I thought I'd made love before Candy, but she opened up thresholds I'd never even dreamed of. We tasted the newness and learned when to go at a slow walk and when to gallop toward the finish line.

Several passionate hours later, we uncoiled long enough to share some coffee and light breakfast. Deliriously happy, I felt sure that I was spent for the day, but while we cleared the dishes from the table, she gave me that look again, along with some ingenious probing with her fingertips and tongue. In one impulsive sweep of my arm, I pushed the few remaining items from the table surface to the floor, lifted her onto it, and renewed our explorations.

I didn't know thirty-six hours could fly by so quickly. We'd planned to ride the horses along the creek bed again, maybe barbecue some steaks and watch some television. Instead, we coupled everyplace from the hayloft to the seat of my pickup to the bathtub and back to bed again. Sometimes we moved to the cadence of the Beatles hollering, "She loves you, yeah, yeah, yeah," and at other times, to Hank Williams crooning about "Your Cheatin' Heart." I felt like the luckiest man alive.

On Tuesday, Jack Ruby called Tommy at the Rodeo and left word that our meeting would have to be delayed until late afternoon. Tommy relayed the message to me when I stopped by. I couldn't be upset about it, since I'd left my phone off the hook while Candy was there and had forgotten to replace it until midmorning, Tuesday.

I met Ruby and Oswald after four at the cafe. During our target practice at the lake, I saw some small improvement in both men, but nothing significant. Oswald said he'd rented a small room in a woman's house on Beckley Street and liked it much better than the previous place he'd been staying. More important, though, he told me that our future sessions would have to be held on weekday evenings, after 5:30, because he'd landed a job in Dallas, at the Texas School Book Depository, from 8:00 to 4:45 each day. And he wanted to visit his wife, Marina, on weekends. Her baby would be born any day now. His announcement about getting a job confused me, because I thought Ruby was going to hire him, but I didn't pry because I really didn't care. It irritated me that he felt I should adjust my schedule to fit his, but I could see some advantages, so I grabbed the opportunity to make my own announcement: "My evenings are mostly taken up with chores I have to do on my place, and some other business. I might be able to mine out one day a week to meet you." I also reminded them that the days were getting shorter, so we wouldn't have much daylight left by the time we got to the lake. Our sessions would be shortened considerably. I pretended to be sorry but inwardly felt a sense of relief.

Ruby frowned and said he might meet with me earlier on some of the afternoons, but he still wanted Oswald to learn more about using guns, so they'd have to settle for whatever we could work out. When they left, I had a strong feeling of dissention brewing between my mismatched students.

John Marshall called as soon as I got home. "Tex, can you break loose for a few days? We've got a job to do over toward Breckenridge."

"You bet, John. When do you want to leave?"

"In about three hours. I know that's short notice, Tex, but this one's pretty urgent. It's going to be a little tricky, too. I've known the man we're going to help out for a long time. I'll tell you more when I get there. How about loading that black mare into your trailer for me? I think we'll need her."

I called Tommy at the Rodeo to pass the word to Jack Ruby, if he called, that I'd be out of town for a few days.

Packed and loaded, with the horse trailer already hitched, I sat waiting in my pickup when Big John skidded to a halt in my driveway. He jumped out, tossed a duffle bag into my truck bed, grabbed his holstered Colt .45 and a rifle, and slid in beside me. I couldn't ever recall seeing Big John look so troubled.

Eleven

"The man we're going to meet," John Marshall said, as I pulled out of the driveway, "has been losing a lot of cattle to rustlers. Ordinarily, that would be a simple job for the sheriff over there. But this has a little different twist. He just found out his own son is the ringleader of the thieves. Carl Williard is the father's name, and he wants the rustling stopped, but it's also very important to him to keep his boy out of jail. I've known Carl for twenty years. He and I have shared campfires more times than I can count, hunting and fishing. His place, Tex, is where I go when I want to get away and not tell anyone where I am. I watched that damn kid grow up, and it makes me sick that he's doing this to a fine man."

"I see what you mean. It's hard to understand why a son would take advantage of his own father that way, unless he felt like he was being abused or something."

"Nothing could be further from the truth. Carl loves that boy. He's always been extremely generous with the kid and given him every possible advantage. Maybe too much. Even named him Carl Junior, but everyone calls the kid Danny. He's about your age, or a little older, and he's had a few narrow escapes with the law before. Carl has always bought off the problems and covered up for the misdeeds."

I headed west toward Weatherford and onto Highway

180. Breckenridge straddled 180 not quite a hundred miles from Fort Worth. With stops for food and gas, and pulling a horse trailer, we'd probably arrive well before midnight. John had been mentally calculating right along with me, and said, "We're going to meet Carl close to town in an all-night coffee shop and work out some details before we go out to the ranch. I'm going to call an old buddy who's with the Texas Rangers to ask for some help." He fell silent for several minutes. "Tex, I'd like you to be the one to take Danny down. He's too close to me and I don't want to make a mistake. I'm asking you, though, to watch yourself carefully. He carries a knife in his boot, and he's pretty good with it. Don't take any chances with him."

"You can bet on that. I ain't exactly looking to get sliced up. It might wreck this pretty face of mine." My attempt at humor got a grin out of John.

"Good," he said. "I know you'll be able to handle it okay. I used to think a lot of that boy, but when Carl called this morning, it sounded like Danny has developed a serious rotten streak."

I could see the whole situation weighed heavily on John's mind. He was right when he said he was too close to the people involved.

We pulled into a truck stop about an hour after dark for fuel, food, and coffee and to check how well the mare was riding. John offered to drive for a spell, but I knew the tension had worn him out and he needed some sleep. Within minutes after we hit the highway again, he dozed off. Traffic thinned out enough to let me keep the headlights on high beam, lowering them only for the occasional oncoming truck. During the long drive, as the dark junipers, oaks, and prairie brush whizzed by, I let my mind wander back to Jack Ruby and Lee Oswald. Just as the job ahead of us troubled John, I felt a growing inner turmoil about my involvement with those two strange people. The most unsettling part was Ruby's underworld connections. I agreed with John's guess that Ruby probably had something shady up his sleeve for which he needed Oswald. But for the life of me, I couldn't figure out what it might be. To get my mind off them, I let images of Judy and little Rae fill my thoughts. Could Rae really be my little girl? I hoped not. They, too, faded out in favor of my incredible time with Candy. I'd never had a more sensuous and satisfying experience with a woman. It would be easy to fall head over heels for her. Should I let myself do it? No, I decided. First of all, I knew I wasn't ready for a full-time relationship, and second, there were some big question marks in my head about her. It'd probably be a good idea, when I got home, to start seeing some of the other girls I knew. There was one named Debbie who had coal black hair and light blue eyes, like Gail Russell, John Wayne's love in "Angel and the Badman." Yeah, I'd definitely give Debbie a call when I got back.

For now, I resolved just to concentrate on what lay ahead in Breckenridge.

After slowing for the climbing curves through the Palo Pinto Mountains, I made good time and reached the city limits at 11:30. John stretched those big arms, yawned, and instructed me to pull over at the first coffee shop on the right. "That's where Carl's going to meet us. He's got an old pickup with 'C & W Ranch' lettered on the doors."

Five minutes later, I spotted the restaurant and wheeled in, ready for a break. The C & W pickup sat close to the entrance, occupied by a man with gray hair and wearing horn-rimmed glasses. John hailed him and jumped out as soon as I'd braked to a halt.

Carl Williard stepped out of his truck slowly, clearly a man saddled with a heavy load. He grabbed John's hand in both of his, saying, "I can't tell you how much I appreciate your getting here so soon. Bet you boys are tired. Ready for something to eat?"

John grinned in my direction. "I'm not a bit tired," he said. "But I can eat, and Tex is always hungry." After I shook hands with Mr. Williard, we attended to the horse, then went inside, where a plump waitress with bleached hair and sleepy eyes took our orders for three chicken fried steaks, gravy, and biscuits.

Carl Williard and John reminisced about old times while we ate, then, over coffee, confronted the problem we were there to help him solve. Lacing his hands together to keep them from trembling, Williard commenced telling us a story he would have given anything to avoid. "Carl, Junior—I still call him that even though everyone else calls him Danny—started getting into some trouble about three years ago. Petty stuff at first, penny-ante poker games and dice. The gambling got into his blood, and he managed to get tangled up with high rollers. Started playing for bigger stakes, and sank deeper and deeper into debt. He couldn't pull himself out of it. I bailed him out several times, and each time he promised to quit. Then I'd find out that he dove in again head-first, repeating the same mistakes, always trying to win the big jackpot. I would have helped him again, but he was too ashamed to ask me, so he started doing favors for the people he owned money to. I think that's why he's working with a gang of rustlers, to keep the kingfish off his back."

"Who do you think they are?" John asked.

"Some people from Las Vegas. They've got hold of him and they're squeezing him tight."

"Did he tell you that?"

"No. His wife, Betty, my daughter-in-law, told me. She's worried sick they're going to hurt him real bad, or kill him."

"Can you trust her?"

"Yes. I have faith in her. Her story is the only thing that makes sense. She came to me to ask for help. They've got a new baby boy. I gave her enough money to go to Oklahoma City until this is all over. Before she left, she told me that the thieves would be loading up a truckload of cattle about twenty-four hours from now, at midnight."

"A truckload?"

"That's right. I've lost over a hundred head already. We found truck and trailer tracks on dirt roads on a remote part of the feeding range. If they raid tonight, it will be the third one against me. I think they're hitting other ranchers, too."

"If your son is caught by the authorities, they could put him away for a long time," John said.

"I know it. And it makes me sick. Please, do what you can to keep him out of prison. He's not a criminal, but he's in a bad situation, way over his head. He's a good boy."

Turning in my direction, John said, "Tex, you haven't had anything to say."

"Sounds pretty bad, and pretty damn big," I said. "Unless they're selling the cattle on the hoof, they've got to have a slaughterhouse to butcher the meat and get rid of the hides. My guess is they're working back and forth across the border to Mexico."

John nodded his agreement, adding, "We're going to have to dig it out one step at a time. We might need more help than my Texas Ranger buddy can give us."

Carl's eyes flashed enthusiasm. "I know some people who will be glad to help out. One's a retired sheriff, and

the other fellow wore a badge for twenty-five years patrolling the highways."

I stayed at the cafe to take care of the truck and horse
while John and Carl went to round up the help. The long
drive caught up with me, and I dozed in the truck seat on
and off until the stars faded out and pale light filtered over
the horizon. I snapped awake when I heard Williard's
pickup and another car rumble to a halt next to me. John
and Carl had rounded up the ranger, the retired patrolman,
and the ex-sheriff. The group made me feel awfully young,
each of them more than twice my age. We moved the meeting to Carl's ranch. Everyone but me knew what Danny
looked like, so Carl showed me a recent photograph. If
there was a shootout, I didn't want to gun down the wrong
person.

Carl provided horses and saddles for himself and the trio
of ex-lawmen and a spare for me. John would ride the black
mare. Our first job was to inspect the ranch perimeter to
develop a plan in which each of us would watch, as soon
as it got dark, from several strategic posts where a truck
might gain access to the cattle. That way, we might have a
chance to ambush the rustlers no matter where they tried
to load the truck. In case we were being watched, it would
look better if all of us were on horseback. Plus, it would
be much easier to conceal ourselves on horses during the
stakeout, rather than try to hide motor vehicles. The ranger
brought radios for each of us to carry, to keep in contact
with the rest of the group. If one of us spotted the thieves,
he could call in the location and hope the other five could
race in to help. We devised some simple code words in
case the bad guys were monitoring radio frequencies.

While the five older men, who were already familiar with the ranch, examined maps, cleaned guns, and prepared the horses, I drove my pickup out to the main road and up a few side trails to get a feel for the hills, gullies, trees, and cattle locations. I came back to the ranch house before dark to join the men in some light supper.

John and I exchanged some thoughts about the operation, agreeing on a few likely spots for each of five men to hide during the stakeout. Carl would stay with me. The ranger suggested, "Let's allow the crooks to get the cattle all loaded and the truck moving. Then we'll stop them before they get to the main road. Otherwise, some motorist could accidentally get in the middle of it out on the highway and get hurt." We all agreed.

At dusk, while there was still enough light to find our ways, each of us rode to his stakeout spot, armed with loaded weapons and a thermos of hot coffee.

More than five hours crawled by, with only the sound of cattle bawling in the distance, and an occasional owl asking who was there. I wondered if we'd been seen and the rustlers had hightailed it to another ranch. Carl seemed lost in his own mental worries. My thoughts wandered again to Fort Worth, my gun tutoring job, and my mixed-up love life. I hadn't had much real sleep and fought hard to keep from dozing. My chin dropped to my chest a couple of times, and I began to dream that I heard the rumble of an old B-61 Mack truck. Jerking my head up with a start, I realized it was no dream.

I jostled Carl and pointed down the slope from my vantage point. We both saw a pair of headlights climb out of a long, low dip in a dirt service road. Unfortunately, another set climbed out of the gully behind it. Now we had two vehicles to deal with. Judging by the smaller space between the headlights of the second truck, I told Carl I thought it was a pickup. He said, "My son has a new Chevy pickup. That could be him."

"I can't tell from here," I whispered. Trying not to speak too loudly, even though the rustlers couldn't have heard me over the roar of the truck engines, I called John on the radio. "Units one and two calling. I think we have objective in sight. There's a complication, though."

"Don't worry about the code, Tex," John replied. "How many of them are there?"

"I don't know yet. There's a big truck pulling a horse trailer, being followed by a pickup. I'm going to ride in for a closer look." I mounted the little roan and headed down through the pasture toward the truck. Both vehicles had stopped, with the pickup parked on the other side of the truck, hidden from my view. I could make out some movement that appeared to be someone taking horses out of the trailer. Staying behind an embankment along the road, and crouching low on my horse, I dismounted within forty feet of the Mack. Now whispering for a valid reason, I told John on the radio, "You're not going to believe this, but they've got three men on horses and two men working portable gates. They're moving cattle up the side ramp into the truck now. Could be fully loaded and on their way out of here in twenty minutes."

The Williard spread was large enough to prevent the cavalry from riding to my rescue in such a few minutes before the rustlers drove off hauling out another fifty head of valuable beef. John voiced the same worry. "Damn, Tex, I don't think we can get there in time to stop them." Three other voices crackled softly, saying they would try but didn't think they could cover the dark ground in such a short time, either. Maybe we'd outsmarted ourselves by not having at least one vehicle to use.

Working rapidly, the rustlers proved to be more organized and efficient than we'd expected. They knew what they were doing. Carl's voice came across on the radio. "Tex, I don't know what to tell you to do. Whatever steps you think you should take, I'll back you up. Forget that my son is out there and use your own judgment."

To me, there was only one logical plan of action. I told John my idea, and asked him to pass it on to the others, with instructions to head toward me as fast as possible. I sat quietly, waiting for the rustlers to finish loading the cattle, looking around from time to time to see if help was anywhere near. I didn't particularly relish taking on the whole group of thieves by myself, but I just couldn't see my way clear to let them get away.

They completed the loading within my estimate of twenty minutes and I heard the engine of the big truck start. Peering over the embankment, I saw the three horsemen lead their mounts into the trailer and a fourth man slam the rear doors, locking the trio inside. That changed the odds considerably in my favor, leaving only the Mack driver, his shotgun rider, and whoever was in the pickup. When the Mack jerked forward, then started to roll, I mounted the roan and spurred him to within fifteen feet of the cab, my .45 in hand. I leveled the gun toward the front of the truck and put two rounds into the tire on the driver's side, then popped another into the air for good measure.

Apparently spooked by the gunfire, the pickup driver floored the accelerator, spinning the wheels in mud, skidded into view, and careened toward the highway. I knew I could have disabled it with a couple of well-placed shots, but I aimed high and the pickup disappeared into the dark. Reining my horse up right next to the driver's side of the big-rig cab, I pointed the barrel at his head and yelled, "Get out of the truck and put your hands on your head. Be damn careful how you do it. I've always wondered what it would be like to kill a man." The last part was mostly bluff.

I could hear clattering inside the trailer, but I knew they were no danger to me. The driver's face sagged, but the passenger said, "Hell, he's just a kid. C'mon, we can take him."

I fired another shot into the air and growled in my most menacing voice, "Yeah, you could try, and I'll blow you away in a heartbeat. Believe me!" They calmed down and sat still. Carl rode over to help and covered the trailer just in case any of the three cowboys inside tried to bust out and make trouble. We waited nearly twenty minutes for the others to arrive, but it seemed like two hours.

John rode up at a gallop and shouted, "Tex, how many are there?"

"Just these two in the cab and three in the trailer."

When the ranger arrived, he unlocked the trailer and yelled, "I want you boys to come out nice and easy when I open this door. We got a well-armed posse out here, ready to blow holes in anyone who doesn't behave." They complied like trained puppy dogs and held out their arms for the ex-sheriff to slap on the cuffs.

Carl watched anxiously as the three men emerged, hoping his son wasn't among them, and breathed a big sigh of relief. We both figured Danny was probably driving the pickup. Carl looked at me and asked, "When you shot at the pickup, you missed deliberately, didn't you?"

"I might have been able to stop it, but I really didn't

want your son to get hurt, if he was in there. Now, it'll be just between you and him."

"Thanks, Tex. I appreciate it."

We let the cattle out of the truck, watched them drift back out across the pasture bawling their displeasure, and unsaddled the three horses. One of the prisoners hollered, "What are you going to do with my cutting horse?"

Carl had a quick answer. "Turn him out in the pasture with the rest of the herd. You won't need him for a while. Where you're going, they don't have many horses."

When we'd delivered the rustlers into the hands of the county sheriff and begun the process of giving official statements, we were surprised to see Danny walk in. He nodded to John, marched over to Carl, and said, "Dad, I've got to tell you something."

Weary and discouraged, Carl replied, "You've got a lot of talking to do, son."

"I'm really sorry. They were forcing me to work for them because of some gambling debts I ran up."

"You could've asked for help. It would have been better than betraying your family."

"I know, Dad. I'll take whatever punishment they want to give me. I was wrong. I handled everything wrong and I hurt you and other people, too."

The young rustler who had asked about his horse, sitting at an interrogation desk, overheard Danny's apology. He too, had something to say. "Mr. Williard, Danny's telling the truth. I got caught up in the crazy game, too, and had to work for them. I'll take what's coming to me, but, sir, could you please take care of my horse? He's a good one. The saddle is mine. I won it. I didn't steal it. I didn't want to do any of this, but I got trapped into it, same as Danny. They threatened my family and were going to burn my father's barn down."

John asked Danny and the apologetic cowboy if they'd be willing to testify against the ringleaders. Both young men said they sure would, and John disappeared into the district attorney's office. He came out grinning and conferred with Carl over in a corner. Tears came to the father's eyes, and he embraced John with gratitude.

After a good night's sleep and a hearty breakfast with Carl, the ranger, and the two jubilant ex-lawmen, we all patted each other's backs and shook hands. Every one of us felt great, especially about the D.A. agreeing to cut a deal to recommend probation for Danny and the unfortunate cowboy. Carl handed John an envelope and told us not to open it until we were down the road aways. As I drove out, John rolled down the passenger window. "Carl, I'll be bringing Tex down here next time we decide to go hunting."

Carl nodded and waved.

About thirty miles east of the ranch, John tore the envelope open. Inside was a thick wad of bills, and a note of thanks. John read it aloud and turned to me just before reading the last sentence: "Please tell Tex he will always be a welcome member of our hunting parties. Thanks again to both of you."

"You must have made a mighty good impression on him," John said. "He's a good man to know."

"He's a lot like you."

It was nearly suppertime when we pulled into John's driveway. His wife came out of the barn where she'd been feeding the horses. "You have four calls from Tommy. Jack Ruby's been trying to get in touch with you. He keeps checking to see if you're back yet."

Twelve

I telephoned the Carousel Club, asked for Jack Ruby, and while I waited, I could hear music in the background. I had a mental picture of Candy moving around on a stage in front of a bunch of leering slobs, displaying her beautiful body, doing bumps and grinds to the brassy tempo. I hated this. Ruby's voice melted away the unpleasant vision. He sounded like he was speaking to a best friend, lost for years, who had just turned up, out of the blue. "Tex, good to hear from you. When are we going shooting again? It's been a week, and I need to get out of this place. Plus, I've got a new gun I want to try out."

"How about Monday or Tuesday?" I didn't want to give up my Saturday or Sunday and I recalled that Oswald had told us he wanted to visit his pregnant wife on the weekends.

"Tuesday will be fine. I'll pick up Lee after he gets off work and meet you at the Rodeo about 5:30. That should give us an hour of daylight at the lake." I doubted we'd have more than a half hour of light, which wouldn't be enough for target practice, but I agreed to meet him, dreading another session with Oswald.

Candy hadn't called or left any messages at the restaurant, for which I felt a certain amount of relief. A possibility had tickled the back of my mind about her. Maybe it was farfetched, but I couldn't shake the idea that she might be in cahoots with Ruby, for whatever he was really after. Could he have paid her to hook me like a dumb fish and turn me into spineless, lovesick slob who would do anything to keep her in my life? I'd seen movies where guys were played for suckers like that. On the other hand, maybe I was being a paranoid idiot. I decided to play the hand close to my chest and wait for her to make the next move.

With a whole weekend free, I turned my thoughts to Debbie. I hadn't seen her since last spring, when she'd completed two years of junior college and left to work a summer job in Oklahoma. We'd had a lot of fun together, and she'd called me in early September, when she'd come home, but I'd been tied up with Ann, so had put off calling her back. I picked up the phone a little nervously and felt lucky when Debbie answered. She pouted for several minutes about my delayed contact and pretended to hesitate about seeing me again, but she accepted a date for Saturday night.

Two hours before I was supposed to pick up Debbie, I stepped out of the shower just as my phone rang. Damn! Was she going to back out after all? I picked it up, ready to be stood up.

Instead, a deep male voice, gruff as gravel in a cement mixer, said, "Pal, you may be getting involved in something that's going to burn you real bad. You'd better think about it." I heard a click and then the dial tone.

Wrong number? Crank call? Practical joke? A series of possibilities tumbled through my mind. I didn't feel frightened, but maybe slightly alarmed. Had someone I'd helped corral with Big John and sent to jail decided to get revenge? No, the veiled threat didn't sound like that. Was it related to Candy? Or Ruby and Oswald? The bastard who'd called had left too many possibilities to make sense. There wasn't really much I could do about it.

Within a few minutes after I'd picked up Debbie, I pushed the weird call out of my mind. She had grown even prettier over the summer. I took her to a Western-style steakhouse for dinner and to a movie in Fort Worth.

They say that life has cycles of good luck and bad luck, in streaks lasting a few days, weeks, or even months. I must have been on a streak of extraordinarily good luck with women that autumn. Debbie told me that she'd been seeing someone since early September and it had ended after a big fight just two days before I'd called. I can't recall the details of her broken romance, but I clearly remember that she was in one of those moods women form when they're on the rebound. She wanted to be wild and free, devil-may-care, adventuresome. Bottom line is, she asked if she could stay all night with me at my place.

At first, I started to be gallant. It wouldn't be manly to take advantage of a broken heart. But when she circled my neck with her arms, then offered her lips and more, she didn't need words to convince me. We had a beautiful evening, night, and morning.

Dreading the next session with Ruby and Oswald more than a trip to the dentist, I was happy when Jack called to postpone it once more. He wanted to wait until Thursday. Acting annoyed, I needled him slightly about the delays, but it didn't faze him.

* * *

We drove to the lake under clear skies on Thursday but could see thunderheads gathering not far away. Our practice was a washout, literally. Within a few minutes of our arrival, the massive gray clouds of a late-summer thunderstorm gathered above us and opened up—a real gully-washer, complete with rumbling rolls of thunder and bright bolts of forked lightning. We tried to wait it out sitting in his car, but the rain wouldn't quit.

Ruby's willingness to talk had increased with each of our meetings, and the rain put him in a gabby mood. He asked me what I thought of Lee Oswald. Trying to be tactful, I said that Lee had a lot to learn about using guns. Vigorously nodding, Jack said, "Yeah, and about a lot of other things, too. He was poking around over in New Orleans, getting himself into some weird things. Handing out leaflets about that Cuba stuff What a waste of time. Hell, if Castro hadn't taken over and put in a Communist government, I would've been sitting pretty. I was right on the verge of sealing a deal to open a casino in Havana. But he screwed it up and set me back plenty. I could have paid off the forty Gs I owe the feds . . ."

Ruby abruptly stopped, as if he realized he was on touchy ground. He watched the rain for a few moments, and changed the subject back to Oswald. "When Lee left Louisiana, he rode a bus down to Mexico City, stayed about a week, then came back here, to Dallas."

"What was he doing down in Mexico City?" I asked the question, even though I really didn't care. It did seem odd, though, that Lee hadn't mentioned the trip. Ruby started to say something but apparently changed his mind. A knowing smile flitted across his face, then faded.

Apparently, Ruby had given up the game of trying to pry information from me. Instead, he meandered into reminiscing about his younger days. "Did I ever tell you I worked as a singing waiter once, in San Francisco?" Amused at his recollection, he said, "That was a failure. Never made any money at all." In Los Angeles, he recalled, he touted horses at the Santa Anita racetrack, then tried door-to-door sales in other parts of California. "I finally gave up on the West Coast and headed back to Chicago. I worked a lot of street scams, then went into business with a buddy, hustling punchboards. We traveled all over the place, made some good dough. Met some terrific ladies that way."

Jack asked me a few questions but mostly seemed interested in having a willing listener to his stories about the past. He said that when World War Two broke out, he helped root out Nazi sympathizers in Illinois. "Those bastards in Germany really treated Jewish people like dirt, and the punks in this country who held rallies and waved German flags around were just as bad. I got a few guys together and raided one of their meetings, and worked a couple of them over pretty good." The subject of fights kept creeping into his recollections. I didn't know if he was trying to impress me with how tough he was, or if he just enjoyed talking about it. He brought up the subject of guns, and how most people really don't know how to handle them: "You're really good at it, Tex. I think you ought to give some serious thought to making some money with your skills. I know some people who can be very generous when they need a favor. A young fellow like you could pull in some big dough. Why don't you mull it over? It would be a shame to waste your talents."

"I don't think I'm wasting anything, Jack. I'm doing fine." I didn't like the way the conversation had turned, so I changed the subject to something more agreeable—food.

I asked if there were any restaurants over in Dallas I should try. Ruby fell silent and stared out through the raindrops making blurred tracks down the windows.

The downpour continued to pound on the Oldsmobile's roof and didn't look like it was going to let up. It was too muddy to continue anyway, so we agreed that the weather had won for today. I ran to my pickup and waved as I headed toward the road, but Jack motioned for me to come close. I maneuvered the pickup next to his driver's door and rolled down the window. Between thunderclaps and the squeak of windshield wipers, he said he'd be busy for a few days, so we agreed to wait until the last Monday in October to meet again. He'd be looking forward to it, he yelled, before rolling up the window and spinning his wheels in mud as he drove away.

The timing turned out to be perfect, since John Marshall decided to take a short vacation with his wife and stay in the little Colorado town where he was born. He came by to ask me if I'd look after his horses and check the house security over the weekend. He knew he didn't have to ask.

The chores on both places kept me hopping, and kept my mind off my strange students, until Sunday night, when I had trouble sleeping because I didn't especially want to see them the next day.

On Monday afternoon, I met them at the Rodeo Cafe. Lee chattered excitedly about his new daughter, who had been born on Sunday, October 20. He complained that she should have arrived two days sooner, on his own birthday.

At the lake, Oswald found himself unable to concentrate on shooting exercises. Ruby continued to practice while Lee ranted about the U.S. Atomic Energy Commission detonating another nuclear weapon in the Nevada desert a couple of days earlier. The veins popped out in his neck and forehead while he bitterly denounced the war-mongering generals in the Pentagon. Jack asked Lee if he held the president responsible. "No, I don't think so," Oswald replied. "I think President Kennedy learned his lesson last year at this time when he played brinksmanship with the USSR over those missiles supposedly in Cuba. I believe that Kennedy wants peace with the Soviet Union, and I think he wishes to restore diplomatic trade and tourism with Cuba. Two weeks ago, he negotiated an agreement to sell thousands of bushels of American wheat to the Eastern bloc of Europe for a fair price. I think Kennedy has made fundamental errors in judgment, but I hold no anger for him."

Both Ruby and I tried to convince Oswald to focus on shooting, but he found another subject to raise hell about. "You know, over a thousand Cubans died this month from that hurricane, I think they called it Flora, that ripped across the island. That's criminal!"

I scratched my head. "What's criminal about it? Isn't a hurricane an act of nature? Who are you holding responsible for that?"

"That's typical," he snapped, his eyes sparking fire. "A perfect example of shallow thinking. Do you believe all those people would have died if they weren't living in flimsy little shanties, in abject poverty?" He stammered with fury. "Something's wrong with the system when that many people are left vulnerable due to economic conditions. It's the same all over the world."

Wondering if Oswald thought he could provide solutions, instead of a whole raft of complaints, I started to ask, then thought better of it. I was weary of his abrasive voice,

which sometimes sounded like Elmer Fudd lecturing Bugs
Bunny while trying to shoot him. For the most part, Ruby
ignored him.

Watching Lee carefully, I discovered one of the problems
that prevented him from firing accurately. He blinked each
time he pulled the trigger. Bringing it to his attention and
suggesting proper techniques didn't seem to help. I got the
impression he really couldn't stop blinking or twitching
when he fired. If he didn't correct it, he'd never be able to
hit anything.

The fading light put an end to our practice and, mercifully, Oswald's bellyaching.

We agreed to meet again a week from Wednesday, November 6. Jack said he'd like to start a little earlier, and
Lee could join us later. I accepted his offer to meet at the
Rodeo an hour before noon. But on Tuesday, Jack called
me at home. "Tex, I'll be about thirty or forty minutes late
tomorrow, maybe an hour at the most. I've got to pick up
some important New Orleans colleagues at the airport at
seven-thirty in the morning. Urgent business. So I'll see
you about noon." I thanked him for letting me know.

I arrived a little early, as usual, and waited. At 12:15, I
turned to see a grim-faced Ruby walk in, followed by three
men, two burly-looking apes and a short, dapper man
dressed in an expensive dark topcoat, gray hat, and gloves.
The man's bearing resonated with power and left no doubt
that he was in charge. All three looked like trouble to me.
They surveyed the interior like they owned it, or planned
to take it over. If these were Ruby's normal companions, I
could see why he needed to learn how to handle a gun.

For the first time, I watched Ruby behave in a subser-
vient manner. He gave me the impression that he was frightened, or at least extremely nervous. "Hello, Tex," he

mumbled. "I just wanted to let you know that our friend and I will be a little late for our meeting this afternoon." I assumed he meant Oswald. "I'll catch you here at about five, after I take these gentlemen to the airport. They're business associates of mine interested in buying some commercial property here in Fort Worth."

The two heavyweights treated me to cold stares, with all the emotion of lizards sunning on a rock. One looked like an ex-wrestler, complete with a smashed nose, scarred brow ridge, and cauliflower ears. The other should have had little bolts coming out of the sides of his neck. I wouldn't want to tangle with either of them in a dark alley, or anywhere else, for that matter.

Both men stayed at close flank to the boss, who reminded me of a shrunken Lee J. Cobb in *On The Waterfront*. He would have had to stand on tiptoe to reach five-four, but he looked tough as a bayou alligator. The thick gray hair I could see under the edge of his hat, along with some crosshatch wrinkles in the neck, placed him in his early fifties. His disproportionately large head looked chiseled from granite, complete with a built-in scowl. And why did every one of these mobster types have a cleft in the chin?

Probably a little too cocky for my own good, and realizing it was probably a foolish question, I asked what kind of business they were in. The two gorillas turned toward their king, snickering. His eyes almost showed some humor. "Tomatoes," he rasped. "I'm a tomato salesman." I nodded and turned back to my iced tea.

Ruby coughed, apparently at a loss for words, and said he'd see me later. The foursome strolled slowly out, still examining the place. I wondered if they really did have an interest in it. I'd never heard Tommy say anything about selling the Rodeo. After they left and Tommy appeared from the kitchen, where he'd been watching, I asked if he'd ever before seen any of the group. "No, I haven't." His voice trembled, and I'd never seen him so tense. "The only one I've ever seen is your student, Jack Ruby."

"Tommy, what's wrong? Did they scare you?" I thought I was joking.

"They looked mighty tough, Tex. I overheard Ruby say something about them wanting to buy some business property. Funny thing is, I've had a few calls lately asking me what I would take for the cafe. I brushed it off and said it wasn't for sale. Yeah, Tex, they made me nervous."

"I wouldn't worry about it, old buddy. They don't look like the type to run the Rodeo." Tommy stared at the floor, shook his head, and returned to the kitchen.

I felt uneasy the rest of the afternoon while I killed time at the saddle shop and the feed store. When Ruby returned at five, he still seemed rattled. Before he could open his mouth, I asked, "Who the hell were those guys, Jack?"

"They're not anyone you want to fool with, Tex. The short guy runs the show over in New Orleans and has interests in most cities in the South, including Dallas. It would probably be a lot better if you don't ask questions."

"Why'd you bring 'em here to the Rodeo?"

"It wasn't my idea. The boss, Marcello, wanted to come. It's his way of letting people know he can cover a lot of territory, and have about anything he wants."

"Does he want something here?"

"Like I told you, Tex, it ain't healthy to ask too many questions."

* * *

Oswald sat outside in Ruby's car, and they followed me to the lake for another short session. It hardly seemed worthwhile to drive all the way out there for only half an hour. This time, Oswald had another reason to complain. Someone from the FBI had visited Marina twice in the Irvine home where she was living. It made Lee furious. He speculated that it had something to do with his activities involving Fair Play for Cuba, or some problems he'd had in New Orleans. Words like "gestapo" and "KGB" dripped from his mouth like snake venom. Once again, he couldn't concentrate on guns or target practice. Ruby thought we might as well let him have a few days off to work out some of his anger. "I've got my own troubles," Ruby said sourly. "I had to fire one of the best strippers at the club. Damn broads, anyway."

We agreed to meet again in one week.

As soon as I saw Ruby and Oswald leave the Rodeo, I called John Marshall to be certain he was home. I urgently needed to ask him some questions.

Thirteen

Big John invited me over for supper, and I gladly accepted. While his wife basted a roast that filled the kitchen with appetizing aromas of cooking beef, gravy, and onions, I nudged him with a signal to go outside for a talk.

Halfway to the barn, I opened up. "John, a couple of thugs and a dapper little dude showed up at Tommy's cafe today with Jack Ruby. They strutted around like they owned the place, or planned to. Tommy acted all shook up, and I've got to admit, they gave me the willies, too. I tried to get Ruby to tell me what the hell it was all about, but he brushed me off with a warning not to ask questions. He did drop a name, though. I'm pretty sure he called the short guy Marcello, from New Orleans, and said he had business interests all over the South. Oh, yeah, Marcello said he was a tomato salesman, but he looked and acted more like a well-heeled mobster."

A deep vertical crease appeared between John's eyebrows, and his mouth turned down at the corners. "Damn, Tex. I've been worried that Ruby's tied up with the big boys. If you saw who I think you did, he's one of the biggest. Are you sure he said they're from New Orleans?"

"Very sure. Jack even told me earlier that he'd gone to pick them up at the airport. Said they were some of his business associates coming in from New Orleans."

"Do you remember when we went to Mexico with my friend Paul Butler and he mentioned a Mafia type from New Orleans? I think this must be the same guy. I don't know who else it could be, other than Carlos Marcello. He's got his thumb on all kinds of things in several states along the Gulf Coast. Gambling, booze, prostitution—you name it. Bobby Kennedy, the U.S. attorney general, deported him a couple of years ago. Dumped him down in the jungles of Guatemala, but somehow he slipped back into the States. There have been lots of rumors, but no one can figure out why the government seems helpless to boot him out again. Maybe he's got the goods on someone high up. He's one tough customer, Tex. If the president's own brother, the top legal eagle in the country, can't keep him out, you know Marcello's got some power behind him."

"Got any idea why he and his goons would make an appearance at the Rodeo?"

"That's what bothers me. Ruby seems to have taken a special liking to the place. His usual stomping grounds are over in Dallas. I wonder if he's sizing up the Rodeo as sort of headquarters, or center of operations for expanding into Fort Worth, and maybe even using it to launder some dirty money."

"I'll tell you, John, Tommy sure got nervous."

"I'd hate to see him pushed out of there. I'll snoop around and see if I can find out anything. In the meantime, I hope you're nearly finished with Ruby and Oswald. I don't like the smell of this whole thing."

"Even if I hadn't seen those guys today, I'm about ready to wash my hands of the whole deal. Oswald's mouth drives me nuts, and I'm suspicious of Ruby, even though he strikes me as a decent guy in some ways. Since the beginning, I've been trying to figure out what he's after. I think he might want to improve his ability with guns, but's that's just a small part of the picture. Next time they come over, I'm going to tell them school's almost out."

"Glad to hear it, Tex. I'll let you know if I find out anything more. Now, let's go in and tackle that roast beef"

Jack Ruby showed up by himself on the appointed Wednesday, and before I could say anything, he held up his hand to stop me. "Tex, I just wanted to let you know I've got a little gift for you, in appreciation of your help. Come on out to the car with me for minute." Reluctantly I followed him. He opened the door, saying, "One of my customers owed me some money but couldn't come up with it. He offered me this as payment." From the back seat, Jack lifted a beautiful little Marlin .30-.30 and handed it to me.

"I can't take that, Jack. You've paid me according to our bargain, and you don't owe me anything."

"I know that, Tex. But when I saw the gun, I wanted you to have it. You've tolerated a lot of crap from Lee and held your temper. I really appreciate that, so I can't take no for an answer. The gun is yours." He paused, admired the rifle, then suggested we get some practice in at the lake without Oswald.

His timing was perfect. How could I tell him I planned to terminate the shooting lessons? All I could do was thank him, accompany him out to Lake Worth, and spend some time coaching him. His skills showed some improvement, but I concluded that if he ever found himself in a real gun-fight, he'd have to move in to point-blank range.

* * *

Later that afternoon, about six, we drove to a restaurant on East Rosedale he wanted to try. He talked with excitement about some weird gadget he wanted to market called a "twist board." Ruby had one in his car, some kind of an exercise contraption. You stand on a board mounted on ball bearings and gyrate your body in the same motions made popular by a singer named Chubby Checker who had popularized the dance sensation called the twist. Jack had even taken one of his strippers to demonstrate it at the Texas Products Show a few day earlier. It didn't interest me very much. Looked like a good way to break your neck. That twist craze had left me cold, anyway. My style was more suited to country-Western music and I was still trying to master the two-step.

While we walked toward the restaurant entrance, I happened to glance at a car stopped for a signal and saw Lee Oswald in the back seat, holding a baby. The small woman beside him, I assumed she was Marina, held a young girl on her lap. An older couple I'd never seen before occupied the front seat. Jack spotted them at the same time, raised his eyebrows in surprise, and said, "Look, there goes Lee. He doesn't see us." I turned my back in a hurry, hoping we'd remain unnoticed. It worked. I had no idea what Lee was doing in that part of town, or who the other people were.

Promising myself that I'd suggest ending the arrangement the next time we got together, I agreed to another session with Ruby on Sunday, November 17. He said he was going out of town for most of the weekend, but would be back in time to meet me late that afternoon. He'd try to convince Oswald to make himself available that Sunday to catch up on the lessons he'd missed recently.

* * *

On Saturday, I took Debbie and two horses to Lake Worth. We rode for hours, wandered around an old casino, and even waded in the chilly water's edge. My short fling with Candy had faded to the back of my mind, and I felt cheered by my decision to end the bothersome sessions with Ruby and Oswald. I'd be free to relax and tend to my horses, my barn, and my house, spend more time with Debbie, and maybe even join Big John on more bounty hunting adventures. My life, I was convinced, was definitely about to change for the better.

Somehow, I failed to see the dark, cloudy spot in my crystal ball.

Lee Oswald started Sunday afternoon off with a big bang. He damn near shot himself in the foot. I'd watched him load a cheap little snub-nosed .38 revolver he'd brought with him and jam it down in his waistband. Words of warning to be careful had just formed in my mouth when out of some idiotic impulse, he attempted a fast draw, barely cleared the barrel from his pants, and accidentally discharged the gun with a loud bang. A wisp of smoke floated up from his waist.

I was torn between laughing my head off or knocking his off. It made me angry that he blatantly ignored every precaution I'd tried to impress on him. But it *was* funny. Ruby covered a grin on his face and said, "Lee, speed isn't everything. I hope this will help you realize that Tex might know what he's talking about when he keeps preaching safety."

"Well, that could happen to anyone," Oswald rationalized.

Oswald told me he was in the marines and qualified as a
sharpshooter. If he did, he must have had some help,
because he had no idea how to handle a rifle.
(Photos courtesy of AP/Wide World Photos)

Oswald's wife, Marina.
He carried this picture of
her in his billfold.
*(Photo courtesy of the Dallas
Municipal Archives and
Records Center,
City of Dallas, TX)*

I saw Lee swagger around like this, pretending to be a gunman.
But I never saw him with any guns that looked like these.
(*Photos courtesy of the Dallas Municipal Archives and Records Center,
City of Dallas, TX*)

Running the Carousel Club
in Dallas kept Jack pretty
busy. He even had to
cancel his shooting lessons
with me because of the
club.   (*Photo courtesy
of the National Archives*)

Jack Ruby loved the ladies
and always had a couple
around him when he
worked at the club.
(*Photo courtesy of the
National Archives*)

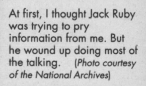

At first, I thought Jack Ruby
was trying to pry
information from me. But
he wound up doing most of
the talking.   (*Photo courtesy
of the National Archives*)

Right here next to Lake Worth was where I taught Jack Ruby and Lee Oswald to use guns. Oswald never did get the hang of it, and couldn't hit any kind of target.
(*Photo courtesy of the Brown & Lasseter Collection*)

The now vacant site of the Rodeo Cafe (just beyond the telephone poles) in Fort Worth, Texas. I can still hear the voice of my old buddie, Tommy, who owned it. The concrete in the foreground marks the site of the gas station where LBJ phoned me.
(*Photo courtesy of the Brown & Lasseter Collection*)

Many people think the shot that killed JFK was fired from behind this wooden fence on the grassy knoll at Dealey Plaza. Just a few days before the killing, I met a Cuban man outside the Rodeo Cafe who might have been the one who pulled the trigger.
(*Photo courtesy of the Brown & Lasseter Collection*)

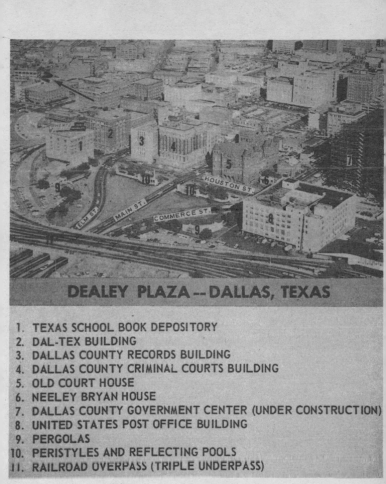

DEALEY PLAZA -- DALLAS, TEXAS

1. TEXAS SCHOOL BOOK DEPOSITORY
2. DAL-TEX BUILDING
3. DALLAS COUNTY RECORDS BUILDING
4. DALLAS COUNTY CRIMINAL COURTS BUILDING
5. OLD COURT HOUSE
6. NEELEY BRYAN HOUSE
7. DALLAS COUNTY GOVERNMENT CENTER (UNDER CONSTRUCTION)
8. UNITED STATES POST OFFICE BUILDING
9. PERGOLAS
10. PERISTYLES AND REFLECTING POOLS
11. RAILROAD OVERPASS (TRIPLE UNDERPASS)

(Photo courtesy of the National Archives)

Lee Oswald couldn't have shot JFK even if he'd used a superior rifle, so there's no way he could have done it with this old Mannlicher-Carcano bolt action weapon. (*Photo courtesy of the National Archives*)

To me, one of the most gut-wrenching photos of all is this one, showing the bloody shirt worn by JFK when he was shot to death. (*Photo courtesy of the National Archives*)

C 32
COMMISSION EXHIBIT
394

Oswald was accused of shooting Dallas police officer J.D. Tippit, but when I heard that the killer stood about ten feet away, I doubted that Oswald did it. His bad habit of blinking and jerking the trigger made him miss even the close shots.
(Photo courtesy of the Dallas Municipal Archives and Records Center, City of Dallas, TX)

Just as he had with me and Jack Ruby, Oswald stayed cocky and arrogant even when held by the police and questioned by reporters. *(Photo courtesy of AP/Wide World Photos)*

Jack Ruby told me he was going to be a hero, then drove off. The next morning, he went to the police basement and shot Oswald. Look at his left arm, bent at the elbow. He never could break the habit of pumping it up and down when he fired a gun.
(*Photo courtesy of Bob Jackson*)

Lee Oswald, silenced forever by one gunshot to the left side delivered by Jack Ruby. Did the shooting lessons I gave Jack contribute to Oswald's death? That question still haunts me.
(*Photo courtesy of the Dallas Municipal Archives and Records Center, City of Dallas, TX*)

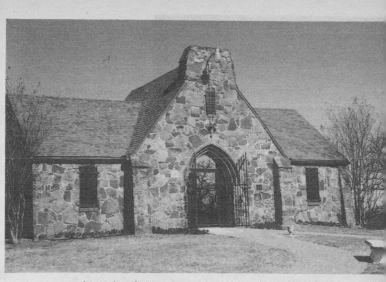

I stood outside a fence, about 100 yards away, to watch the graveside service for Oswald. A gang of reporters had to be recruited to carry the casket from a little hilltop chapel.
(*Photo courtesy of the Brown & Lasseter Collection*)

Oswald's funeral was pitiful, attended only by his wife Marina, his brother Robert, his mom Marguerite, his two little daughters, and some reporters. (*Photo courtesy of the National Archives*)

In February 1996, I visited Oswald's grave, now marked only by this small stone slab. The original headstone, engraved with his full name and dates, was stolen years ago. (*Photo courtesy of the Brown & Lasseter Collection*)

OSWALD

DALLAS POLICE
36398
11 24 63

Jack Ruby, looking mighty grim after his arrest for shooting Oswald. He had the same expression the day I refused to accept his offer of a million dollars to kill someone. (*Photos courtesy of the Dallas Municipal Archives and Records Center, City of Dallas, TX*)

The president told me to call him Lyndon, like one cowboy talking to another. He admired my Appaloosa, Chief, and was a pretty fair rider himself. (*Photo courtesy of the LBJ Library*)

The first time I met LBJ, he arrived at my campsite on the Pedernales River, driving this Continental convertible by himself. It's now on display at his ranch. (*Photo courtesy of the Brown & Lasseter Collection*)

LBJ, his wife Lady Bird, and two daughters at the Texas ranch home. When he died in this house in 1973, I had mixed emotions, but still stuck to the promise I'd made him. (*Photo courtesy of the LBJ Library*)

LBJ and Governor John Connally, wearing bandannas at a ceremony overlooking the Pedernales River. They say the bullet that killed JFK was the same one that wounded Gov. Connally. I'm not so sure. (*Photo courtesy of the LBJ Library*)

You might be able to tell by my expression how much I hated
returning to Dealey Plaza on a cold day in Februry 1996.
It brought back too many painful memories.
(Photo courtesy of the Brown & Lasseter Collection)

"Sure, it could," I said. "But you aren't going to have many toes left if you keep doing it."

"Okay, let's see you draw, then." Sometimes, he reminded me of a schoolkid squabbling on the playground.

At first, I felt like turning my back to him and walking away. On second thought, I figured I'd better guide him through it and maybe prevent a serious injury. "I'm going to show you the right way to do it with the hope that it might keep you from becoming a cripple. Now, pay attention. I'll go through it in slow motion, then fast." I pulled the Colt .45 from a locked compartment in my truck bed and strapped my leather holster on my left side, so the grip of the gun would face forward.

Oswald watched, his arrogant smirk even more intense. "What are doing it that way for? Doesn't it take more time to reach all the way across your body, then have to bring the gun back over? They don't do it that way in the movies."

"A cross-handed draw has some advantages," I explained, struggling to remain patient. "And for me, it's just as fast, if not more so. Think about it for a second, Lee. If you're wearing a coat or a vest, like I always do, the gun is usually covered. It's a lot easier to reach into the left side of the vest than to try to lift the right side, then draw." He acted as if he hadn't heard a word I'd said.

Oswald decided to increase the challenge by setting up four cans and asking that I not only draw and fire rapidly, but demonstrate accuracy as well. He made it clear that he hoped I would miss. But I didn't. And he didn't bother to acknowledge that, either.

Forsaking the fast draw, Lee tried to aim accurately, but still missed. "The gun's off center," he complained. I tried his weapon and found it reasonably precise, to which he finally admitted, "Maybe it's in my grip, the way I handle it."

"Let me show you." I placed his right hand correctly on the grip with forefinger inside the trigger guard, and his left hand cupping and gripping the right wrist, arms extended at high aim, and explained that this method provided balance along with preventing some of the kickback. "Now, remember, fine shooting starts in the mind. You gotta *think* you're going to hit that target. Then the mind works the hand, and the hand works the trigger—all in a smooth sequence." I stepped back and told him to fire. He actually knocked off one of the cans and turned up the corners of that taut little mouth into a silly grin.

The tidbit of success improved Oswald's disposition and ignited his desire to talk. He was fascinated with the new baby, he said, and hoped the world would improve by the time she grew up. Laughter relaxed his defiant expression when he described the infant and his other daughter's antics. Marina, he told us, was a good mother, even though she still could speak very little English. The woman she was staying with spoke Russian.

Just making conversation, I asked how he'd met Marina. Lee said that he'd attended a dance at the Palace of Culture in Minsk, Russia, and noticed her immediately because she was beautiful. "She was very surprised when I told her I was an American, because I speak the Russian language fluently and she thought I was probably from somewhere else in the Soviet Union. I asked her if she would meet me at another dance the next week, and she accepted my invitation. Before that, I'd been dating another girl, named Ella, and that was a serious relationship. But I decided I wanted Marina."

Ruby stopped shooting long enough to ask about Marina's background. Lee seemed proud as he told us. "Marina was educated in Leningrad at the Pharmacy Teknikum, and earned a diploma to become a pharmacist, but the cell party leader assigned her to work in a warehouse. That made her unhappy, so she left Leningrad to live with her aunt and uncle in Minsk. She got a job in a hospital. Just before our second date, I got sick and had to be hospitalized myself. Marina visited me every day. She even brought me a colored egg on Easter Sunday. I proposed to her from my sickbed, but she had to think it over. She was nineteen at the time."

Nineteen seemed old enough to me. "So how long did it take you to convince her to marry you?"

"About a month. Her uncle was an official in the Communist party, and I worried that he might discourage her from marrying an American. But they both accepted me, and we had our wedding on April 30, 1961. Her family gave us a nice reception in their home, with plenty to eat and drink. Someone started a fight with her uncle, and the whole place was thrown into total darkness when a fuse blew. But it turned out nice. Our honeymoon was nothing more than three days off from our jobs. I worked in a factory. We took boat rides on Lake Minsk and long walks in the park and went to the opera and the circus."

"Was your first daughter born over there, or here in this country?"

"She was born in Minsk on February 15, last year. I wanted to name her June Marina, but there's a stupid law over there that requires a child's second name to be a derivative of the father's name. Can you beat that? So we named her June Lee."

"When did you come back to the U.S.?"

"Last year, in June. Same as my daughter's name. But

there is no significance to that. Sometimes I wonder if we made the right move. Political considerations brought us here."

I didn't want to hear his "political considerations," so I suggested we try some more shooting. Lee and Jack continued to practice, trying to hit a garbage can lid on a swinging rope, while I let my thoughts wrestle with annoying questions. What in the world did Ruby have in mind for Oswald? If Jack was trying to make the arrogant little cuss into some kind of an armed guard, he'd picked the wrong person. Lee would never become competent with a gun. Any target more than ten yards away was completely out of his range. How he had qualified with a rifle in the Marine Corps was a real mystery to me.

Oswald hadn't expended his desire to talk. "Tex, have you ever heard of General Edwin Walker?" I said I'd heard someone had taken a potshot at him last spring in Dallas, but had missed. "Yes," Oswald said, "and it was an unfortunate miss." The expression on Lee's face made me think he knew a lot about the case.

"Why do you say that?"

"Because Walker is a right-wing fanatic racist member of the John Birch Society. He goes all over the country trying to stir up a war against Communists, and he tried to keep that young black man, James Meredith, from enrolling at the University of Mississippi. I can't believe that over one hundred and thirty thousand people in Texas voted for him for governor last year. If he had won out over John Connally, there would have been a race war in this state. Did you know that President Kennedy relieved Walker of command of an Army division over in Germany last year, and Walker resigned his commission as a result?"

I nodded, but didn't recall any of the details. Oswald was on a roll. Whether I wanted to hear more or not, I was sure he was going to tell me.

"I have some very influential friends," he continued, growing red in the face, "who say that anyone who killed Walker would be a hero and deserves a medal. He's a menace to peace and social harmony."

Oswald's tirade made me wonder if he had tried to kill Walker. If he had, the outcome would have been certain. He would have missed.

Oswald interrupted my troubled thoughts. "You know, Tex, you could make a living with guns."

I saw my opportunity to let them know the lessons were nearing an end. "I don't think so, Lee. I'm just about finished coaching you two guys, and I don't think I want to be a teacher anymore. Never did get along very well with teachers in school, and I don't think I'm cut out to be one."

Ruby also saw an opportunity. "Maybe there are other ways to earn money with guns, more profitable than teaching."

"That's true, Jack. You saw Big John and me in a very good example. That's as far as I'd ever go, and I keep hoping that I won't have to actually shoot anyone. I'll never break the law with my guns."

"If someone offered you a lot of money, more money than you'd ever seen in your life, would you consider it?" I hoped it was a rhetorical question, but his eyes looked dead serious.

"No one is going to buy me, Jack."

With a grim smile, he shot back, "Anybody can be bought." I chose to disregard his words and suggested they practice for a few more minutes before we headed back into town.

* * *

In the Rodeo parking lot, I started to tell them that today was the last lesson, but Jack interrupted to ask me for help in a crucial matter. He pulled me out of Oswald's hearing range, hinting that he wanted to share something very confidential with me. In a low voice, he described a one-in-a-thousand rifle he would like me to examine, a collector's item Winchester. It was for sale, and Ruby was thinking of buying it. My evaluation of it, he said, would help with the decision. The man knew exactly how to bore right in on a person's weaknesses. In his extremely persuasive manner, Jack convinced me to allow him to bring the owner to my house that same evening.

For the first time, Oswald waved, with that goofy grin, as they drove away.

It would be the last time I'd ever see him alive, in person.

Fourteen

I dug out some books I owned and did some quick research on Winchesters so I'd have a better idea how to evaluate the rare rifle Ruby had described. I was reading when I heard Jack's car pull into my driveway. Outside, I greeted him and shook hands with his companion, who spoke in a distinctive Cuban accent but was unusually tall for people born there. Suave, intelligent, and well groomed, he leaned back into the car to retrieve the rifle, in a case, and we went into the house.

Opening the case as if it contained the crown jewels, he carefully lifted out a classic Winchester rifle. At first, I was positive that it was a rare Model 73 One of One-Thousand that causes gun collectors to drool and beg. Only 136 of them were manufactured back in 1873, and each was worth $10,000 or more. I craned my neck, looking for the engraving on the barrel that would identify it, but couldn't see it. So I figured it was a Model 73 lever-action repeater made sometime in the early 1920s, and still worth a lot of money. It had a plain straight grip stock and forearm, with a twenty-four-inch barrel. The Cuban said it was chambered for caliber .38-.40 with a fifteen-shot magazine.

When the rifle owner excused himself to use the bathroom, I whispered to Jack that the gun was probably worth more than a thousand dollars. Ruby's eyes widened. "Hell, I was going to offer him five hundred for it."

"You could probably resell it for two or three times that much. If I had the money, I'd buy it."

Ruby gave me a long look, and said, "Maybe I'll just give the gun to you if we end up with it." The Cuban came out of the bathroom, cutting off my chance to respond. Just as well, because I was speechless at Ruby's professed generosity.

Following some more general chitchat about guns, Ruby asked if I could meet them tomorrow, go to the lake, and try the Winchester out.

"Okay, Jack," I said. "But I think that will be our last time. I'm quite sure that your other buddy is not going to make any more improvement, and I've shown you about all I can."

"Well, give it some thought, Tex. You and I get along well, and I've got some contacts that you might find useful. Don't slam the door 'til you know what opportunities you might be missing."

"I've made up my mind, Jack. But I'll see you at the Rodeo Cafe tomorrow."

"We'll be there about three in the afternoon, if that's okay with you." I didn't realize, until they'd left, that Ruby had never even mentioned his Cuban pal's name.

I decided to arrive at the Rodeo early. Two weeks had passed since the odd visit to the cafe by the men from Louisiana, and Tommy hadn't been the same since. Normally an easygoing fellow, he'd been acting edgy, nervous, and close-mouthed lately. Sometimes, he didn't even show up for work, leaving the restaurant in the hands of a part-time cook and a couple of waitresses. I thought I'd better see if I could do anything to help him.

The waitress said Tommy would be in later, so I sat at my usual table and ordered a hamburger. I knew most of the regular customers and exchanged greetings with the ones sitting around over coffee and exchanging tall stories. Maybe my concern for Tommy's worries made me overly sensitive to strangers because I found myself eyeing newcomers with critical curiosity. One man, sitting only a few feet from me, rang my internal alarm.

Over six feet tall, in his mid- to late twenties, and wearing a long gray topcoat, he occupied a booth by himself. A neatly trimmed beard covered the chin of his big, square, rugged face. The flesh over his right eye angled downward toward his cheekbone, giving him a sleepy look, but the eyes burned brightly. A full thatch of wavy brown hair had been mussed up by the morning breeze. When he folded his newspaper, I noticed that his fingernails were clean and neatly trimmed, in stark contrast to all those of the other cowboy customers. I tried not to stare overtly, but something about the man, I wasn't sure what it was, riveted my attention. It's almost always true that if you keep looking at a stranger, that person will somehow pick up the vibes and look back, and he did. But he paid little attention, just calmly returning to his newspaper and coffee. When he spoke to the waitress, his voice rumbled with self-assurance in a slow, husky drawl.

When Tommy came in, he sat with me for a while, exchanging greetings and asking about Big John. He seemed much more relaxed than before, so I didn't plague him with questions. We chatted about more pleasant things and planned to attend the big Cotton Bowl Rodeo on the day after Christmas. He bragged about the professional football

performance of Dandy Don Meredith on Sunday, and glo-
ried in the Dallas team beating the Philadelphia Eagles 27
to 20. Meredith had completed 25 of 33 passes in the game,
Tommy said. It reminded me that Lee Oswald had mentioned watching football on television during the weekends
he visited Marina, and I wondered if he'd been peeved
about missing out on them last Sunday. Oh, well, he could
watch all he wanted from now on. I didn't want to see him
anymore. Tommy seemed to be in better spirits, so I left to
pick up some hardware I needed.

I made it back to the cafe a little before three, a few
minutes before Ruby and the Cuban arrived, and they followed me to the lake.

Expecting Jack's companion, whose name I still didn't
know, to pull the Winchester from the trunk of the Oldsmobile, I was surprised when he lifted a different leather case
out instead. Fancy tooling decorated it, and I could make
out the name "H. Carlos." He opened it to reveal the dis-
assembled components of a weapon like I'd never seen before.

"Con permisso Señor," he said, "I'd like to try some
shooting weeth thees one first." Hoping he meant that we'd
still use the Winchester later, I said it was fine with me.
He screwed and snapped the rifle, including a powerful
scope, together in seconds, then loaded it. After turning his
cap around and hanging his dark glasses on the neck of his
shirt, he pointed his finger at a crow sitting on a limb about
a hundred yards away. Slipping his hand through the sling
which he looped over his elbow, snapping the butt to his
shoulder and his eye to the scope, he popped off one shot.
A cluster of black feathers exploded in the treetop. The
Cuban grinned, displaying the sparkle of a gold eyetooth
and the glint of mean brown eyes.

We marked off targets at gradually increasing distances, and he never missed once. It punched the wind out of my sails in a hurry, making my ability to knock over tin cans look like a third-grader with a BB gun. I'm sure he could have hit a bullseye at a half mile. When he dismantled the scope rifle and returned it to the fancy case, he produced a long-barreled German-made fully automatic pistol, and scored equally well with it. Even considering his expensive, high powered equipment, the guy was an eagle-eyed dead shot.

We never did get around to using the Winchester. I'm not even sure he had it with him. If the purpose of the demonstration was to impress me, it worked.

Before we left the lake, Jack told me he was going to drop the Cuban off in Fort Worth, and would like to talk to me, but not at the Rodeo. We agreed to meet for supper at a steak house on Twenty-eighth and Sylvania Street. He couldn't stay very late, he said, because an associate had invited him to a party that night.

We met at the restaurant, and I'd never seen Ruby so fidgety. He kept glancing around at other tables, unable to concentrate on the menu. He took a container of pills from his coat pocket and washed one down with water. When we'd finally ordered our meals, he said, "Tex, I know you don't like to talk business while you're eating, but this is important and can't wait. I've been asked by some other people to make you an offer. I'm just a middleman, here, but I hope you will give this serious consideration." He reached into his inside coat pocket and withdrew an envelope. "I'm supposed to open it for you, hand you the written proposition, then take the paper with me. Okay?"

My first inclination was to get up and walk out of there.

The hair stood up on the back of my neck. Suspicion crawled over me like flies on horse manure. But curiosity overcame my good judgment, so I nodded.

He opened the unsealed envelope, slipped out a single-folded sheet of paper, and handed it across the table. I held it next to the dim lamp and read:

Dear Tex,
    I do not know you, but I've heard you are good with a rifle. How would you like to be one of the richest men in North Texas for one day's work? Price tag, one million dollars.

I felt the heat start down around my toes and rise to my face. My temples throbbed and my teeth ground together. It took all I could muster not to spring out of that chair and throw something at him. "Jack," I growled, "what the hell have you gotten me into?"

"Calm down!" It sounded more like an order than a request. "Read the rest of it." I struggled for control, and looked again at the paper:

If you choose not to accept this offer, there are no hard feelings. If you accept, the bearer of this note will give you the details of the job we have in mind. I know we can trust you to be discreet.

No signature. I had to clear my throat of a boiling anger before speaking. "Jack, if this means what it sounds like, you're asking me to kill someone. If that's true, I'm really disappointed. I thought you knew me better than that."

"I think they'd give you even more money than the letter offers if you do the job properly."

"Good God, man. Aren't you listening to me? I'm not interested. I don't use my guns like that. There ain't enough money in the state of Texas to hire me to be a killer. Even if I thought that way, you can't spend money while you're sitting in the electric chair." I felt like wadding up the note and shoving it down his throat, but I simply pushed it back across the table.

His face sullen, he picked the sheet up, carefully folded it, and returned it to the envelope. As he inserted it, I thought I saw the word "Miami" printed on the outside, but I couldn't be certain.

My appetite was wrecked. After our steaks were served and I'd partially calmed down, I said, "Jack, in some ways, I've enjoyed working with you. There have been a lot of questions in my mind about the kind of business you're in and the people you run with. But that's none of my business and I've avoided asking questions. I don't know where this note came from, and I don't want to know. Just tell them I'm the wrong man for the job."

"I told them that," he muttered. "But they wanted me to approach you anyway." We picked through the rest of our meals in awkward silence.

As we walked to our cars, I said, "Look, maybe you *are* just a middleman, but you must have told someone that you thought I'd do this. I'm trying not to be mad. But this ends our bargain. I've got other things to do with my life. So we'll just say *adios*."

"I'm sorry you feel that way, Tex. I'm in kind of a bind. If you change your mind, you know where you can find me." When he pulled into traffic with that Oldsmobile, he laid about ten feet of rubber. He never looked back.

* * *

John Marshall called that evening, asking if I'd like to accompany him to Waco for a little job. As usual, his timing was perfect. If I ever needed to get away, that was the night. I said I'd be happy to go, and that I had something to tell him.

The drive down Highway 35 took less than two hours. I gave John all the details of my encounter with Ruby. He listened to the whole story without interrupting, then said, "I'm proud of you, Tex." That was all. With that simple comment of approval, he made me feel like I had truly come of age. I was no longer his youthful sidekick, but more like a full partner—no longer a kid, but now a man of equal status. He couldn't have said anything that would have pleased me more.

We easily found our fugitive in Waco that same night and delivered him to the authorities. The guy was all spaced out on drugs and had tried to kill his own mother. I don't think I'd really realized, up to that time, how serious the growing drug problem was. This halfwit kept slobbering and talking to himself the whole time we had him handcuffed and chained in the truck. He didn't know where he was or what was going on around him. How anyone could let themselves sink that low by injecting stuff to make themselves feel good was beyond my understanding. I knew that if drug use continued to grow, our bounty hunting expeditions would keep us as busy as we wanted to be. John said it was the easiest thousand dollars he'd ever made.

Clouds had started to gather on Wednesday, November 20. I finished patching some leaks in the barn roof before driving over to pick up a load of hay on North Houston Street. As I passed a popular hamburger stand, I caught sight of someone familiar walking out of the place. The long gray coat tipped me off at first, then the height. He moved with that same self-assurance along the sidewalk. But the beard had been shaved off. I took a second look, and a third to be sure, erasing all doubts. It was the same well-manicured stranger who had looked so out of place in the Rodeo Cafe on Monday. Odd, running into the same person, who'd caught my attention, twice in such a short time.

Perhaps it wouldn't have registered as such a coincidence if another one hadn't happened immediately afterward. Within a couple of blocks I spotted two more familiar faces. Jack Ruby and the tall marksman Cuban were standing near the Oldsmobile, talking. They didn't see me, and I turned right to avoid moving into their line of vision. I had no desire to talk to either man. My mind kept seeking a connection between the two sightings, but my conscious logic rejected it. Just because I'd seen the topcoated man in the Rodeo didn't mean there was any link to Ruby. Or did it?

It felt good to work up a sweat unloading my hay back in the barn. Physical labor can drive out mental demons. I found more work to keep me busy, brushing the horses, shoveling out the barn floor, patching another couple of leaks in the roof. A hot shower helped, too. But I wasn't hungry, and that convinced me something must be wrong.

I followed the same routine on Thursday, working as hard as I could. More rain was forecast for the next day, so I battened down everything, covered the hay with tarps, and checked for any more roof leaks. By that evening, I felt my appetite returning, and with it the desire to be around people. I called Debbie to ask if she'd like to go into town tomorrow morning for something special. The president had flown in yesterday and spent the night at the Texas Hotel in Fort Worth. According to the news, he'd make a speech Friday morning to the Chamber of Commerce, then be driven out to the airport for a short flight to Dallas. I thought it might be fun to go in early, find a parking place, and hang around near the hotel, where we might get a chance to see him.

I had no special love for John Kennedy, because I'd heard that his father had used to deal with racketeers in the bootlegging era, had made millions, and had virtually bought the presidency for his son. But I had to admit that the young chief executive possessed a lot of charisma and had sparked hope for the future among the younger generation. They called it the new Camelot, and that had a nice sound to it. I regarded myself as a loyal, law-abiding American citizen and felt responsible to see the president if I had the opportunity.

Unfortunately, Debbie couldn't ride in with me. She had to work at least until 11 A.M., then would meet me for a drive to the lake. Maybe we could catch a movie later. I glanced at a Dallas newspaper to see what was currently playing. The entertainment section contained an ad for Jack Ruby's Carousel Club. Someone name Bill Demar, with the title "Master of ESP," was part of the entertainment there, along with "5 Exotic Dancers on 3 Large Runways." I wondered how many customers would be attracted by the top line of the ad, which read, "Free Admission to Ladies." Not me. They couldn't have paid me to take Debbie there.

She wouldn't be able to meet me until 11 A.M., but I still planned to see Mr. Kennedy, even if I had to do it alone, and even if I had to stand in the rain.

I threw a steak on the grill, fried up a mess of potatoes, and settled down to watch *Cheyenne* on television. It was an interesting episode in which he faced death several times during a dangerous trip. I'll always remember the episode's title, which turned out to be eerily prophetic. It was called "The Road to Three Graves."

Fifteen

The weather prediction had been accurate. It rained steadily before dawn and continued to drizzle as I drove into town. A sense of excitement elevated my mood, though, which usually needed the energy spurt provided by a hearty breakfast to chase away the pre-coffee crankiness. I had never seen a president before, and it might be fun to mingle with an excited crowd.

Throngs of people had already arrived by the time I did, and traffic was thick. I lucked out, finding a parking place near the Greyhound Bus depot, where, by standing on the pickup bed, I would have a pretty good view of the Hotel Texas and the adjacent parking lot. The rain had tapered to a drizzle, but dark clouds threatened a new downpour any minute.

I bought a paper cup of coffee in the bus depot and sat in my truck. Somewhere around 8:45, a ripple of excitement buzzed through the crowd, and I hopped out, jumped up into the truck bed, and craned my neck toward the hotel.

Sure enough, I saw President John Fitzgerald Kennedy. No one could have missed that bright, gleaming smile and that shock of unruly dark hair. There truly was something magic about his presence, as if a glow surrounded him. The rain even stopped for him, and rays of sun broke through. He stepped up on a raised platform to speak to the crowd, but I couldn't hear his words. It didn't matter. The moment still had electric excitement, the realization of being on the spot of a historic moment, crossing paths with greatness.

The vice-president, our own Texan, Lyndon B. Johnson, stood behind Kennedy, to his left, Governor John Connally directly behind Kennedy, and Senator Ralph Yarborough to his right. The crowd chanted, *"Where's Jackie?"* He grinned, pointed up to a hotel window, and said something else. In a few more minutes, he finished his short speech, moved through the admirers, and went toward the hotel entrance. I waited for a few minutes, enjoying the moment, watching the people. Most of them shared my excitement, but a few grumbled criticism and complaints. It crossed my mind that no matter what business or activity anyone does, you can't please everyone. And that certainly included the president, probably more than any other person in the world. I didn't envy Mr. Kennedy his job.

When the traffic eased, I drove out of the downtown area to pick up Debbie. I felt terrific. I wouldn't be seeing Jack Ruby or Lee Oswald or any of their mysterious associates anymore. A huge burden had been lifted from my shoulders, freeing me of the weight of doubt, questions, and a growing feeling of indefinable guilt. It was going to be a beautiful day, and a little rain certainly wasn't going to spoil it.

I picked Debbie up at 11, and headed southwest, toward Benbrook Lake. We stopped and bought some fried chicken, chips, and soft drinks, a makeshift picnic, planning to park close to a spot overlooking the lake. If the clouds broke, we'd walk around to find a place with a romantic view and enjoy an outdoors afternoon in the rolling hills. If the skies opened up for another downpour, we'd sit in the pickup cab, listen to music on the radio, and find other ways to while away a rainy day. We talked about going to a movie. She wanted to see Elizabeth Taylor in *Cleopatra.* My preference was for John Wayne in *McClintock* or James Garner in *The Wheeler Dealers,* because the cast also included one of my favorite character actors, Chill Wills.

By the time we reached the dam, it began to drizzle again, so we opened the packages of food inside the cab and took our time, laughing and eating. We had a lot to talk about: her work, my horses, our goals in life, some intimate matters, and our futures, and we took our own sweet time. Both of us felt that the relationship was moving in the right direction, and we agreed to see each other more often. I felt calm and satisfied for the first time in weeks. Some good music, we both thought, would enhance the peaceful afternoon. Somewhere around 4 o'clock, I turned the dashboard switch on and touched the button for my favorite station.

My life would never be the same after that moment.

We did not hear the music we expected. Instead, the tense voice of an announcer reeled off the incredible news that the president of the United States had died from bullet wounds three hours earlier at Parkland Hospital in Dallas!

Debbie and I looked at each other in horror and shock. She shrieked, "Oh my God!," put both hands over her face, and began trembling uncontrollably. Good Lord, I had just seen him that morning, full of life, grinning and waving. This was absolutely unbelievable. I looked at her and groaned, "What is this country coming to?" I turned up the volume. We learned that someone had shot the president while the motorcade had driven through Dealey Plaza, on the western side of downtown Dallas. Governor John Connally had also been wounded and was being treated at Parkland Hospital, where Kennedy had died. Vice-President Lyndon B. Johnson, now our thirty-sixth president, had already flown out of Love Field back to Washington, D.C., in Air Force One.

Speechless and stunned, we sat in silence and listened. The announcer's voice rose to a new level of excitement with another news development. A police officer named J. D. Tippit had been shot to death in the Oak Cliff section of Dallas. My mind leaped back to Jack Ruby, who had once mentioned living in that neighborhood. Something else spun into focus, bringing with it the first seed of worry in the pit of my stomach when I recalled that Lee Oswald had also moved there. No, there couldn't be any connection. That was absurd. Debbie whispered a prayer for John Kennedy and Officer Tippit.

I started to reach for the ignition switch to head back to town when my hand froze in mid-air. The quivering voice boomed in my ears. A suspect had been arrested in a theater on Jefferson Boulevard, a few blocks from the Tippit murder scene. The man arrested had been identified as a Dallas resident named Lee Harvey Oswald! He even matched the description of an employee of the Texas School Book Depository in Dealey Plaza, who officials sought as a possible suspect in the presidential assassination.

My thoughts bucked and reeled. A Texas twister whirled around in my head. I couldn't grasp the nightmarish reality. My next reaction shocked Debbie, and myself: I laughed out loud!

Lee Harvey Oswald? That seemed so ridiculous it struck a bizarre part of my funny bone. Good Lord! That little twerp couldn't hit anything with a gun, whether it be a rifle or a pistol. How could he have shot anyone to death, especially a trained police officer? Of course, I had this vague picture of a high-noon shootout on a dusty Western street, where the sheriff and the villain stand twenty or thirty paces apart, draw, and shoot. The other possibilities didn't even occur to me—that Officer Tippit might have been ambushed at point-blank range. If I had thought of that, I probably would have rejected it as well. Oswald didn't have that kind of grit. There must be some serious error. Lee, now known to the world as Lee Harvey Oswald, could not have committed such an outrageous act. And the thought that he'd shot the president from a distance with the target in a moving car was so absurd it didn't even warrant serious consideration.

With the shock beginning to subside, I could think of only one place to go—the Rodeo Cafe. People I knew, including John Marshall, would probably be there. I needed his agreement that Oswald couldn't have been the killer. This was too big to keep inside, and Debbie really didn't know that much about it. We'd planned to go to a Mexican restaurant for dinner, but I started the pickup, jammed it into gear, and headed for Twenty-eighth and Main.

As I had expected, a crowd of regulars had gathered, including Marshall. Tommy had placed a television set on the counter, and everyone moved into a semi-circle to watch the black-and-white images. Newscasters continually interrupted with updated bulletins. There were scenes of people standing in groups all over town, especially at Dealey Plaza, sobbing and consoling each other. They replayed the heartbreaking scenes of Kennedy's last ride, as he waved to a cheering, festive crowd, and showed again the dramatic announcement by Walter Cronkite removing his glasses and choking back the tears as he announced that the President was dead.

The solemn group listened in crushed silence, too stunned to speak. I'm sure that some of them shared one of my thoughts. First, I deplored the killing of the president and wished that it had never happened. Then I asked, Why in Texas? We're a proud state, a loyal people. Why in the hell did the killer have to besmirch Texas with horror and shame? I wondered if citizens of other states felt relief that it had not happened to them, or if they could understand the hurt, pain, and agony that the people of Dallas and all of Texas felt.

On television, they showed a photo of Lyndon Johnson taking the oath of office, administered by a small woman, Judge Sarah T. Hughes, inside Air Force One. Tears came to the eyes of some of the viewers when they saw that Jacqueline Kennedy, who stood to the new president's left, still wore her fashionable suit, described as pink by the announcer, stained with the blood of her late husband. Johnson's grim face reflected the pain of a nation. Immediately after the brief ceremony, the plane took off from Love Field for Washington, D.C. The slain body of John Fitzgerald Kennedy was aboard for his last earthly flight.

That same morning, when I'd seen him, he'd spoken to the crowd outside the Texas Hotel. I hadn't been able to hear his words, but the television news had repeated them for me. In his usual good-humored way, with that big, radiant smile, the president had said, "Mrs. Kennedy is organizing herself. It takes longer—of course, she looks better than we do when she does it." At the Chamber of Commerce breakfast, he'd made another reference to his beautiful wife's appearance. "Two years ago, I introduced myself in Paris by saying I was the man who had accompanied Mrs. Kennedy to Paris. I am getting somewhat the same sensation as I travel around Texas. Nobody wonders what Lyndon and I wear."

We learned from the news that the president had been shot at about 12:30, moments after his open limousine had turned left from Houston onto Elm Street, and moved slowly past the seven-story red brick building known as the Texas School Book Depository. Witnesses said they'd heard three loud reports, like firecrackers, many of them believing the shots came from the window on the southeast corner of the depository's sixth floor. Others thought the shots came from somewhere on a grassy knoll, a hundred yards from the building. The limo had sped up and raced to Parkland Hospital, four miles away, where Kennedy was pronounced dead a half hour later.

Texas governor John Connally, who had been riding in the jump seat directly in front of Kennedy, was wounded on his right side, ribs, arm, and thigh. He'd undergone surgery, also at Parkland, but did not appear to be in danger of dying. Neither Mrs. Kennedy nor Mrs. Connally was wounded. Mrs. Kennedy, though, had done an odd thing when her husband was shot. She leaped up from the limousine's back seat and crawled out on the trunk lid. Some speculated that she was trying to help the Secret Service agent who had jumped out of the following car, run forward to the President's vehicle, and leaped on the back bumper. As the car sped up, Mrs. Kennedy returned to her seat. (Investigators would later learn that she'd crawled back there to retrieve a piece of her husband's skull she'd seen when his head had virtually exploded after the final gunshot.)

More details came on the news reports about the other killing. At about 1:15, near the intersection of Tenth and Patton in Oak Cliff, Officer J. D. Tippit had been patrolling slowly, driving east on Tenth Street. According to reports, he'd seen a man walking in the same direction who fit the description given to the police of the assassination suspect: a slender white male, about thirty years old, five-eight, 165 pounds, wearing a light jacket, white shirt, and dark slacks. He stopped the pedestrian, who came to the passenger window. They spoke briefly, then the officer exited the car. When Tippit reached the left front fender, gunfire erupted and he fell to the pavement, dead. Later, several blocks away, a witness saw someone enter the Texas Theater without purchasing a ticket. The police were called, and after a struggle, they arrested Lee Harvey Oswald for the murder of Tippet. Oswald had a Smith and Wesson .38-caliber revolver in his possession at the time.

I could picture that damn little gun and the erratic shooting ability of Oswald, the way he blinked, and jerked the trigger, and missed targets ten feet away. In my opinion, he couldn't have shot the officer. And the news reports were saying he was a suspect in the president's death. When I heard more details about the distance from the sixth-floor window to the limo, and the downward angle of the bullet's trajectory, the idea that he'd shot Kennedy became even more ridiculous. In the first place, anyone sitting on that sixth floor planning to shoot a figure in a moving car wouldn't have waited until it turned onto Elm Street. It would have been a far easier shot while the limo was slowing on Houston to make the sharp left turn. I was even more convinced that Oswald had been set up to take the rap for the real killer.

And I wondered just how deeply involved in the horrible events Jack Ruby was. I decided right then that I wanted to talk to him.

Sixteen

After I'd dropped Debbie off that Friday evening, I mulled over what I wanted to ask Jack Ruby. The questions would have to be formed with extreme care. If he was involved in a conspiracy to kill President Kennedy, as I strongly suspected, he might react like a cornered cougar.

It didn't seem likely to me that Ruby wanted Kennedy dead, but he had probably been pulled into the mire for money, which he always needed, or because he owed some favors. And I felt sure that he had tried to recruit me as a shooter, maybe to fire the shots at Kennedy, or to silence Oswald later. In my mind, Oswald was nothing but a fall guy, a scapegoat they'd gone to an awful lot of trouble to paint with the colors of guilt. They'd hung a big sign on his back saying "Arrest me, I'm the assassin."

Now, how could I ask Ruby all that? And would he give me any answers? Probably not. He was a very talkative guy, but not stupid. There would be no reason in the world for him to tell me what he had done, or why.

If I slept on the problem, maybe I could do a better job of finding the right words, the clever strategy, to get the information I wanted. Before I went to bed, I telephoned the Carousel Club to ask if Ruby was there, with hopes of arranging a meeting. Whoever answered the phone told me curtly that the club was closed indefinitely, in honor of the late president. No, Mr. Ruby wasn't in, and the speaker didn't know where he was.

I called his apartment in Oak Cliff, but got no answer.

Earlier, at the Rodeo, I had briefly chatted with John Marshall, too overwhelmed to discuss the incredible events in any detail. He'd patted me on the back, signaling his understanding, and said we'd talk later. Unable to reach Ruby, I decided to try again to tell Big John my plans to ask Jack some questions.

Marshall answered on the second ring. I described my efforts to reach Jack, and, as usual, John had up-to-date information. "Hell, Tex, Ruby's been hanging around in the police station all evening. A reporter friend of mine told me Jack even tried to walk into the captain's office, where detectives were questioning Oswald, but they turned him away. I swear, that guy's got the crust of a buzzard. I knew that he hung around some of the cops, but I didn't realize they'd let him up there where the biggest murder case in history of Dallas is being investigated. He's smart, though. He brought a bunch of sandwiches in for the cops, so how could they toss him out?"

"I sure need to talk to him, John. I have to ask some questions, to find out for my own peace of mind what was going on, and if they really planned to frame Oswald."

"I understand, Tex. But what makes you think he'll tell you anything?"

"He probably won't, but I can't rest until I at least try."

"Well, I sure wouldn't recommend that you search for him at the Dallas police station. I think you should stay as far away from there as possible. And I wouldn't go to his apartment, either. His clubs are closed, but he's bound to show up there sooner or later. Maybe you could go over there tomorrow and park where you can keep an eye on who comes and goes. I'd suggest you stake out the Carousel."

"Maybe I'll try that. I can't just sit around. It's worth a try. Thanks, John. I'll let you know if I find out anything."

Figuring that Ruby had probably been up all night, I waited until early Saturday afternoon to drive over to Dallas. Downtown, at the corner of Commerce and Field, I saw a marquee with the words "CAROUSEL—BURLESQUE" and "Girls, Girls." Another sign, with removable letters, held the names "Ember," "Tammy," "Kathy," and "Kay." On the left side of the entry to the joint, near an arrangement of photos picturing scantily clad dancers, someone had mounted a hand-lettered poster with the word "Closed" scrawled on it.

I circled the block and pulled over to the curb near Nichols' parking garage. If John Marshall was right, Ruby would probably show up pretty soon.

Big John was always right. At about 1:30, the white Oldsmobile wheeled into the garage entry. I waited to see if Ruby would walk to the club. He'd been inside the garage about five minutes, when I saw his car nose out the exit. I jumped from my pickup, ran, and leaped in front of the Olds, waving my hands for him to stop. He did. I moved to the driver's window and waited while he rolled it down.

"Jack, I've got to talk to you," I said, louder than I'd intended.

"Not now, Tex," he shot back, his tone agitated and serious. "I've got urgent business. Maybe we can get together later."

"When? You've gotta let me know just what the hell was going on." Not exactly the carefully worded, tactful approach I'd promised myself to use.

"It'll have to wait. Just watch who you talk to, Tex. You could be in a lot of danger, so it's best to keep your mouth shut. And watch old Jack, too. I'm going to be a hero!" His last few words were loud and spoken with an intensity I'd never heard from him before.

I started to protest, but he rolled his window up and shot out of the driveway, squealing the tires as he turned onto Commerce. Thoughts of chasing him rushed around in my mind, but I dismissed the idea. Ruby had made it clear he had no intention of taking time out to talk to me. All those trips to Fort Worth to seek me out had been when he'd wanted something. Now, my usefulness to him had passed, and he didn't have two minutes to spare.

I drove back to Fort Worth half angry, half befuddled, and determined to pin Ruby down for some answers in the near future.

Back in my house, I tried to watch television, but every station had canceled normal programming to concentrate on the aftermath of the assassination. Watching it just made me sicker and more confused. My brain went on overload, refusing to accept any more stress. I switched off the TV and wanted to switch off the world, too. Trying to occupy my time with something useful, I puttered around the barn for a while, but couldn't concentrate on that, either. Food usually helped pull me out of a rotten mood, but the thought of eating made my stomach turn. When I flopped down to

sleep, I tossed and bucked for a while, then had nightmares
in the color of blood.

Sunday morning, November 24, I wanted to be alone.
Curiosity bedeviled me, but my stubbornness prevailed. I
didn't want to hear news about the horrible events of Friday,
so I worked for a couple of hours. Finally, I switched on
the television, and heard the sad strains of "Hail to the
Chief," the song always played when the President makes
an appearance. Only this time, it was for his funeral. I
changed channels, but couldn't escape it. Distraction was
what I needed. I knew of a calf-roping contest scheduled
that afternoon out on Riverside Drive, so I decided to keep
my mind off the tragedies by attending it. En route, about
noon, I stopped at a 7-Eleven store to buy some lunch meat,
a loaf of bread, and a bottle of Dr. Pepper. The sales clerk
was glued to a television. While fishing out some money,
I inadvertently glanced up at the screen and felt like I'd
been hit by a bolt of lightning. The incredible nightmare
became worse.

The news announcer reran a piece of tape that had been
repeatedly shown, probably hundreds of times, since 11:21
that morning, when the event was shown live to millions
of television viewers across the nation. I watched it in absolute disbelief and stunned horror.

The grainy images had been taken in the basement of
police headquarters on East Main Street in Dallas, where
a group of reporters and television camera operators milled
around near the bottom of a car ramp. Within a minute or
two, their chatter rose as double doors opened to a hallway
which led from an elevator that provided access to the upstairs jail area. Lee Harvey Oswald, flanked on his right

by an official wearing a light-colored suit and hat, and on his left by another man dressed in dark suit and hat, marched between them. His wrists were cuffed and his arms held by both escorts. Of course, he had that tight-lipped, perturbed expression, the one I'd seen so often. The soft tissue above his left eye looked dark and swollen.

From out of the crowd, someone wearing a dark suit and light hat, with shirt and tie, stepped into view. The television camera caught a slight look at his profile, but mostly his back. He lunged instantly toward Oswald and thrust his right arm forward, while his left arm, bent at the elbow, pumped twice. No one, including Oswald, seemed to see the revolver in his hand until he fired it.

Lee Oswald grimaced in pain and dropped, with a bullet hole through his ribs. The officer in the light suit leaned back in horrified surprise. Pandemonium reigned. Several of the men wrestled the shooter to the floor. A newscaster yelled, "Oswald's been shot! Oswald's been shot!"

It was easy to recognize the assailant. It was Jack Ruby!

I forgot the calf roping event. I almost forgot where I was. The crazy world moved around me at the speed of old silent movies, while I trudged along in excruciating slow motion. I could hear people speaking, but they made all the sense of an auctioneer trying to hurry. I was drowning in confusion.

Somehow, I managed to find my way home. I wanted to dig a hole, jump in, and pull it in after me. Any contact with other human beings was completely out of the question. The blank television screen stared at me, threatening to reveal more insanity, so I pulled the plug out of the socket to be sure it didn't come on by itself.

The last words Ruby had spoken to me echoed in my mind: "I'm going to be a hero." So that's what he meant, that he was going to kill Lee Oswald. But how did that make him a hero? Did he think that the American public would be grateful because he'd wiped out the man most people believed to be the president's assassin? That didn't make a whole lot of sense to me. Oswald wasn't going anywhere. He would have faced trial and almost certain conviction, even though I felt sure he was not the shooter. But more important, he might have revealed what had really happened. With him dead, the truth might never be exposed.

Or did Ruby have something else in mind? Was he going to be a hero to the real killers, the conspirators? By silencing Oswald forever, Ruby would keep the truth from coming out, protecting those who bore the true guilt. I supposed they would regard him as a hero and probably hire the best lawyers available to keep Ruby out of prison. Unless they decided to sacrifice him, too, in an underhanded, sneaky doublecross.

I had to start giving some serious thought to telling the authorities what I knew, regardless of the consequences. It might open the dam to a flood of witnesses who could help reveal the truth. But right now, I felt too dumbfounded and bewildered to make any important decisions.

I sat in a stupor nearly all night, unable to sleep or function normally. At dawn, I finally drifted off for a while, but kept snapping awake, with the instinct to draw my guns and blast away at some menacing threat.

At last I allowed myself to turn the television on, sort of hoping that a calm announcer would say everything had been a gigantic mistake, or that nothing had really happened. Maybe I'd dreamed it all. No such luck. They showed that heart wrenching shot of little "John-John" Kennedy, wearing a short coat and raising his tiny right hand to his forehead in a military salute to his fallen father. Tears welled in my eyes, and I unplugged the set again.

John Marshall and his wife rode to my rescue, as they had so many times in the past, bringing food and comfort. They talked to me several hours Sunday night as a mother and father might, trying to soothe the mental wounds suffered by their son. I knew I could never repay them enough for their thoughtful kindness. John also reminded me that it would be wise to keep silent until I understood all of the consequences, and dangers, of telling what I knew.

Now it was out of the question for me to pry any answers from Jack Ruby. Obviously, I needed to steer clear of him.

Lee Harvey Oswald was dead. No more arrogant smirks, no more lectures about the wonders of Marxism, and no more futile efforts at learning to use a gun. I'd been relieved when my teaching chores ended. But, damn it, I felt the emptiness of a journey uncompleted or a task unfinished, like a thriller with the last two pages missing.

There was something I had to do, even if I risked arrest, torture, or being shot to death by some faceless marksman hiding around the next corner.

Seventeen

A wise man once said, "The more I know, the more I realize how little I know." My formal schooling had ended early, but I regarded my education in the ways of life more complete than that of most men who hadn't yet seen their twentieth birthday. In the world of rough-and-tumble men, cowboys, bounty hunters, lawbreakers, innocent girls, and scarlet women, I had learned a great deal about human nature. I could verbally fence with considerable agility, recognize the subtleties of most con games, and hold my own in a contest of common sense. But the dark events of November 22 and 24, 1963, shook my self-confidence to the core. I felt mentally and physically shattered.

Each time I saw a cop in a police car, I fully expected him to screech to a halt, leap out, level a gun at me, and snap the cuffs on. I jumped every time I heard a sharp noise, wondering if some mobster had been hired to silence me forever. Feeling vulnerable to both the law and the underworld, I couldn't think of a logical place to hide. Misery is poor company, and I had about all I could tolerate. The image of Jack Ruby shooting Lee Oswald repeatedly ran through my mind in slow motion.

I told John Marshall that I wanted to attend the graveside services for Oswald when they buried him. Not because I liked the guy, and not because I sympathized with anything he believed or did. I couldn't explain exactly why I wanted to be there. Somehow, I had a compelling desire to express condolences to his wife Marina, to his mother, and to any other family members he might have in attendance. Maybe I felt a kernel of guilt deep inside stemming from my role in training Lee to shoot, which might indirectly have led to his death.

Marshall made some phone calls and jotted down on a slip of paper when and where Oswald would be buried. It would be on Monday, and I knew the exact location of Rose Hill Burial Park, about eight miles east of downtown Fort Worth on Lancaster Street, close to Lake Arlington. I'd been by there hundreds of times, but the time that popped up in my memory was the day Big John and I had driven over to Dallas to capture a burglar who liked to beat up his prostitute girlfriend. I recalled passing the cemetery en route that day, and later meeting Jack Ruby, for the first time, inside the sleazy bar. That seemingly innocent event opened the gate to a flood, an unpredictable chain of events leading to this whole life-changing predicament. Now, I'd visit Rose Hill again, feeling nothing but torment and anguish.

Anyone searching for the burial grounds couldn't have missed it. All along Lancaster street, outside the perimeter fence, the shoulder was lined with parked vehicles, most of them equipped with television relay antennas. The general public had been excluded from the cemetery grounds during the services and burial, and that included me. I didn't ask to be allowed inside as a friend of the deceased. To call myself a friend wouldn't have been entirely honest. Besides, I had mixed feelings about intruding on the somber event, even while groping for a way to help ease the family's pain. A whole raft of conflicting emotions troubled me.

On top of a knoll in the center of the cemetery stood a small chapel constructed of stones colored in various earthen hues. At about 4 that afternoon, from my vantage point outside the main gate, flanked on both sides by two pillars of the same colored stones, I could see a small group of dark-suited men standing in the bright sunshine near the arched entrance to the chapel. Someone came from inside and appeared to speak to them. They followed him in, in a neat file, and emerged later carrying the white oak casket. A buzz of conversation passed among the assembled television camera people near me, and from them I learned that the pallbearers, recruited on the spot, were newsreporters who'd been allowed inside to cover the story. They'd been asked to perform the duty ordinarily reserved for friends, family, or associates. I felt a surge of pity. Oswald didn't even have enough friends to carry his casket.

An older woman, wearing dark-rimmed glasses, her gray hair pulled back in a knot, and dressed in black, carried a blanketed baby from the chapel. Close behind her, a younger woman in a light-colored coat, leading a small child, also dressed in summer colors, followed in the slow procession. The whispering newshounds said the women were Marguerite, Oswald's mother, and Marina, his wife, along with her two daughters. A man who resembled Lee slightly stayed close to them. I heard he was Oswald's brother. I didn't even know Oswald had a brother.

The assembly moved down the slope to the canopy-covered gravesite. They placed the casket inside a vault on the mechanism that would lower it into the ground, while lower, the pitifully small group of family mourners sat in folding chairs. If there was music, I couldn't hear it, nor any of the words spoken. But I felt the sadness and loneliness of the two women, the brother, and the confused little girl, who appeared to be no more than two or three years old.

A frustrating bleakness flooded over me, along with confusion about what to do. Should I wait for them to exit the gates and try to talk with them? No, that wouldn't work. They'd be shielded from the hordes of reporters and I'd have no chance. Should I try to follow them home? Or perhaps it would be better to wait a few days, and with John's help, track them down to express my feelings. Maybe that was the best solution. But if I faced them, what would I say? I'm the guy who trained Lee to use a gun so he could wind up dead? How would that help? I'd never been at a loss for words before, and here I stood, unable to think of any appropriate way to express my sympathy to the family.

Something odd happened under the canopy. I'd never heard of a coffin being opened at graveside services, but while I watched, someone stepped over and raised the cover of Oswald's casket. Marina moved close to it and reached in. I couldn't make out just what she did, but the moment touched me deeply. After a few minutes, they solemnly closed it.

A sense of time deserted me. I didn't know if the ceremony lasted hours or minutes. Even as the crowd dispersed, I stood there waiting for . . . I didn't know what. The whole world moved around me at a distance, detached from reality. I made my way back to my house, still groping my way through confusion and heartache.

The man who had provided an anchor for me as a drifting youngster threw me a lifeline again. When I arrived home,

John Marshall was there waiting for me with food and information.

"Look, Tex," he said, his deep voice full of stability and confidence, "I know you're carrying the weight of an anvil on your shoulders. But I'll tell you, son, you got no call to feel bad. You did an honest job that a man paid you for, and you made the right decision when it got suspicious. I want you to realize that you had nothing to do with any of those three deaths. I've been asking questions in some confidential circles. You already know that Jack Ruby was running with some heavy-handed people. I think he was under orders to use Lee Oswald, then get rid of him. Some of their plans might have gone sour, and Ruby probably had to do a hands-on execution himself. There's something else. You remember Ruby was complaining about being in debt and broke? Well, the police found out that he had seven thousand dollars in cash three hours after JFK was killed."

I fumbled for a response. "Boy, he must have been in it up to his butt. I appreciate your letting me know, John. My brain feels like it's all swelled up and I just can't think straight. I'm convinced that Oswald didn't shoot the president. We both know he couldn't have hit that barn out there. And his encounter over in Oak Cliff, where Officer Tippit died, seems mighty peculiar as well."

Big John nodded. "There's something weird going on with Oswald. You mentioned that Ruby said he was in Mexico for a week before he came to Dallas. My buddy at police headquarters got a look at the report the captain made out after they interrogated Lee. He admitted being in Russia and working on some outfit for Cuba down in New Orleans, but completely denied being in Mexico, except for a trip to Tijuana when he was in the Marines. He also denied being in the upper floors of the building when the shooting was going on. He told them that he was downstairs eating his lunch at noon on Friday, then went up to the second floor for a Coke. Says he left the building after he heard the president had been shot, because he figured they wouldn't work any more that day. Y'know, he was a contrary, opinionated little twerp, and I reckon he's tied into the mess somehow, but I'm not convinced he did any shooting at all.

"I'm damn sure he didn't hit anything, whether he pulled a trigger or not.

"When they arrested Lee and searched him, they found an identification card in his billfold that said his name was Alek James Hidell. When they asked him about it, he got real cocky, as usual. He said something like, 'I know your tactics. They do it the same way in Russia. You go real easy on a guy at first, hoping to worm information out of him.' He claimed he didn't own a rifle, but he'd seen one in the book depository a couple of days before, and some guy named Truly was showing it to some other fellas.

"I think they could have asked him a thousand questions, and none of 'em would have proved that he shot anyone. Ruby had a lariat around Lee's neck and was jerking it up tight.

"There are some other forks in the trail, too. I don't know if you've ever heard of Jimmy Hoffa, that guy who heads up the Teamsters' labor union. He and Bobby Kennedy have been at each other's throats for years. I can't pin it down as pure fact, but I've heard that Ruby might have some connections to him. I don't think there's anyone who would celebrate more over Kennedy's death than Hoffa. But the thing that bothers me the most was going on right in Dallas. You know, Ruby was in thick with a lot of cops on the Dallas force, always hanging around and handing out personal favors, like bringing them food, and kissing up to them. Word is that some of the officers were often seen after hours in his clubs, taking advantage of free drinks and women. One cop, Roscoe White, even married a gal named Geneva who had worked for Jack. Some people say that Ruby had been seen talking to J. D. Tippit. By itself, that might not mean anything, but when you start putting it all together, it gets worrisome. I even heard speculation about why Tippit was patrolling over in Oak Cliff, between Ruby's apartment and Lee's rooming house, maybe looking for Oswald."

"John, are you suggesting that some Dallas cops might even be involved in this thing?"

"I can't say that for sure, Tex, but I think we'd both better proceed with caution. I found out that the little .38 Colt revolver Ruby used to shoot Oswald was bought for him by a Dallas cop named Joe Cody. We don't know who all is tangled up in it, so that means we don't want to say the wrong thing to the wrong people, and wind up dead, too."

"But the president was killed, and a cop, and now Oswald. Shouldn't we be ready to tell investigators what we know about Ruby and Oswald working together, and being in such a hurry to learn how to use guns? I sure as hell don't want to get nailed for withholding evidence and wind up as Jack Ruby's cellmate."

"Tex, there's a man with the Fort Worth police who I can trust all the way. Name's Duke Jordan. You and I are going over to see him tomorrow and ask for his advice. And whatever he says, that's what we're going to do. Can you live with that?"

"You bet, John. Right now, I'm willing to listen to any good advice. I've never felt so screwed up in my life."

"It'll pass, Tex. In the meantime, though, we both had

better hang on to the saddle horn, or we're apt to get throwed pretty hard."

In the booth of a restaurant selected by Fort Worth detective Duke Jordan, John detailed our dilemma, including the brushes with the New Orleans mob leader, Carlos Marcello, the sharpshooting Cuban, Oswald, Ruby, and the training sessions. I mentioned Ruby's emotional state after the president's death and his boast that he was going to be a hero.

Jordan drew thoughtfully on his cigarette, inhaled deeply, then flicked it over an ashtray. He exhaled a cloud of smoke and looked at both of us with worry in his eyes. "John, the best advice I can give you and Tex is to keep your mouths shut. There are some weird angles to this triple shooting that are going to keep people guessing for a long time. It's damn hard right now to know where to turn. If Marcello's involved, you risk getting the mob on your neck. If there are some dirty cops, your lives aren't worth a plugged nickel there, either. Hell, I've even heard rumors of covert government agents who wanted Kennedy dead. There are some federal agencies who can literally get away with murder. Now, you tell me a Cuban sharpshooter was hanging around Ruby. We know that some attempts have been made on Castro's life, so maybe there's some kind of revenge factor tangled in this mess. I don't think we've seen an end to the bloodshed yet. Play it smart, guys. Don't tell anyone anything. Not for now, at least."

"Sounds like good advice to me," John said. "We sure do appreciate your help, Duke. You'll let us know if the picture changes?"

"Of course, John. You two watch your step. We go back too far to let this get us in trouble."

At home that night in bed, I tossed for hours, trying to work things out in my mind. I knew that the advice given us by the Fort Worth detective was probably the right way to go, but a deep moral sense of justice pulled me in the other direction. If law and order meant anything, then shouldn't I help the investigators who'd be working night and day to solve the assassination? Of course, I couldn't help anyone if I spoke to the wrong people and wound up at the bottom of a lake, or shot full of holes. I wrestled with it until mental fatigue mercifully blurred everything. I'd finally dozed off when my phone snapped me awake again. "Hello?"

"Tex, we want to help you. Now, listen carefully. You know a few things that could get you hurt real bad. Some people have died, and it would be easy to hush up a few more in the same way. If you want to stay healthy, stay quiet. Don't shoot off your mouth to anyone. Don't go to the police, and don't give them anything if they come to you. Understand?"

My natural resistance to being shoved around made me flush hot. "Just a damn minute. Who is this? Who the hell are you to be telling me what to do? I don't have to . . ."

"I told you, this is someone who wants to help you. Getting hostile isn't going to do you any good. Shut up and pay attention! Maybe you don't value your own life, but there's a certain redheaded lady you used to know, and a little girl named Rae. Do you want to see them get hurt? There are some people who could have a lot of fun with that shapely redhead. Now, you can fuss and fume all you want, but I'm dead serious. There is nothing to negotiate and no room for mistakes. Keep your mouth shut." Click! Dial tone.

It sounded like the same sandpaper voice I'd heard a few weeks ago giving me a similar warning. Anger boiled inside me. I wanted to hit something. Dirty bastards! Threatening Judy and little Rae. I had rejected the idea that she was my daughter, but I felt affection and loyalty for her the same as if I had been her father.

The menacing ultimatum put a whole new twist on my decision-making process. It really took the decision away from me. I had no choice. I could not risk the safety or the lives of Judy and Rae. Whoever had called obviously had access to unlimited information about me and people I cared for. It sounded like they would go to any lengths to keep me silent.

With the decision out of my hands, I tried to return to a daily routine of intense, sweat-inducing, muscle-straining work. I fixed everything in sight on my place, tuned my truck engine, saddle-soaped every piece of tack and leather I owned, cleaned my guns, then drove over to John's place to join him in similar labor. We talked about the telephone threat and watched television at night to keep up on any new developments. We even watched the new president, Lyndon Johnson, speak to the nation in that distinctive drawl of his, sounding as if he read every word from a script, and beginning with, "Mah fellow Amurh-uh-cuns . . ." His voice became easily recognizable.

On the fourth day following the funeral, I felt a little better, rationalizing that I really had little choice but to remain silent. In the Rodeo Cafe, I kidded with Tommy about hiring some pretty new waitresses, then watched two dudes wearing suits walk in and approach me. Following their instructions the next morning, I picked up the ringing phone at the Texaco station. I heard that familiar drawl ask me to do something for my country and virtually order me to move to South Texas, where jobs would be waiting for me. Back in my pickup, I counted $5,000 in fifties and sat there in a daze.

If I thought I'd been left with few choices before, now I had to accept the complete absence of any alternatives. With the most powerful man in the world telling me what to do, there was no argument left.

The most difficult part in preparing to leave Fort Worth was saying goodbye to my friends.

First, of course, I discussed it in detail with John Marshall, who said he'd help me in any way he could, including taking care of my horses until I found a place in the south. My property, which I'd purchased from him and was legally still in his name, would revert back to John. He offered to pay me considerably more than I'd paid him for it, but I wouldn't hear of it, so he handed me an equal sum in cash. (When I counted it later, he'd slipped in a ten percent profit.)

Next, I spent an evening with Debbie. I couldn't tell her why I was leaving, so I glossed over it with excuses about a young man needing to experience some different places and people before settling down. She didn't believe me and kept asking, between tears and sobbing, what she had done wrong. My best efforts to assure her that she was blameless had no effect. We said goodbye on the basis that maybe sometime we would meet again. I hated to part that way, but it wouldn't have been fair to drag her into the mess I'd made.

Tommy immediately understood my need to depart but didn't know about the president contacting me. He just figured that I wanted to get away from any possible link to Ruby and his racketeer friends. Before I walked out of the Rodeo for the last time, Tommy and I lifted tall glasses of iced tea as a departure toast. I noticed that his was a slightly different color than mine and took a sniff of it. He'd spiked it liberally with bourbon. Tommy still acted depressed and worried over the recent visits to his restaurant by Ruby's cohorts. I shook his hand, gave him a big hug, wished him the best of luck, and told him with all sincerity that I'd miss his great cooking and his friendship. We both felt lumps in our throats from emotion before I finally drove away.

After bidding fond farewells to a few other buddies, and ladies, I packed up my clothing, tack, guns, and personal belongings. I secured a home-made camper shell to the back of my truck, threw everything in, took a last look around, and headed south for a new life.

house. Also for that, wasn't any going that against mountain peaks. Yet this startling landscape that I crossed me with its beard communities or my sweeping valleys...

By the blurred roadside! Soon down every miles to me Austin, up to the... dividing line at both shopped a waterbed of money, and my subway was stopped I rolled over this point, right I...

Eighteen

It seemed to take forever to drive the fifty miles down Highway 35 to the fork at Hillsboro where the east and west divisions of the road converge, then continue south another forty miles to Waco. Having no idea where I planned to settle, I figured I'd just keep rolling until someplace struck my fancy. Waco? I knew it was a cowtown from way back. The historic big cattle drives north to Kansas, along the Chisholm trail, had stopped there to water thirsty herds in the Brazos River. Cowboys still populated the town, so I'd be among my own kind. But when I arrived there, I knew I hadn't yet moved far enough.

Passing another hundred miles of brushy junipers, live oaks, cattle, and dun-colored dry grass, I continued down the highway to Austin. Sixty miles west of there, the new president's ranch sprawled along the Pedernales River on the other side of Johnson City. Did I want to live in the state capital? Maybe I just felt a streak of orneriness, but I felt that was too close to LBJ. A sneaking suspicion still gave me reason to worry that someone might suddenly decide to want me dead, including possibly government agents.

Austin's a very attractive place to live, on the Colorado River, and can offer thriving industries, agriculture, big ranches, and the great University of Texas with its Longhorns. But football wasn't my game, and neither industrial success nor dirt farming interested me. I crossed the wide river and continued driving south.

By the time I reached San Marcos, forty miles below Austin, my bones ached, my muscles felt like I'd bull-dogged a whole herd of steers, and my energy was sapped. I pulled over to a motel, checked in, found a cafe with decent chicken fried steak, and called it a day. On the restaurant bulletin board, I absentmindedly scanned a list of houses for rent. My eyes landed on an ad for a small spread a few miles out of town with a fenced pasture, horse pen, small older house, and good water originating from the ice-cold San Marcos springs. "Will rent cheap to the right person" the ad said. Maybe I was the right person. The idea of living in a small town for a change appealed to me. Somehow, it sounded right.

The next morning I drove out to see if the place offered for rent matched my mental pictures of it. It looked perfect, with plenty of room for my six horses, and just the kind of rustic house I liked. Similar to my little spread near Fort Worth, it had a screened-in porch for sleeping on hot nights, two bedrooms, and a handy kitchen. The exterior needed a coat of paint, but I could take care of that. I drove back to a pay telephone and called the owner. Within two hours, we shook hands to seal the bargain.

Early the next morning, I pointed the pickup north again and drove faster this time. I arrived at John Marshall's home by noon. We recruited another friend who owned a horse trailer and caravaned to my old place. We loaded two horses in each of three trailers, threw my remaining possessions into the truck beds, and formed a convoy along the highway, southbound again.

All three of us, especially John and I, dreaded completing the task of unloading, so we took it slow. We knew that this marked a real change in our lives, a separation that could last a long time. Words came hard. We finally gripped hands, said a few sentimental things, and walked out to the trucks. One of the most difficult moments in my life was watching Big John Marshall's taillights disappear into the distant darkness.

The sense of loneliness diminished rapidly the next morning when I tackled the chores of settling in and arranging stalls for feeding my horses. I worked feverishly at repairing fences, whitewashing them, and painting the house. Despite the chilly weather, I worked up a good sweat each morning during the next week, making my new home sparkle, tending to the horses, hauling hay from the local feed store. Each evening, I rode Chief, the only friend who was still with me, around the area, exploring, thinking, wondering where to turn next.

Try as I might, I couldn't exorcise the ghosts of Oswald and the president, or the image of Jack Ruby and the crazy days of October and November. Reliving the bizarre events, trying to recall every conversation, they became etched in my memory like a motion picture compulsively viewed time and time again. And the absence of explanations for what had happened taunted me like a complex, sinister puzzle. Each time I mentally assembled the pieces into some logical order, they'd fly apart again, hopelessly scrambled. I realized that constant speculation in the absence of more hard facts was probably driving me toward a nervous breakdown. It would become an obsession unless I found a substitute to occupy my mind.

The substitute arrived at the end of my second week in San Marcos in the form of a rattling, rust-covered 1951 red Ford pickup. The driver braked to a squeaking halt in my driveway, causing the engine to backfire. My heart did a triple jump while my right hand automatically reached across my waist for the Colt .45 I kept as a full-time companion.

"Hold on there, cowboy," the driver yelled out his window. "You ain't gonna' need no gun. I'm a peaceful fellow and mean you no harm."

Relaxing to some degree, I asked who he was. "I came calling with some news for you. Okay if I get out?" I gave him permission. A man about forty climbed out of the battered pickup, brushing the front of his red plaid shirt and faded jeans. He wore a straw cowboy hat that had seen years of weather and dust. A cigarette dangled, Western-style, from the corner of his mouth, and his deeply tanned face bore the damage of sunbaked days on horseback. If he wasn't an authentic cowboy, I'd never seen one. I figured I was as good a judge as anyone about cowboys. That's why the next words he spoke completely surprised me.

"The president wants to talk to you, Tex, in person."

"The president? You mean President Johnson?"

Smiling good-naturedly, the stranger replied, "Well, yeah. He's the only president we have right now."

"Boy, you guys know everything, don't you? I don't even have a phone yet, and only two people, close friends of mine, know where I live. How the hell did you find me?"

"C'mon, Tex, you know the chief has ways to find anyone he wants to. Ever heard of the CIA? Ever heard of the Secret Service, or the FBI? I ain't saying which one is keeping tabs on you right now, but all three agencies have mighty long arms. You ought to know that by now."

"Yeah, I guess. So the president wants to see me, in person? When? Where?"

"That'll come later. My job is just to tell you to stand by. You'll be notified when he's ready. It would be a good idea for you to keep your schedule flexible for a last-minute request to meet him. Keep your camping gear handy, too. Got any coffee brewed?"

"No, but come on in, I'll make some."

The stranger introduced himself as Sherman. He'd been doing work for the government for longer than he cared to remember. His background was similar to my own. He was a young cowboy who'd got caught up in some problems after which he was given the opportunity to become an operative for a federal agency. He enjoyed his work immensely and was well paid for it. The old Ford pickup served as excellent camouflage.

Curious about how much he knew of my situation, I asked, but he was too cagy to give me any direct answers. "I know a lot, cowboy. You were simply in the wrong place at the wrong time, and it will take a while for you to work your way out of it. If I were you, I'd do a lot of listening and very little talking. You'll find some things coming your way that'll occupy you and be right profitable at that. The chief is a good man to have on your side. Behave yourself and you'll be all right."

Sherman drank black coffee while I had my usual iced tea. We spent the rest of the time talking about horses. Few people I've met demonstrated more knowledge about the subject than Sherman. He also knew nearly everyone in

South Texas involved in the horse business, plus a long list of other influential people, including executives of the telephone company. My application to have a phone installed would be expedited, he promised. Before he left, he handed me a map of Gillespie County, with details of the hill country along the Pedernales River between Johnson City and Fredericksburg. He also laid a folder on my kitchen table containing literature about the area and the new president. "You might want to learn a little about the chief," he said, lighting a fresh Marlboro.

The old Ford clattered out of the driveway, boiling up a small twister of dust.

Examining the map and the other material Sherman had left, I saw some penciled entries marked along the edge of the Pedernales River noting places to camp out. It also included a layout of Lyndon Johnson's extensive ranch, mostly on the north side of the meandering river, fourteen miles west of Johnson City. If you drove past the ranch another sixteen miles along Highway 290, you'd come to the old German community Fredricksburg. It was the birthplace and boyhood home of another famous American, Admiral Chester W. Nimitz, commander in chief of the U.S. Pacific fleet during World War II. It surprised me that two such important men in our nation's history had been born so close together in the rural hill country of Texas.

Many people thought, just like I did, that Johnson City was named for the new president, who had been a powerful member of Congress since 1937, when he was only twenty-nine years old. Not true. The little town had been established in 1879 by James Polk Johnson, a nephew of Lyndon's grandfather, Sam Ealy Johnson, who had returned from the Civil War, rounded up a herd of half-wild longhorn cattle, and driven them to Abilene, Kansas, for a tidy profit. He later acquired the ranch in 1887. Lyndon Baines Johnson was born in a small house on the ranch August 27, 1908, when his grandfather galloped a horse, Old Reb, to nearby Stonewall and fetched a midwife to deliver the infant. Sam Ealy, Jr., Lyndon's father, had served two terms in the Texas state legislature, but he'd returned to farming after his son's birth.

Little Lyndon grew up exploring the surrounding woods and the rolling acres on which his father had planted cotton. At age three, his grandpa gave him his first horse and saddle, and he learned to roam the land among a thick population of white-tailed deer, coyotes, javelina, and all sorts of other wildlife. He began his formal education in a one-room school up the road.

Sam Ealy, Jr., though, hated farming, so he moved his little family to a house on the corner of Ninth and G Streets in Johnson City when Lyndon was seven. The boy still liked to ride to his favorite spots along the Pedernales and spend leisurely hours skinnydipping or soaking up the warm Texas sunshine. His father ran for a seat in the state legislature and won again.

After graduating from Johnson City High School in 1924, Lyndon announced he was finished with school forever. He joined a group of young men in an adventurous journey to California, where he worked as a laborer, fruit picker, and finally, law clerk. Discouraged, he returned to Texas and entered college in, of all places, San Marcos, where he earned a teaching degree. A small school in Cotulla, eighty miles south of San Antonio, hired him. In 1931, Lyndon left teaching when a U.S. Congressman offered him a secretarial job in Washington, D.C. Six years later, he ran for and won a seat in the House of Representatives. His next election campaign landed him a position as one of our two senators from Texas in 1948.

The ranch had passed to the hands of Lyndon's aunt. In 1951 he bought it from her and began a long series of improvements. His political career took off like a shooting star, and he became a power broker, dealmaker, and then the majority leader of the Senate before John F. Kennedy accepted him as the vice-presidential candidate in 1960.

So this was the man who wanted to meet me, face to face for a talk. His Texas roots weren't that different from mine, but I couldn't see my path in life ever being anything like his. It seemed like a dream, or a nightmare, that I would be facing him one on one.

In my new digs, I tried my best to keep busy to avoid thinking about the recent months, and to ward off loneliness. I dreaded the birthday coming up on Christmas Eve, and even more, I dreaded Christmas. Two feelings came over me. First, I wanted to be left alone. Second, I felt sorry for myself for being alone. Christmas was when families got together, exchanged gifts, and celebrated over a big dinner. John Marshall and his wife had invited me, as he had for several years, to join them. But I was afraid my deep mood swings wouldn't lend much to the holidays, so I'd politely declined.

To avoid sitting around in sour depression, I threw a few things into my pickup in the late afternoon of December 23 and drove to the highway. I flipped a coin: heads, I'd go north; tails, south. Tails won. Merging into traffic on the main artery, I headed toward San Antonio. I toyed with the idea of spending some time exploring the town, looking over the Alamo, walking along the shops on the riverbanks. But instead, I just kept going. Two and a half hours later, I parked in Laredo, close to the Rio Grande. Not hungry, I checked into a motel and slept until after ten the next morning.

I woke, bathed, dressed, and drove to Augustin Plaza, the center of the town back in 1840 when it was the capital of an independent country called The Republic of the Rio Grande, which included parts of South Texas and a good portion of northern Mexico. It was first settled ten years before a bunch of colonists back East decided to have a revolution and make the United States a new independent country. Texas still belonged to Mexico then, and Mexico belonged to Spain. The Lipan Apaches and the Comanches lived in the area where the river, called Rio Bravo Del Norte, was shallow enough in spots to wade across. But they were eventually driven out. Laredo became a battleground and military post during about every war in the turbulent history of Texas.

I wandered around the Plaza, strolled along Zaragoza Street, then drove into the shopping area, where people scampered around trying to find last-minute Christmas gifts. Finally feeling the growling of hunger in my innards, I sat down in a Mexican restaurant and ordered a couple of tacos and a bean burrito. *Happy Birthday, Tex.*

Later in the afternoon, I walked along Guerrero Avenue and over the International Bridge, one of the two spans across the Rio Grande, into Nuevo Laredo, Mexico. Other people sang Christmas carols, but with my dampened holiday spirit, I hummed Gene Autry's old song, "South of the Border, Down Mexico Way." Strolling around El Mercado at Guerrero and Calle Belden, I browsed among open front shops and sidewalk vendors, searching for something to buy for myself. A birthday present or a Christmas present? The heck with it, I didn't want either one. Instead, I stopped in a cantina and had a shot of tequila, complete with a slice of lime and salt on the back of my left hand. *Merry Christmas, Tex.*

Christmas day dawned quiet and clear. Everyone had someplace to go, and most shops were closed. I watched TV in my room, walked around for several hours, crossing the border twice, had a "home cooked" dinner in a Laredo coffee shop, and hit the sack early. The next day, I drove home. I wondered when "the chief" would summon me.

The invitation, if you could call it that, came a week after Christmas, on New Year's Day. My telephone, which had been promptly installed the day after Sherman had left, rang, and he was on the other end. Sherman wished me a happy holiday, chatted briefly about the weather, horses, and asked how I was getting along. Finally, in an afterthought, he advised me to be certain I checked my mail tomorrow.

Following his "suggestion" on Thursday morning, I opened the box and found a plain envelope with my address handprinted on it. I nervously slipped a piece of typing paper out, on which were printed the words:

> Be at campsite #2 (marked on your map) early Sunday morning.
> Wait there. Do not leave the camp on that day.
> You will be visited before sundown.

I unfolded the map Sherman had given me and located the penciled notation indicating campsite number 2. It was on the south bank of the Pedernales River, not far from the main gate to the LBJ ranch. The drive over there would take at least an hour, maybe more. I didn't particularly want to camp overnight, but I knew that I'd better not be late, so I decided to make the trip on Saturday afternoon and sleep in my truck at the campsite. After I thought it over in more detail, I figured it might be a good idea to take my horse, too, and scout around the area where I couldn't drive. The Secret Service would probably be watching every step I made, so I'd have to be cautious not to give them an excuse to shoot me.

I hoped that no one planned to end my problems on the banks of the Pedernales River, or at the bottom of it.

Nineteen

Hoping that someone was calling to cancel my weekend appointment with LBJ, I answered the phone on Friday morning. That familiar deep voice drawled, "Hullo, is this Tex?"

"Speaking," I said, not quite positive it was who it sounded like.

"This is Lyndon. Are you going camping Sunday?"

"Yes, sir. Actually, I'd planned to be there Saturday night so I won't be late on Sunday."

"That's fine, son." I still felt the surge of resentment at being called "son," but didn't object, considering the source. "Cowboy, I just wanted to tell you that what you're doing for your country is a good thing. I want to meet with you, eyeball to eyeball. You have the map that tells you where to be, don't you?"

"I sure do, Mr. President."

"Just call me Lyndon. I used to camp there myself a long time ago."

"Sir, I don't want to sound paranoid, but it has come to my mind that I could be in danger. Is there any chance I'm going to be ambushed?"

There was a chuckle on the other end. "No, son. Nobody's going to hurt you. On the contrary, we want to provide for you, set up your future in the state of Texas. You've done a fine job of keeping your word. I suppose you've got it all written down somewhere."

I wasn't sure if his last sentence was an idle comment or an outright question. It really hadn't occurred to me to record anything in writing or keep a diary. Not a bad idea, though. The threat of a hidden record might provide me with some margin of safety. I'd start one right away. "Yes, sir," I lied, "I've got two copies of my written records of the whole thing. They're in separate places with instructions to be opened if anything happens to me."

Another chuckle. "Well, son, nothing's going to happen to you, so you won't need that kind of insurance. We're just going to have to trust each other. I'll see you on Sunday." He hung up.

With the horse trailer in tow, I wound westward on narrow country roads to Highway 281, turned north for twenty miles, then swung left into Johnson City. The word "city" was an ambitious description of the little Blanco County seat. It had once been the gathering place for cattlemen and farmers who congregated in the hotel, stores, and saloon near the first steam-powered gin- and gristmill in the region. Many of the old Western-faced buildings had been demolished, some replaced by nondescript modern shops, restaurants, and gas stations. I made another left off Highway 280 onto G Street, drove one block, and paused to look at the corner house where young Lyndon had lived during his boyhood and teen years. Painted white, sporting two chimneys and gingerbread trimmings above the front porch, it was a much nicer-looking place than I'd expected.

Back on 290, through a sweeping curve a half mile from the town center, I caught a glimpse through some trees of an ancient windmill, and beyond it the original log house occupied by Lyndon's grandfather, Sam Ealy Johnson, a century earlier.

Growing more apprehensive over the next fourteen miles, I crossed small bridges over Towhead Creek and Rocky Creek and passed through a hamlet called Hye consisting mostly of a Western-facade post office and store. Past the Gillespie County marker, I slowed and swung right on a dirt road to the Pedernales River. Ten minutes later, I stopped at a clearing close to the sandy south bank and recognized a small island in the river designated on my map. I found a wooden stake someone had driven into the ground. A cloth hung from it, lettered with the words "Campsite #2."

I didn't bother to pitch a tent, planning on sleeping under my camper shell in the bed of the truck. I saddled up my Appaloosa, Chief, locked my truck doors, and took a ride.

Walking Chief slowly, we covered a mile or more along the riverbank. On the other side, I could see spreading groves of bare, leafless pecan trees and an old building near a bridge. A road paralleled the river on both sides, and twice I saw unmarked cars traveling at a snail's pace. I figured they were security people keeping me in sight, although they didn't acknowledge my presence or make any moves in my direction. Under some spreading live oaks, ahead of me, across the water, I spotted a small, peaceful cemetery.

I pulled Chief's head around and returned to my campsite, then reconnoitered in the other direction for half an hour. I whiled away the rest of the afternoon reading, listening to the radio, and eating some sandwiches I'd brought. In the late afternoon, I heard a car stop out of sight about fifty yards away. A man wearing whipcords, an Eisenhower jacket, and an old campaign hat approached me on foot, watching as my right hand reached under the left side of my vest. He spoke in a strong, firm voice. "If you're reaching for a gun, cowboy, you won't need it. I've got a message for you."

"Okay. Let's have it."

"You're going to have a visitor between noon and one o'clock tomorrow. He'll probably be with you about half an hour."

"That's fine. Thanks for letting me know." He gave me a casual salute and left. I breathed a sigh of relief. Not long after the sun went down, I stretched out on my sleeping bag, padded by an air mattress on the truck bed, and dozed off.

Before sunrise, I woke, made a campfire, and boiled some water for coffee. The open air and fresh breeze made me hungry, so I fried some bacon and scrambled some eggs. After I'd cleaned up, I scouted on horseback some more. The morning crept by with the pace of a sleepy tortoise. I waited, trying to ignore the growing knot of tension in my gut.

At 12:40, a big, white Lincoln Continental convertible, with the top down, rolled into my campsite. I immediately recognized the president of the United States, Lyndon Baines Johnson behind the wheel, by himself. He wore a blocked tan Stetson and a blue-and-white checked shirt under a tan jacket. When he stepped out, I could see a pair of good cowboy boots and wrinkled khakis.

The classic Texan face, with furrowed forehead, dark eyebrows squared off at the corners, the squint of a man constantly looking into the sun, permanently etched crows feet, a strong nose, deep creases in both cheeks, and a virtually lipless mouth closed to a tight grimace, was bigger than life. He stood well over six feet, but with his imposing presence, it seemed more like eight.

"Howdy, Tex," he boomed. "It's good to see you. That's a fine-looking Appaloosa." The "s" sound, at the end of his words, had a slight "sh" slur.

"Thank you, Mr. President. It's a pleasure to meet you, sir." I looked behind him to both sides, and across the river, fully expecting to see a platoon of men pointing weapons in my direction. I saw no one, and all I could hear was the chirping of some unconcerned birds. If any of his Secret Service guards were observing us, they were well hidden.

"Call me Lyndon," he drawled. "We're on the ranch, by my favorite river. No need to be formal. It's kinda nice to relax and shoot the breeze with a fellow Texan. You know what, I used to swim pretty close to this spot. What do you say we take a dip right now?" I looked at him to see if he'd been drinking or maybe was joking. The sun shone brightly, but the air temperature was in the low sixties, and the water would probably be a lot colder.

"Well, sir—uh, Mr. Lyndon, I didn't come prepared to swim. No swimmin' trunks." I guess it's a trait of powerful, successful people to put the other guy off balance and keep him there. He knew how to do that, all right.

"Hell, son, I cain't ever remember wearing anything while swimming in this river." He slipped out of his jacket, tossed it into his car, reached for the buttons on his shirt, and had half of them undone before I could even respond. And when I did, I was shocked at my own words.

"What are you going to do? Get me in there and drown me?"

A grin deepened his facial creases, and he broke into that chuckle. "No, cowboy, I'm not going to drown you.

To be honest, I think it would make us both feel better to know neither one of us is wearing a wire. No recorders."

By the time I looked up from pulling my boots off and self-consciously dropping my jeans, he was already wading into the water, naked as a jaybird. I hurried and leaped in, too. The water was bracingly cold, but not as icy as I'd expected. We paddled out into the slow current, chest deep.

"Tex," he said, no shiver in his voice, "we're gonna' talk business now, you and me. Don't consider me as the president, just a fellow cowboy. What you know about certain events, son—that should never be told to anyone. And I mean anyone. What you know about that young Communist SOB should never be mentioned. You've got a good future, if you can do what I'm telling you, Tex. My people tell me you're a bounty hunter. I believe we can find plenty of work for a fellow in that business. You're going to be kept busy from one border to the other, all across this great country. I'm told you're pretty well acquainted with the folks and the terrain around the Mexican border. Well, you're going to learn a whole lot more about it in the years to come. Son, what you're doing for your country is a service not many people get the opportunity to perform. And you're going to do it right."

"What's that mean, sir?"

"You'll be getting jobs offered to you. If there are some you don't want, you don't have to take them. If they appeal to you, then you'll do 'em. It's that simple. I think you'll be happy with the way things will work out for you."

All I could think of to say was, "I ain't got anybody to take care of my horses."

Another hearty laugh echoed across the water's surface. "You'll find somebody." He headed for the shore and asked if I had a spare towel. I hurried past him, glad to get out of the water because my skin was turning blue, and handed him the only towel I'd brought. I dried off with one of my blankets. While he vigorously rubbed himself dry, he spoke. "Water felt great, didn't it? Like being a kid again. Sure is good to be here on the ranch. Isn't this grand country? When you're up here, the water is more pure, the moon is bigger at night, and the stars are brighter. I was born right over there, Tex." He pointed in a northwesterly direction, toward the center of the ranch. Dressing quickly and donning his hat, he said, "Remember one thing. What you know must stay between you and me. It's a matter of trust and honor."

"I'll remember, sir. Is it okay if I head back to San Marcos now?"

"Head on back, son," he laughed. "You'll be hearing from someone with job offers very soon. I know I can trust you. Adios, cowboy." He slid into the white Continental and drove away.

I don't even remember breaking camp, loading Chief into the trailer, or driving the first fifty miles. Then the realization slammed into me like a Mack truck rear-ending a stalled Volkswagen. I'd just been skinnydipping with the president of the United States, who had treated me with respect and courtesy.

But had he really? Wasn't I just a pawn in his game of power? He'd been as slick as a greased pig about it, but he'd cornered me into a commitment I didn't like. Was my silence going to help someone get away with murder, while the blame was piled on a dead man? No matter how you slice it, the whole idea of covering it up didn't seem right to me.

A seething sense of anger replaced the awe I'd been feeling for Lyndon Johnson. I had agreed to live a lie and to be paid for it in the form of government jobs coming my way. I wondered how long it would take for the guilty feeling to go away. Or if it ever would.

Twenty

Just as Lyndon Johnson had promised, the first job offer came a few days later. Sherman arrived one evening in his noisy red pickup, asked me how my camping trip had gone, and handed me an envelope. I told him nothing about my meeting or the skinnydipping episode. We shot the breeze over general topics for half an hour before he rattled off into the distance.

I chewed on the offer all night. Should I take it and lock myself into a career? Even though I had worked dozens of cases with John Marshall, I'd never planned to make it a full-time profession. All I wanted to do was raise Appaloosas for showing, racing, and selling. I could have made a good living at it. Now, I'd been pressed into service as a narc, a bounty hunter, a cop without a badge. I don't think I really had the option of refusing. Why LBJ, or his expert in those matters wanted me in this kind of work, I wasn't sure. Maybe just to keep me compartmentalized and controlled, vulnerable to their whims. If they finally decided to silence me permanently, all they'd have to do is set me up to get killed in some remote, godforsaken village or desert roadside south of the border. My body would never be found. *Old Tex just disappeared. Wonder what ever happened to him?*

Was I being paranoid? My experiences over the past few

months had squeezed all the trust for anyone, except John Marshall, right out of me. If they, whoever they were, wanted me dead, couldn't it be done without all these complex shenanigans? Maybe the president really was trying to give me a chance to work my way through this crisis with honor. Perhaps I truly would be serving my country. That's what he said. Why didn't I believe him?

In the morning, I dialed the number of my contact. You can't just sit at every intersection or fork in the road you come to. You have to make a decision, put it in gear, and stomp the accelerator. A career had been chosen for me. I might as well make the best of it.

The voice on the other end of the line gave me information and instructions for my first job. He said a stolen racehorse had to be recovered. *A stolen racehorse?* I thought I was going to be chasing human fugitives, the way I had with Big John. Oh, well, as an independent operator, I had to start somewhere.

The horse, a thoroughbred stallion worth more than $50,000 had been taken from his stall in southern Oklahoma. It would be easy to identify the chestnut horse without a photo, due to the white lightning-shaped blaze on his face and white markings on both fetlocks. A tipster had informed authorities in Mexico that the horse had been hauled down to Monterrey, 125 miles south of the border. Oklahoma police didn't have the authority or resources to go after it, so they had requested help from the feds. Officially, there wasn't much they could do, either, so that's why the case fell into the hands of Ray "Tex" Brown, horse fancier and bounty hunter, without portfolio.

I drove to Laredo, walked across the border, and met with my contact in Nuevo Laredo, Chico Fernandez. My recent and lonely birthday/Christmas visit was still fresh in my mind but pushed to the back burner by the excitement of the chase. At his direction, I crossed back into Laredo, hired a cab to follow me twenty miles out of town to a spot picked by Chico, parked my truck, and rode back in the cab. Once more across the border, and in his truck, pulling an empty horse trailer, we bounced and bumped for three hours before crawling out to rest our sore bones in Monterrey.

The tipster met us in a noisy dive where brassy mariachi music bounced from the peeling walls. For a stack of paper pesos probably worth twenty dollars, the snitch agreed to lead us to the *ranchero,* six miles out of town. He also told us the stallion was being used to breed a stolen thoroughbred mare, in hopes of producing valuable foals that could be sold in *Del Norte,* the States.

Chico and I staked out the *ranchero:* five or six adobe buildings, a ramshackle barn, and four pens in which we spotted the proud stallion. You could tell he felt out of place in these surroundings.

Three ragged, lazy *vaqueros* moved in slow motion between the buildings. We watched for several hours from a clump of trees in a dry gulch and finally decided the honcho wasn't around. So we waited until three in the morning, simply walked over to the pen, quietly opened the gate, slapped a bridle on the horse, and led him into the desert. We walked the half mile to Chico's trailer, loaded our big guy, and drove back to Nuevo Laredo. Twenty miles out of town, Chico pointed out a spot in the river I could easily ford on the horse's back. It reminded me of an episode not long ago with Big John Marshall. I paid Chico his $500, told him we'd probably be doing business again, and halfrode, half-swam across the muddy water.

In Oklahoma, I delivered a happy horse to a delighted

owner, accepted my first bounty payoff, and returned to San Marcos.

I tried to avoid reading or watching anything about the assassination or the events afterward, preferring to avoid the sick feeling that came with thinking about it. In the latter part of March, though, I did hear that Jack Ruby had stood trial for the murder of Lee Oswald and had been convicted of premeditated murder. Later, he was sentenced to be executed for it. I shoved the whole thing out of my mind.

By the end of March, I had completed three missions chasing humans. I brought back two heroin dealers, a small ring of warehouse burglars, and a man who had killed his mother-in-law. In those three months, I collected a bundle of money, all in cash. A new worry struck me: the income tax would be staggering. Then it occurred to me that I could probably get away without reporting the cash payments, which no doubt came from some flexible government slush fund with no IRS forms involved. It sounded tempting at first, until I realized what a stupid move that would be. I didn't need to make myself vulnerable to a tax evasion rap and a long term in the federal pen. They'd closed Alcatraz the previous year, but Leavenworth and several others would gladly accept me. I figured they could do without my presence.

With a few weeks off between jobs, I relaxed. As LBJ had said when I'd worried about someone to tend my horses, a cowboy in San Marcos had shown up the evening before I'd left to perform that first job, and agreed to take care of them and watch my place for very reasonable fees. Each time I got home, it was a pleasure to relieve him and give the six Appaloosas my affectionate attention. My life seemed to be getting back on an even keel when I was broadsided with shocking news.

I hadn't heard from Tommy, my good old friend from the Rodeo Cafe, even though I'd left word in March for him to give me a buzz sometime. I was still bothered by the change of mood I'd seen in him after the odd visit to his restaurant by Carlos Marcello. He and I had both worried that racketeers wanted to take over his place to use as a base of operations.

The call from Tommy never came. John Marshall and I maintained regular phone contact with each other and during one of our confabs, I mentioned that I hadn't heard from our old buddy. The very next night, John called me with devastating news. Tommy had been paying a call to someone in Decatur, northwest of Fort Worth. His car had stalled on the highway north of town, and when he'd stepped out to open the hood, a dump truck full of rocks had crushed him to death. In John's opinion, Tommy's car, which he'd always kept in top shape, had been tampered with. The truck driver hadn't been charged with anything, because he'd struck Tommy in the middle of a traffic lane. It made no sense to John or me that our pal would have been wandering around in the middle of a highway. Someone must have pushed him out there, or knocked him unconscious and dragged him onto the pavement to be run over. But there were no witnesses, so his death was recorded as an accident. We'd never know if the mob had pressured him to sell the Rodeo and dealt with his refusal by violently snuffing out his life.

On the way to Fort Worth to attend Tommy's funeral, I admired the fresh growth of bluebonnets, Indian paintbrush, and poppies lining both sides of the highway but felt sad that my old buddy would never see the glorious bursts of spring again. I decided to refuel, the pickup and the stomach, at a truck stop outside Waco. Halfway through my hamburger, I idly glanced at another customer sitting in a booth. When I'd walked in, his face had been hidden by a newspaper he was reading. Now, when I caught a full view of him, I nearly strangled on my food. It was the same man in the long topcoat, with the sloping right eye, who I'd seen in Fort Worth in November. He'd been in the Rodeo Cafe once, and at a downtown hamburger stand just a couple of days before the assassination. I had no reason to connect him to anything, but the coincidence bothered me. I don't think he recognized me, so I avoided any further eye contact with him.

It was good to see John Marshall, but I would have preferred circumstances other than saying goodbye to our dear old sidekick. We made a last visit to the Rodeo Cafe to raise a final glass of iced tea in remembrance of Tommy, then went to the church services, where his army of friends and cronies from the Rodeo packed every pew.

Afterward, John told me he'd heard that Debbie had married her new boyfriend following a whirlwind romance. Just as well. I certainly was in no position to offer her a stable relationship. I wished her all the happiness in the world. He hadn't heard of or seen Candy since the assassination. Judy and Rae, he said, were doing just fine, but he didn't know if she'd found any new romantic ties. I thought I'd better not try to renew anything with her, either, although I felt deeply affectionate and curious about her and little Rae.

I returned to San Marcos feeling sorry that we'd lost Tommy, but somehow stronger. I was now totally independent, both financially and otherwise, and my life had taken on new dimensions. I'd weathered the emotional storm of the involvement with Ruby and Oswald, and the loss of a great pal. I don't know how you measure maturity, but mine had grown several notches.

Sherman had delivered a new envelope, so I arranged for my horse-sitter to do his duties and headed east this time, for Louisiana. A young Houston woman had shot her older husband to death in an argument over who would use their new Cadillac one evening. He had pulled the revolver from the glove box, and during a lull in the name-calling and screaming, he'd placed it on top of the dashboard. She'd grabbed it and put a bullet in his heart. Of course, she claimed there'd been a struggle and the gun had gone off by accident. Charged with manslaughter, she'd made bail and promptly skipped across the state line. I wasn't sure how this case had fallen into Sherman's hands, but the government, like other high deities, worked in strange ways. He provided me with some photographs, attractive images that made this assignment rather easy to take, plus some vital statistics and background on her. She'd been a lady of dubious repute before becoming the bride of her financially secure lover.

With the help of an informant recommended by Sherman's contacts, I spent three nights in the Latin Quarter of New Orleans and found her in a restaurant. The stakeout had given me the chance to try some food that had always sounded exotic to me, ever since I'd first heard Hank Williams sing about jambalaya and crawfish pie and filé gumbo. As soon as they served it, I was sorry. Way too spicy. I couldn't finish it. I longed for chicken fried steak and biscuits. Fortunately, my lovely fugitive sauntered in and took my mind off the experiment in food.

She wasn't the least bit suspicious of a cowboy dressed in jeans, a red shirt, a black vest with matching Stetson, and pointed-toe boots who found a way to strike up a conversation with her. Not until we stepped outside to my pickup and I poked her ribs with the barrel of my revolver still hidden under the vest. She paled, breathed a soft, high-pitched moan, and nearly fainted when I put the cuffs on her and helped her into the truck.

Making a fast recovery, she pouted for the first hour, then began hinting at very personal favors she could do for me, even before we crossed the state line into Texas. By the time we reached Beaumont, she was making the offers graphic and specific. I was glad Houston was only another hour away, because I think I might have caved in if it had been two hours. She was a very attractive, supple, and curvaceous lady. I accepted my bounty payment without mentioning that if I had known in advance how pleasurable the task would be, I probably would have done it free of charge.

Following another couple of forays into Mexico, I had the good fortune of running into Big John again. On my way to another assignment, this one in Grandview, about twenty-five miles south of Fort Worth, I made a pit stop in Hillsboro. As I was paying for my lunch, John marched into the cafe, filling the place with his size and presence. Damn, I was glad to see him. We both grinned, made goofy comments about the restaurant allowing bums inside, then slid into a booth. He ordered a hamburger for himself and a glass of iced tea for me.

After he'd caught me up on events around Fort Worth and listened to my stories of chasing bail jumpers and drug dealers, he tactfully mentioned the unpleasant subject of the assassination. Because John knew me so well, he was sensitive to my hatred of discussing the topic. I'd decided to put it behind me, to try to forget the whole thing and stop tormenting myself with guilt and unanswerable questions. The only person I would allow into that territory was John.

He knew that, and would have avoided the subject, but he had a good reason to bring it up. "Have you been paying attention to news about the Warren Commission?" he asked. I'd read only headlines about the investigation being conducted by a group of Washington, D.C., notables, deliberately avoiding the details.

"I've heard of them, but when I see something in the paper about all that, I try to skip over it. When I hear mention of it on the news, I turn off the TV or change stations on the radio. Damn it, John, it gives me ulcers and headaches to think about a murdered president, a dead cop, and Jack Ruby blasting Oswald to hell. If I'd had any inkling what was about to happen, I would never have spent five seconds with Jack and Lee. It drives me nuts, and the only way I can survive is to avoid it like I would a mad dog."

"I know that, Tex. But you might want to give some thought to the possibility that the investigators could come after you. If they do, you need to know in advance what you'd be willing to say or not say. It might save you a lot of trouble to think it out before they show up on your doorstep."

"That's occurred to me. I don't know what I'd do."

"You'd have to make a choice. It'll be a tough decision whether to tell them everything you know, or keep your mouth shut and deny any knowledge of or association with Ruby and Oswald. I've been trying to keep tabs on anyone who knows we met them. Naturally, Tommy can't say anything, bless him. I don't know how much you said to Debbie. I'm also concerned about that other gal, Candy. She left Dallas and I can't get a line on where she went."

"Debbie doesn't know anything. I kept that business away from her. Candy knew a lot. I introduced her to Ruby, but you know what, John? I'm not sure they weren't already in cahoots. It was too smooth, the way she flirted with me, wanted to 'meet' Ruby, went right to work for him, then spent that time with me like she fell in love at first sight. I've thought a lot about it, and I'm wondering if it was a setup to lure me into Ruby's game. He wanted something from me, and I hate to even think what it was. John, I believe he was trying to recruit me to shoot the president."

"I wouldn't be surprised, Tex. But in my opinion, Ruby was under orders from somebody a lot more powerful. I think he liked you and gave you that note with the proposition on it because he was told to do it. He got cornered and had to do some of the dirty work himself."

"Maybe so. Do you think there's much likelihood that the commission investigators will come after me?"

"It's hard to say. If they're interested in the truth and your name comes up, they'll contact you. In any case, I think you need to be prepared. I know you don't want to keep wallowing in the mud about those killings, but, if I were you, I'd at least study a little bit about it. I'm going to get some stuff together about the commission and send it to you. Read it if you want, or toss it out. You've got some decisions to make, partner."

It's funny. All of the deadly serious stuff we'd been talking about faded into the background in the light of that one word, "Partner." John had always called me "son," or "Tex." That was the first time he'd ever called me "partner." It meant something special, an acknowledgment of our relationship. A full-fledged equal. I grinned and he gave me a nearly imperceptible nod. *Partner.*

We shook hands a little longer than usual that day. It would have been nice if we could have spent the whole afternoon together, but business called both of us. He gave me that big, sweeping wave of his long arm, along with his wide, infectious grin, as he drove his pickup out of sight.

Twenty-one

I arrived home in San Marcos four days later, after delivering another bail jumper into custody and collecting an envelope full of cash. My cowboy-caretaker had collected the mail and stacked it on the table by my bed. It included a manila envelope from John Marshall containing details about the Warren Commission, some personal notes, and a photograph of him and his wife on horseback. He still looked like the actor Clint Walker, despite the gray hair, especially when he sat tall in the saddle, astride his big horse.

If John had gone to all the trouble to put together this information, the least I could do was read it.

The Warren Commission, I learned, was a misnomer. It was officially the President's "Commission to Report upon the Assassination of President John F. Kennedy," but it had taken on the name of its chairman, Earl Warren, the ex-governor of California and currently the chief justice of the U.S. Supreme Court. Within one week of JFK's death, Lyndon Johnson had assembled a group of powerful, knowledgeable men, and issued an executive order directing them to "ascertain, evaluate, and report upon the facts relating to the assassination of the late President John F. Kennedy and the subsequent violent death of the man charged with the assassination." They would use the FBI as the main investigating body but were directed to also examine any evidence uncovered by "federal or state authorities" and report their findings and conclusions directly to President Johnson.

Marshall had consulted with a government insider he knew and scribbled some notes for me to consider. "What if the investigation revealed Fidel Castro was involved? Americans would demand revenge. Then the Soviet Union might come charging in to rescue Cuba. Could that lead to a war and the possible use of nuclear weapons? Would it be worth the risk to the whole population of our country just to solve a couple of murders?" Wouldn't it be easier, and safer for our government, John noted, to let everyone think that Lee Harvey Oswald did it all by himself.

That idea raised my level of bile, because it didn't seem like proper justice. But if revealing the true facts might start World War III and blow up half the people on earth with nuclear bombs, maybe the truth should remain hidden. I read on.

Among the six-man panel of commission directors, LBJ had picked two senators: Richard Russell from Georgia, and John S. Cooper of Kentucky; and two members of the House of Representatives: Hale Boggs from Louisiana, and Gerald Ford from Michigan. Rounding out the group were John McCloy, the ex-president of the World Bank and high commissioner of Germany after World War II, and Allen Dulles, the former top man of the CIA. They would coordinate the investigative and reporting activities of fourteen assistant counsels and a dozen staff members. Armed with nearly unlimited legal powers, and financed by an "Emergency Fund for the President," they should be able to ferret out any information they needed or wanted.

It sounded like LBJ expected a meticulous and thorough

sifting of everything connected to the shootings, which could very well include pulling me in and giving me the third degree. I dreaded that idea worse than a rattlesnake bite.

More written notes from John: "Don't forget, this is an election year. President Johnson wants to be elected to the office on his own right, not just be a Kennedy hand-me-down. It sure wouldn't sit well with the public to hear that we let JFK get murdered by a mobster involved in an organized crime conspiracy, or that some radical government agents played a part in it. That would cook LBJ's goose. It wouldn't cause an atomic war, but it would get a Republican elected to the White House. I don't know which is worse."

If the commission dug out all the facts, including my knowledge of Ruby and Oswald, I wondered how LBJ would treat me then. Would my life be expendable?

I shuffled through some more of the material John had sent but felt my stomach tighten into a painful knot. I didn't want to relive the torment I'd felt right after the killings and ever since then. Damn Jack Ruby. Why did he have to pull me into this? Why couldn't he have been somewhere else that day, other than the dingy bar where John and I had grabbed our fugitive? More and more, I was convinced that Ruby had never cared about the shooting lessons. Now I believed that he was actually trying to recruit me to kill the president. And I felt sure that it didn't matter to Ruby whether Oswald learned anything about marksmanship or not, because he was being set up as a fall guy. The whole deal smelled like a sewer, and I'd been dragged right through the middle of it.

Before shoving the papers back in the envelope, I read John's final note. "LBJ has some tough decisions facing him, and so do you, partner. They are not easy for either one of you. I know that whatever you do, it will be the right thing. If I can help you in any way, you know I will do everything I can." It was signed with a simple J.M.

Like that ornery little gal in *Gone with the Wind,* I decided I'd think about that tomorrow.

An idea had been rattling around in the back of my head for some time, and I decided to act on it. John Marshall had supplemented his income for years by hauling loads in his eighteen-wheeler, sometimes using it as a cover for his bounty hunting activities. He'd taught me to drive the big rig competently. Why not get hold of one and use it in the same way?

I presented the idea to the man who acted as my liaison for government assignments, and within a week he obtained approval. The feds would even finance the truck for me and let me gradually buy it at cost, paying it off in small chunks. Four days later, I was the proud owner of a spotless black late fifties model Mack truck. I hired a sign painter to letter "Texas Outlaw" on the back of the trailer and adopted the nickname as my two-way radio identification.

To establish a reputation as a trucker, I learned how to convince brokers to assign loads to me, everything from produce to pottery, and hauled the payloads up and down the network of highways. I made it a point to start conversations with fellow big rig jockeys at every truck stop and to be on my radio constantly, making sure everyone knew the Texas Outlaw. My experience several years earlier, learning the side roads that circumvented weigh stations and patrol traps, came in handy, and I used it often to ingratiate myself with the circle of operators on the shady side of the law. To let them know I'd be willing to transport anything for a profit, legal or illegal, I dropped hints that I was desperate for money, that my truck was about to be repossessed, and that I'd do just about anything for a payload. Within a few weeks, my government contact suggested that I hang around a truck stop close to Laredo, and spread the word about my financial problem and my disregard for the law.

It didn't take long for my plight to be heard by the right people. I was sitting at the counter, bemoaning my problems to a bored trucker, near a trio of bikers. One of them moved to the stool next to me and asked a few questions. I must have given the right answers, because he suggested that I stand close to the pay phone in a booth outside later that evening, answer it when it rang, and identify myself as *El Negro Toro*. I had waited nearly three hours and planned to give up if nothing happened by midnight. At 11:45, it rang. A voice with a Spanish accent asked who he was speaking to, and when I told him it was the black bull, he asked if I would be willing to pick up a load and drop if off up in Oklahoma. I haggled over the pay for a few minutes, trying not to sound too willing, and arranged for my first contraband load. Ninety pounds of high-grade marijuana, grown south of the border and smuggled across the river, needed transport to Oklahoma City, where it would bring quick and handsome profits. He gave me instructions where to show up at noon the next day.

At a rusting, littered warehouse that looked like a WWII quonset hut, just outside Laredo, I met the distributor, who planned to rake in big bucks for placing the weed in the hands of kids who would sell it on the streets. The easy money would forever turn the youngsters away from trying to earn honest wages, and doom them to lives of corruption and eventual imprisonment. I hated the bastards who were behind this. They were polluting our country as surely as big industry polluted water and land.

It took all my acting skills to behave like a greedy goon who would do anything for a few filthy dollars. To convince the distributor of my underworld experience and credentials, I dropped some names given to me by an agent from the U.S. Customs Service. The sleazeball bit like a channel catfish and ordered the bales loaded into my trailer. As soon as I cleared the gate in the surrounding chain link fence and turned the corner, I radioed a preset code. It was a pleasure to watch while a team of feds screamed through the open gate, raided the warehouse and cuffed the dazed distributor and his hired hands. But I'd forgotten one thing. They made a beeline for my truck, pulled me out, slammed me to the ground, and hauled me in with the rest of the bums. Only after we'd all been booked and put in cells could they drag me to an interview room and come to my rescue. Of course, the agent pointed out, it had been necessary to arrest me, too, in order to maintain my cover.

Two more similar drug busts had been successfully completed before I took a few weeks off to spend on my place. In San Marcos I met a new lady whose company graced my evenings, while the days were used up with work on the house and horse stalls, and riding Chief across the countryside.

One evening, a little after nine, I answered the phone expecting the honeyed voice of my lady friend. It was, instead, a girl I used to date in Fort Worth. She was calling to deliver the most devastating news of my life.

Twenty-two

I sat stunned, speechless, and heartsick when the young woman in Fort Worth completed her message, offered her sympathy, and hung up. My heart pounded and I couldn't move.

John Marshall had been murdered!

No son ever suffered more hurt at hearing of a parent's death. No friend was ever more saddened when informed of the loss of a loved one. Questions floated indistinctly around in the stormy, pounding emotions of my mind. Why? Who? Oh, God, not John Marshall!

The caller had little information to offer. John's wife, too broken up to call me herself, had given the girl my telephone number and asked her to break the sad news to me. But the details were sketchy.

John, she said, had been found in the back pasture of an acquaintance's ranch outside North Fort Worth. He'd been shot in the back five times! The ranch owner was in town, not on the property, when it had happened. No suspects had been arrested or even identified. No bullet casings had been found near his body, which suggested the possibility that he'd been murdered elsewhere and dumped out in the pasture. That was it. No more information was available. The funeral would be held in two days.

I don't know how long I sat there in shock. Some time

later, maybe an hour, the phone rang again. I didn't feel like talking to anyone but mechanically reached for the handset and mumbled a hello. John's wife, her voice shaking, said she had to call and apologize for not being the first one to tell me. It took all the strength she could summon to finally pick up the phone and contact me. I struggled for words of consolation. We both had lost the person we cared for more than anyone else in the world. Words weren't really necessary. We spoke the necessary ones, and I told her I'd be there for the funeral. Her composure broke into a flood of choking tears just before she hung up.

The drive up to Wichita Falls, where Mrs. Marshall had requested that the funeral be held, was the longest and loneliest I'd ever made. My insides had turned to lead. The only stops I made were for gas, because I felt like I'd never eat again. The whole damn world seemed empty.

I couldn't remember the last time I had cried; probably long before I'd left my aunt and uncle in Fort Worth. I'd remained dry-eyed even at Tommy's funeral, but my eyes kept filling to the brim, and the tears finally cut loose during the services for John. The sad hymns filling the little chapel broke down my macho barrier against crying, and the touching eulogy delivered by a minister cracked my resolve. I felt the hot tears trickle down my cheeks. John's wife sat next to me, her red eyes hidden behind a black veil, sobbing silently.

Several old cowboys, their weather-creased faces also tearstained, stood up to recall their days in the sun with their revered companion. No one pretended that John Marshall had been a saint, but he was the best man and the best friend any of us had ever known. He'd always been there when we'd needed him, our rock of stability, and it was hard to imagine what life would be like without him.

On my return home, I paid a call to Detective Duke Jordan, John's old buddy in Fort Worth. He'd retired just a few weeks earlier and planned to move out of the state. There were very few clues related to John's murder, he said, and no leads to a likely suspect. Jordan seemed nervous and reluctant to say very much. He'd keep me posted, he promised, if there were any new developments. I headed back to San Marcos, knowing full well that I'd never hear anything more from him about the case.

Over the next couple of weeks, I pondered my next course of action. Up to that point, I had convinced myself that it didn't really matter to me whether the assassination was ever solved, or the true facts about the deaths of Oswald and Officer Tippit were ever revealed. Trying to heal, I had avoided newspapers, radio, and television news. I didn't want to hear anything about death or the ongoing Warren Commission investigation. I did see a magazine article which showed a photograph of Lee Oswald, dressed all in black, holding some pamphlets up to his chest with his right hand, in his left a rifle that looked like the one police had recovered from the sixth floor. A handgun stuck out of his right pocket. His face bore that tight-lipped smirk. I wouldn't read the article. Whether the photo proved Lee owned the rifle or not, no one could ever convince me that he'd fired the deadly shots.

But now, some dirtbag had shot John Marshall in the back, and that changed everything. I wanted the killer hunted down and either shot on the spot, or brought to a jury and convicted of capital murder. The possibility that

Marshall's death was somehow linked to the others disturbed me, and that connection grew more plausible in my mind with each passing day. There was only one thing left to do.

From a public telephone, I called the office of Governor John Connally, who had been wounded when JFK was shot, and asked how to contact the Warren Commission. An aide gave me the information and a telephone number. I realized that I might be exposing myself to serious danger, but I no longer gave a damn. Armed with a sack full of change, I dialed the operator and asked her to place a long-distance call to Washington, D.C.

A woman answered, business-like, and I asked to speak to someone with the Warren Commission. Not a flunky, I said, but someone with authority. After a couple of minutes on hold, a deep male voice said he was a supervising investigator.

Mustering my courage, I said, "I've got some very important information regarding the man they accused of shooting President Kennedy, Lee Harvey Oswald, and the guy who shot him, Jack Ruby." I didn't give my name, planning on revealing it only when I could sit face to face with the person who would take my statement.

The voice paused for a second, then said, "We appreciate your call very much, sir, but the investigation is nearly concluded, and we have the information we need."

"You don't have the information I can give you."

"It really won't be necessary, sir. We've had thousands of calls and most of them are quite repetitious. Our questions have been answered, and there's nothing more related to this that will change the outcome. Thanks very much for calling, sir. Have a nice day." The line went silent.

Government bureaucracy had always left me cold, but

this was beyond belief. What absolute arrogance. What un-mitigated, narrowminded, jackass-stubborn stupidity. Didn't they want the truth?

It took several hours for my anger to cool down. I decided to hell with it. No one could say I hadn't tried. The wise men of the commission had already made up their minds. Might as well wash my hands of the whole thing. I couldn't bring John or Tommy back. Probably all I could do was get myself killed, too. John Marshall had said, "Whatever you choose to do, I know it will be the right thing." I had tried, and they'd rejected it. The right thing to do now was to survive this mess and do the best I could with the rest of my life.

Throwing myself into the bounty hunting work, I vol-unteered for even more cases, the more dangerous, the bet-ter. Maybe I had a subconscious urge to get knocked off and end the turmoil and wondering if someone was out to get me. Or maybe the intense concentration required in locating and subduing the fugitives kept my mind off the tragedies and personal problems.

I liked working with my big black Mack. One especially memorable case involved a high-speed chase in which I jammed the pedal to the metal to keep up with an escaped felon who had a female hostage with him. That took some driving. My speedometer was maxed out, so I don't really know how fast we were going. You can bet every other vehicle on the road scooted out of the way in a big hurry. My adrenaline was pumping faster than the diesel into my engine. I finally managed to subdue him when he lost con-trol and wrecked the car. The felon was banged up, but his hostage survived unscathed.

A half dozen drug busts and several other captured felons during the next few months kept me busy. Then I ran into the lowest form of life, even among lawbreakers. Few criminals make my skin crawl more than someone who produces child pornography and sells it. A major dealer in the filthy business named Don Williamson had been operating in Louisiana. It turned my stomach when I saw the explicit color photos of pubescent young girls, engaging in perverted sex acts with adult men, preteen boys, and each other. It never fails to astonish me how low some people can sink in their perpetual quest for dirty money. *Someone ought to shoot that S.O.B. and I'd like to be the one to do it.*

Police in Louisiana had been on this sleazebag's trail for months and had arrested him once on an unrelated charge, hoping to jail him long enough to finalize collecting childporn evidence. But a shyster lawyer had convinced a judge to let Williamson out on bail. He skipped across the border at Brownsville and had been spotted down in Torreon, Mexico.

With the information my contact provided, I traveled deep into Mexico, where I'd been just twice before, to Torreon. On a previous case in the same little town, I'd worked with a young man who could ferret out greedy informants willing to betray their own mothers for a few pesos. I was fortunate enough to find him again.

Because the sexual deviant had another bad habit, cocaine, our job was made easier. A local dealer accepted a moderate bribe to lead us to the fugitive. We ambushed the slimeball in a country village, where he had already started his vile business again. He hadn't waited long. We found that he'd recruited four young peasant girls, twelve or thirteen years old, and photographed them. He'd paid them the

generous sum of five dollars each. For the first time in my
life, I truly wanted to use my guns to kill someone. That
pervert deserved it, if anyone ever did. It was a real effort
to restrain myself, and focus on my real responsibility; to
bring him back to authorities in Louisiana. We used a small
plane to transport him back into the United States, carrying
with us his new collection of prints and a dozen rolls of
unexposed film. Rapists and sexual abusers of children
rank at the bottom of the scale among prisoners. I doubted
that Don Williamson would last long enough to face trial.
Even if he did, his existence wouldn't be a very pleasant
one.

As the months rolled by, I collected more cash than I'd
anticipated. I didn't want to start a bank account that could
build a paper trail for the use of revenge-seeking felons,
or anyone else who might want to put some hurt on me.
So I stored the bundles in buried coffee cans, in hidden
compartments in my cabinets, and in my truck. I'd bought
a new saddle, and my pickup was paid off. The job offers
came in as often as I wanted. I turned a few down but
accepted most. Lyndon Johnson had kept his word, and
with the exception of calling the Warren Commission when
I'd been crushed by John Marshall's murder and felt the
misery of tormented anger and sadness, I'd kept mine. I
hadn't leaked a single word of the information I'd promised
to keep secret.

Several weeks after my return from the satisfying incar-
ceration of the child porn peddler, Sherman came rattling
into my driveway again. I asked when he was going to junk
that old red jalopy, but he said he had developed a certain
fondness for it. He had a message for me. "The chief" had

requested the pleasure of my company again. Sherman "suggested" that I make some time, when notified, to drive down to Cotulla, a small town seventy-five miles north of Laredo. The meeting would be close to an old schoolhouse, shown on a map he gave me. Then Sherman made a comment that bothered me. "Lyndon kept his word. You need to keep yours."

My face heated up. "Look, I'm going to tell you something, Bud. I haven't talked to anyone. I've been minding my own business, exactly as I promised."

"We told him that," Sherman said. "But there's been a leak somewhere. It's keeping things stirred up in certain circles."

Indignation colored my response. "Geez, Sherman, it's no wonder. How many times has a president been killed in Texas? Do you think it's just going to die down like the murder of some wino in a back alley? Of course people are still talking about it, and they're going to keep on talking for a long time. There's been so much covered up, and so many rumors. It's the biggest mystery of this century. The public wants to know who the hell orchestrated the killing. Not many people believe that Oswald acted alone. For Chrissake, am I going to be called on the carpet every time someone starts a new rumor?"

"Calm down, cowboy. He just wants to talk to you. Probably needs a little reassurance."

His answer didn't satisfy me. "You're making a mistake if you think I've been talking. I sure as hell don't want anyone to know I had any connection with any part of it."

"I believe you." He held up his hands, palms forward, in a show of earnest. "I can't see that you've done anything wrong, so far. They say that you've done a fine job on every one of your assignments."

Realizing that Sherman was trying to settle me down and change the subject, I eased off, but had to add, "I'm tired of being suspected. I can keep my word. I always will, unless I feel that you people have let me down."

"That sounds like a threat."

"It's not a threat. I promised to keep my mouth shut, and I plan to keep that promise. But if I find out someone's trying to wreck my life, or mess around with anyone I care for, I can be an obstinate mule. The chief, as you call him, doesn't scare me. I just want to be treated with respect. I've done what I said I'd do." Most of my comments were exactly what I meant, but a little bit of it was bluster and bluff. "Just tell him that this Texan will keep his word."

Sherman seemed relieved to end the discussion. "I'm sure you will, cowboy. I'll let you know when to be in Cotulla." He took a few steps toward his pickup, stopped, half-turned, and said, "Oh, by the way, when you go down there, there's a stop you really ought to make on the way. It's a candy store in San Antonio. You'll be given the address. Buy five pounds of their special peanut brittle. The "chief" loves that stuff. It'd make him real happy if you would do him that little favor."

The message came from Sherman three days after our heated conversation.

Cotulla was about a three-hour drive from San Marcos. On the appointed day, I waited in the shadow of the school, which had been built in the early part of the century. Once again, I wondered if someone was looking at me through the crosshairs of a scope mounted on a high-powered rifle, calmly fondling the trigger.

Twenty-three

I'd waited about an hour when three cars halted a block away. Some men scurried around them before one car lurched forward again and moved toward me. The driver parked. A familiar figure stepped out, and took long, leisurely strides in my direction. This time, Lyndon Johnson wore a dark suit, white shirt, and diagonally striped tie. His graying hair was combed straight back. For the first time, I noticed his ears, which lay back at the sides of his head, but were larger than most men's, with long, thick lobes. His relaxed expression appeared pleasant, the eyes in that perpetual squint, the thin-lipped mouth drawn back into a crease-deepening smile.

"How are ya', cowboy?" he asked. I replied that I was doing fine. He invited me to take a little walk with him. Glancing at the old schoolhouse, he said, "I used to teach here, Welhausen School, a long time ago, and I was the principal, too. Had three grades at the same time: fifth, sixth, and seventh. All the kids were Mexican Americans, and most of them spoke very little English. My ability with the Spanish language wasn't all that great, either, but we managed to get along. Poverty-stricken children, poor, hungry. I think they survived mostly on frijole beans. They didn't have the slightest idea about hygiene. One time I arranged to get toothpaste for every last one of them." He gazed around the place, evidently in a nostalgic mood.

I listened, sincerely interested. I knew he had arranged to see me for more than a personal history lesson, but I felt privileged that he would take the time to share it with me. Just as I started to relax, his face tensed and he got to the point. "Tex, have you been talking to anyone?"

"Mr. President, I . . ."

"I told you once, call me Lyndon."

"Mr. Lyndon," I continued, "I never said nothing to nobody, and I ain't going to."

His eyes, squinting, looked directly into mine, as if he could see behind them and watch exactly what was playing on the movie screen of my mind. Those facial muscles of his big features relaxed again. "Well, I think I can trust you. We're both men who can keep our bargains." Without skipping a beat, he changed back to his memories. "Those kids who went to school here didn't know anything about sports or games. At recess, all they'd do is fight. I taught them how to play games instead, and it made a big difference in them. Right here is where I learned about the extreme importance of education."

"I sure agree with you, sir. I wish I'd had more formal schooling."

"Did you drop out early to start working?"

"Yes, sir. I had that stubborn streak of Texan independence, so I lit out on my own and took any job I could get, including shooting coyotes, to scrape by."

"Well, son, I think hard work helps form character in a man. I picked cotton and ran a little shoeshine business up there in Johnson City. Rode a donkey to school. I love that hill country, but it made for hardscrabble living at times. How do you like it in San Marcos?"

Impressed that this world leader could remember where I lived, I said, "It's a nice town, good water, friendly people."

"When I left here, I moved to San Marcos to finish college. Southwestern State Teacher's College. Taught some high school after that, before I got into politics. Those were tough times, cowboy. You'd better hope this country never goes through another depression like that one."

"I reckon so, sir. Thanks to those jobs I've been getting, I'm doing great, financially."

"Glad to hear it, son. Your country, and I, appreciate what you've done. Keep it up." He started to turn, stopped, and said, "Oh, did you happen to make a stop in San Antonio on the way here?"

"Yes, sir. I sure did." I handed him the bag of peanut brittle. His face broke into a satisfied grin.

"Well, boy, I appreciate it. Here's a little remembrance for you." Pulling a toothbrush from his pocket, he handed it to me, saying, "Every time you brush your teeth, I want you to use this. It's from the White House. It'll remind you to keep clean." He grinned as if he'd cracked a clever joke, raised his hand in a waist-high wave, turned, walked briskly back to the car, and climbed in. It sped out and rejoined the others, and they convoyed out of sight.

I examined the toothbrush, which had "The White House" printed on it, and shook my head. When he'd reached into his pocket, I'd been tempted to dodge, but had controlled the impulse. If he wanted me knocked off, he wouldn't do it personally. But I was nervous. A *toothbrush*. What a strange way to remind me to keep my mouth shut, or as he put it, "keep clean."

* * *

I kept clean over the next few years, busy with covert activities for several federal law enforcement agencies, the Texas Department of Public Safety, and various county officers. As Johnson had said, I became intimately familiar with the border between Texas and Mexico. I knew every mile of the winding Rio Grande, every shallow ford, all the bridges, and the drug smugglers' favorite locations. People who wore badges on both sides of the border became my friends and associates. I saved some of their skins, and they got me out of life-threatening tight spots more than once. One of my favorites was a colonel in the *federales* with whom I worked to help bust a giant marijuana ring. The smugglers used a reconditioned DC-3 plane, built during World War II, to bring the drugs across to Texas. When we made the raid deep in Mexico, and stood over four captives who belligerently refused to cooperate or answer questions, I watched the colonel administer his brand of justice. One by one, he asked them to reveal information he wanted, and when each one refused, he drew his revolver and put a bullet in their brains. It was the opposite extreme to the detailed investigations, capturing, jailing, expensive trials, lawyers seeking to free them on technicalities, years of costly appeals, and early release we probably would have seen in our country for the same criminals. To me, either extreme could use some extensive modification.

The money poured in. I bought everything I needed, plus a few things I didn't need. My Mack truck was soon paid off, and I had a string of horses that won championships for me at various shows across Texas. I felt that the emotional scars of 1963, and the heartbreak of losing both Tommy and Big John, had healed nicely, when I heard news that ripped the stitches out and nearly killed me.

A few days after I'd had a sweet dream about Judy and

little Rae, John Marshall's widow called me. She'd been trying to reach me for two days, she sobbed. Ice-cold tremors ran up and down my spine and chill bumps covered my skin. I didn't want her to say what I feared. But she had to.

Judy and Rae had been in a horrible auto accident. A dump truck had broadsided their car. Both of them were killed instantly. The funeral was tomorrow. Mrs. Marshall asked if I could possibly show up for it. When I could force the words out, I told her I would be there.

Afterward, I couldn't go home. I drove aimlessly through several states, not caring where I was or what happened to me. A man can take only so much. Why was it that every person I truly cared for met with violent death?

It took nearly three months for me to regain some semblance of normalcy.

Eventually, I gave up my little place in San Marcos, and I changed locations several times. Arizona was my home for two years.

I met the woman who became my wife. She was the sunny side of my life as a bounty hunter. There were some terribly dark sides, as well.

Three times, I thought I was going to die in a bloody heap of beaten, stabbed, or gunshot flesh. One night, in a dark alley in Mexico, four men got the drop on me before I could draw. They beat me for what seemed like hours. Broke my nose, several ribs, and my left leg. I was a whisper away from joining my old mentor, John Marshall, up there, or wherever. But some good samaritans found me and hauled me to a clinic. After they patched me up and sent me back to Texas, I spent two months in a hospital, and several more recuperating at home. My wife begged me to give up the chasing and concentrate on horses. But I couldn't.

Another time, some bad hombres threw me from a car moving fifty or sixty miles an hour. The hospital stay was even longer, during which they put enough metal in my body to set off the detectors in airports. My leg needed pins, this time, to patch the bones together. A few months later an icepick pushed up to the hilt in my back missed my heart by a quarter of an inch.

The third time, they used baseball bats to try to pulverize me. They would have succeeded, but some DEA agents pulled me to safety before my brains could be spilled on the pavement. This time, my wife wondered if some of the gray matter had, indeed, leaked out, because I still refused to quit. My decision cost me my marriage.

Living alone again, I accepted as many assignments as I could handle and continued to avoid news relating to the assassination. Now and then, though, bits of information would leak through my wall of emotional protection. I heard some odd reports about Jack Ruby.

While Jack was in jail, he gave some strong hints of his connection to the assassination, but he never said anything specific. He begged the Warren Commission to take him to Washington, D.C., to be interviewed, but they refused. Ruby reportedly denied the existence of any conspiracy or the involvement of other people. But what would he be expected to say? If powerful organized crime figures were involved in the murders, Ruby could kiss life goodbye if he informed.

His stated reason for killing Oswald was to prevent Mrs. Kennedy the ordeal of returning to Dallas for a trial. He'd read a newspaper on Sunday morning after the assassination, he said. In Ruby's words, he'd shot Oswald because he hated the possibility that ". . . Mrs. Kennedy may have to come back for the trial of Lee Harvey Oswald. I don't know what bug got ahold of me . . . I am taking a pill called Preludin. It is a harmless pill and it is very easy to get in the drugstore. I use it for dieting." It sounded like he was suggesting the pills drove him to murder.

I remembered Ruby popping pills, and how they seemed to give him a lift. In those last few days I saw him, he swallowed a lot of them. He must have downed a whole bottle on the day he killed Oswald, because he told investigators that he wanted to show his love for the Jewish faith, and ". . . suddenly the emotional feeling came within me that someone owed this debt to our beloved president to save her (Mrs. Kennedy) the ordeal of coming back."

It had been reported that Ruby shouted an obscenity at Oswald a split second before the fatal shot was fired. Ruby denied it. "I never called the man by any obscene name because as I stated earlier, there was no malice in me. He was insignificant, to my feelings, for my love for Mrs. Kennedy and our beloved president." I found that comment very odd. He'd never expressed to me any great love for Kennedy. If he had such affection for the president, I wondered why he hadn't even bothered to try to see him during the motorcade.

Someone overheard Jack muttering in jail, "They're going to find out about New Orleans, find out about everything . . ." I could understand the meaning of that cryptic comment, but authorities ignored it.

Jack Ruby never faced an executioner for killing

Oswald. In jail, he began having delusions about a new holocaust, ranting that "they" were going to kill all the Jews, and that 25 million Jews had been slaughtered on the floor below, in jail. He thought he could hear planes going over and dropping bombs on the Jews. He told his visiting sister that he could hear and see Jews being boiled in oil. Police guards reported him putting his ear to the wall, and moaning, "Shhh! Do you hear the screams? They are torturing the Jews again down in the basement."

According to some reports, Ruby even tried to commit suicide several times by banging his head against the wall and attempting to electrocute himself with a light socket. No conclusive tests were conducted to determine if he was truly suffering mental deterioration, or faking it to escape execution.

After an appeals court granted him a new trial, based on technicalities in the law, he fell sick. At Parkland Hospital, where both Kennedy and Oswald had died, doctors at first thought Ruby suffered from pneumonia, but found that he had cancer in his brain, lungs, and liver. Jack Ruby died on January 3, 1967, at the age of 55.

I felt no sense of loss at Ruby's death. He'd pulled me into a mess that had changed my life, much for the worse. But I felt no bitterness or anger, either. It just didn't matter anymore.

I never met Lyndon Johnson face to face again, but he and I talked on the phone a few times. In 1971, I'd hauled some prized Appaloosas to Las Vegas for a horse show at the Stardust Hotel. They were owned by the Bar B Ranch, and I had been entrusted to transport and show the three champions named Skip, Spring, and Splash. I

telephoned the owner with the proud news that we'd won
blue ribbons, but our achievement was overshadowed by
some bad news. An epidemic affecting horses had broken
out across the country, and crossing state lines would be
a bundle of red tape, inoculations, and delays. For all
intents and purposes, the state borders were closed. The
owner was frantic, because he needed the horses back for
another show as soon as possible. I told him I'd see what
I could do.

The trip would take me through Nevada, Utah, and Colorado. My old trick of circumventing the state line inspection stations wouldn't work, because I couldn't haul the
horses over tiny, bumpy roads. The risk of injuring a million
dollars' worth of horseflesh was too great. I'd made a commitment to attempt a hurried trip but found myself against
a stone wall.

Stonewall! That reminded me of the community next to
the LBJ ranch. I had never asked Johnson for a favor since
we'd sealed our first bargain over a pay telephone in Fort
Worth.

Surprised at my own brazen idea, I called the White
House, identified myself, and asked to speak to the president. I was even more surprised when he picked it up. After
apologizing for bothering him, I described the problem.
He chuckled and instructed me to load up my horses and
go where I needed to go. I wouldn't have any problems.
Another voice came on and asked for a description of my
truck and the license plate number.

At each inspection station, I found extremely courteous
officials and the red carpet treatment. I delivered those
horses in record time to an astonished and happy owner.

* * *

Over the years, I had a few other telephone conversations with LBJ. Mostly, he wanted to tell me that I'd done a good job serving my country. Translated, that meant I had never said a word to anyone about the dark days of 1963.

The highs and lows of Lyndon Johnson's presidency reminded me of driving a big rig to California, down into Death Valley, and way up over the Donner Summit, which I did a few times during his years in the White House. He accomplished some lofty goals with his Great Society, in which he ramrodded unprecedented social changes through his old buddies in Congress. On the other extreme, he suffered the pains of hell by the mess in Vietnam that drove a wedge into our national unity. It caused the biggest division among Americans since the Civil War and cost 58,000 young American lives, plus the immeasurable damage to hundreds of thousands who returned with physical and mental damage. Back in '63, we'd heard that the little problem over in Southeast Asia, where John Kennedy had sent some troops to act as "advisers," would be all over by 1965. But in 1968, it had escalated to a raging inferno from which Johnson couldn't seem to free himself, or the American military. No one knows for sure, but it may have contributed to the heart problems he suffered. In 1968, he announced that he would not accept his party's nomination for another term in the White House, and retired to his ranch in the hill country of Texas.

Ironically, another man who sought the nomination died that same year at the hands of a lone gun-toting assassin. At least, that's what the controversial trial concluded. Robert F. Kennedy, the martyred president's brother, had just won the June primary in California, and confidently said to his celebrating audience, "Now, on to Chicago." But he would never reach the national convention. In the kitchen of the Ambassador Hotel in Los Angeles, Kennedy fell to the floor, mortally wounded. An immigrant named Sirhan Sirhan was wrestled to the floor, and later tried and convicted of killing Kennedy. But just as in JFK's death, controversy swirled around the investigation, and questions were never answered. Suspicions were batted around that the same conspiracy killed both brothers.

Periodically, after Lyndon Johnson retired to his ranch, I saw television news stories about him. It looked strange to see his gray sideburns stretching down to the bottoms of those long ears and the fuzzy white hair at the back of his head curling down almost to his shoulders. He looked older than he was. Long hair was still worn by the so-called hippies of the sixties, but it didn't look right on a retired president.

That era seemed to last several lifetimes, but the turbulent sixties finally passed into history. I was happy to see them go.

January 1973 started off with a bang in the District of Columbia. Football fans watched history in the making when the Miami Dolphins completed the only perfect season ever recorded in the NFL by beating the Washington Redskins 14-7 in the Super Bowl. Richard M. Nixon was sworn in on January 20 for his second term as president of the United States. Boxing fans watched a young fighter named George Foreman, who had won a gold medal in the Olympic Games of 1968 in Mexico City, take the heavyweight championship away from Joe Frazier on January 22. That same month, G. Gordon Liddy and James W. McCord were convicted of plotting to spy on the Democrats during the recent campaign that had reelected Richard

Nixon. And ironically, headlines announced that the United
States had, at long last, signed a peace agreement in Paris
to end the Vietnam War.

In the east bedroom of the sprawling white ranch house
overlooking the Pedernales River, Lyndon Baines Johnson
suffered his final heart attack on January 22. A private
plane took off from the landing strip a hundred yards behind the house and hurried him to a San Antonio hospital,
where he was declared dead. LBJ was sixty-four years old.

I was driving my truck, pulling a trailer full of horses,
to Pompano Beach, Florida, when I heard the radio
announcement of Johnson's death. The news put me in
an introspective mood. It certainly represented the end of
an important segment of American history, and a demar-
cation in my life. But did it release me from my promise
to LBJ never to utter a word about Oswald, Ruby, and the
assassination? No. I was still being assigned well-paying
jobs chasing outlaws and making a lot of money. And there
were plenty of people still alive who might react in a dan-
gerously negative way if I spilled the beans. Johnson's
death changed nothing for me.

The announcement, though, marked the beginning in a
long string of deaths that did influence my life.

Twenty-four

We all face the sad fact that loved ones, friends, and acquaintances are going to die. I'd certainly already had my share of losses by the time I learned of LBJ's death. His passing left me feeling mixed emotions. But not very much sorrow.

I felt much worse, for example, when the actor Chill Wills died. I'd been fortunate enough to meet him at a horse show, and had developed a real affection for him.

There was a nice bonus to visiting the horse shows besides winning ribbons with my Appaloosas. I met some exceptionally nice people—ordinary folks, politicians, wealthy businessmen, and actors. It reminded me of the old days at the Fort Worth exhibitions, when I rubbed elbows with similar types, but they hardly noticed the kid with stars in his eyes who shoveled out the stalls to pick up a few bucks. Now, they treated me as a fellow horse showman.

Three of the most memorable people I met were cowboy actors. I'd admired Chill Wills for years. And he was just as down to earth in real life as he was in his movie roles. He admired one of my Appaloosas at a big event in San Antonio, and that led us into some fun conversations. I found out that he was a fellow native Texan, from Seagoville, right next to Dallas, which I'd suspected all along from his drawl and ways of expressing himself. By the time I met him, he was seventy, and his hair had turned white. Most people didn't realize that besides being the movie voice of Francis, the Talking Mule, Wills was a singer, too, and had a group in the early thirties called the Avalon Boys. Watch closely, sometime, and you can hear him, accompanied by the Avalon Boys, perform the song Laurel and Hardy did that classic dance to, in front of the saloon in *Way Out West*. By the time I met Wills, he'd made over thirty movies, including some classics like *Giant*. He was even nominated for an Academy Award for his role in John Wayne's epic picture about my favorite historical event, *The Alamo*. I told him that I'd planned to see him in James Garner's movie *The Wheeler Dealers* on the weekend President Kennedy was killed. He seemed grateful that I knew so much about him, and pleased that I admired him. I wish all actors had such good hearts and friendly, pleasant personalities.

The second actor I met at a horse show was Slim Pickens, whose real name was Louis Lindley, Jr. Although he sounded like a Texan, he was born in California. He'd worked in rodeos for years, and been a rodeo clown, before he got his first break in movies, in 1950. I was able to hold my own with him talking about calf-roping and bronc-riding, and found that he was really a nice guy. We both laughed when I told him how much I admired the way he rode that nuclear bomb out of the plane in *Dr. Strangelove*.

And when I met Ben Johnson, it was a pleasure to have it confirmed that he, too, was a real cowboy. A native of Oklahoma, he was a stunt wrangler in movies before his big break as Travis Tyree in the classic John Ford Westerns. Ben starred in several movies before he took a one-year break to try his hand at rodeos and won a world's championship in 1953. Back in acting, he took home an Academy Award in 1972 for *The Last Picture Show.* Altogether, he made forty-six movies. Like Wills and Pickens, Ben Johnson was a congenial, warm-hearted country boy who really knew his horseflesh, had the most authentic drawl ever heard on the big screen, and set people at ease with his sincere Western sociability. The conversations I had with him were just like talking to a good old-boy ranch hand.

One of the politicians I ran into was the ex-governor of Texas who had been wounded when JFK was killed. John Connally strolled between stalls at the Joe Freeman Coliseum horse barns during the San Antonio livestock show, admiring the competing animals. I was brushing an Appaloosa scheduled for "showing" that afternoon when Connally stopped, glanced into the stall, then moved in close to praise the horse. I was astonished when he called me by name. "How're you doing, Tex?" Then I realized that a placard on a stall post bore not only my horse's name but mine, too.

My relief was short lived, though, when Connally leaned forward, making sure no one else could hear, and asked if I'd ever talked to the commission investigators or the more recent congressional inquiry. I knew what he meant, but played ignorant. I wondered how he knew, and what he knew about me. Had LBJ broken his word to keep silent? Or did Connally have contacts who had informed him of my associations in 1963? He winked, and in that slow drawl, in his dignified manner, said, "There's a few things I'd like to know. If you're ever in the mood to have a little talk, here's where you can reach me." He handed me a business card.

"Mr. Connally," I said, smiling, "anytime you want to

talk about these great horses, I'd be happy to join you. I sure don't know what else we'd have to discuss."

"Okay, Tex. Good luck in the showing this afternoon." He strolled on as if we had been chatting about the weather. It wasn't too long after our brief encounter that he faced a jury and was found not guilty of accepting questionable gifts from wealthy owners of dairies. Even though he was exonerated, his aspirations to spend four years living in the White House crashed and burned.

The congressional inquiry Connally had referred to was the Select Committee on Assassinations, of the U.S. House of Representatives, who were conducting a new examination of evidence and testimony connected to the murder of both Kennedys. I wasn't very optimistic that they would arrive at any better conclusions than the Warren Commission had.

In 1978, I heard that Chill Wills had died and felt regret as if an old friend had passed on.

And then, six years later, when we lost actor Slim Pickens, I felt the same kind of depression.

During those late 1970s, my bounty hunting activities increasingly focused on drug dealers and smugglers. The problem had expanded all across the country after the war in Vietnam had finally tapered to an inglorious end. Druglords south of the Rio Grande became multimillionaire businessmen. The DEA found a growing need for my services.

Many of the dealers I dragged back across the border were taken to San Antonio to face charges in a federal court. I got to know a few of the judges on a first-name basis. One of them, Judge John H. Wood, Jr., commanded respect from the whole law enforcement community. Many of us called him "Maximum John" because he'd lost patience with criminals in the drug business, and routinely sentenced them to the maximum prison terms allowable. Wood was a fellow Texan by birth, from Rockport, and had been appointed to the federal bench by President Nixon in 1971. He once told me that his great-granddaddy had moved west from New York with a group of men who wanted to help Texas win independence from Mexico. John Howland Wood had been paid for his gallantry with a nice parcel of land, which later became a big ranch.

In his early sixties, Judge Wood maintained a fine sense of humor and a level-headed attitude about the difficulties faced by DEA officers, and their unofficial helpers, like me. We enjoyed working with him.

In May 1979, some of the agents and I were particularly interested in a case we'd help break, over which Judge Wood was scheduled to preside. Two El Paso brothers had smuggled over 20,000 pounds of marijuana into this country over a period of several years. They had acquired it in Colombia, stored it in Mexico, and distributed it in the United States. A lawyer for one of the defendants was so worried about the tough reputation of Wood, he tried to get the judge thrown off the case, but it didn't work. Some of us figured we might just spend some time in San Antonio and watch the trial.

On the day before Memorial Day, 1979, I had dozed off with the television set playing. A newsreporter brought me out of a groggy sleep when he announced that the famous silent film star Mary Pickford had died out in California. He said she was eighty-six years old. Still half asleep, I vaguely felt surprise, because I thought she had died years earlier. I'd almost fallen back into deep slumber when the announcer's voice became tense, and seemingly louder, as he started his next news story. It hit me like an icicle pushed into my heart, and brought me bolt upright on the couch.

A federal judge, he said, had been murdered in San Antonio, Texas. Judge John Herbert Wood, Jr., had just left his apartment and walked to his car when he was dropped in his tracks by a single gunshot from a rifle. The FBI had cordoned off the surrounding area and would devote every possible resource to solving the case. So far, no suspects had been identified.

I guess when your work takes you into the depths of man's greed, depravity, and disregard for human life, you have to expect tragedy. When you walk through a pit of rattlesnakes, you might expect to get bit. But a judge, up there in a safe courtroom or in his upscale home seems safe from the dangerous vipers and vermin. Judges were rarely the victims of killers, and no federal judge had ever been murdered. The sad part was, John Wood had recently dismissed bodyguard service provided by the U.S. Marshal's Service, which had been protecting him ever since the life of another judge, who specialized in drug cases, had been threatened.

Once again, I had to accept that a person I knew and liked had lost his life at the hands of a criminal. It made me wonder how I had escaped so long.

I hoped I would be able to assist in finding John Wood's killer. Bringing him to justice would give me a great sense of satisfaction. But there were no clues, and no witnesses had been located. No matter how hard lawmen try, some murders are never solved.

* * *

The House of Representatives issued the results of their new investigation of the assassinations in 1979. At least they cut a little slack in the old verdict that Oswald had acted alone and suggested that a conspiracy might have existed. While that represented some progress, I think most Americans felt no closer to the truth than they had fifteen years earlier.

Dragging drug dealers back across the border became routine during the next year. I had a fine string of horses, two big rigs running for me, and more money than I'd expected to earn in a lifetime. I needed a change.

A grand idea slowly took hold in my mind. I explained it to my federal contact, and after some wrangling, got approval. I opened the wildest, woolliest, hi-falootin' topless bar in South Texas. The idea was to attract a clientele of underworld creeps by giving them a likely place to gather. It wasn't long before the word got around that Tex Brown's joint was a haven away from cops, and a good place to make some deals. Drug sellers and drug buyers flocked to watch the bare-skin dancers and to negotiate price and delivery of everything from marijuana to methamphetamine. As the manager of a gaggle of beautiful women with naked assets, I was able to gain the confidence of the dealers and pass on information leading to a whole series of major busts. Pardon the pun.

Greed, unfortunately, spreads not only among the underworld; it sometimes infects people who are supposed to be protecting the good citizens. Some shifty-eyed city officials got wind of the high cash flow in my place and wanted their palms crossed with silver. Their corruption complicated things enough to wind up closing my venture. But it was a nice diversion while it lasted.

Some of the other operations were horribly gruesome.

A Rio Bravo gang planned to bring a ton of marijuana across the river. I infiltrated the group and watched in horror as they dealt their own brand of justice to an informer. In an isolated spot out on the dark desert, they made him dig a deep pit. After they'd pushed him in, one of the gang pulled a five-gallon can of gasoline from a truck bed and soaked the begging double-dealer. Someone tossed a match into the hole and the gang watched as the human torch screamed, flailing and twisting in agony for several minutes. I had to grit my teeth real hard to keep from throwing up or pulling both of my revolvers and blasting away at them. Instead, I hung around long enough to discover they were using the false bottom of a butane tanker to transport the drugs. I personally participated in the arrest, with a great deal of glee.

I didn't escape scot free every time. I took some beatings I'll never forget—the pain in my legs from several fractures won't let me. But they healed, and I kept at the jobs with an obsession that even I didn't fully understand.

News stories about the assassination seemed never to go away. In 1981, I heard that the body of Lee Harvey Oswald had been exhumed, with his widow's permission, to assure doubters that it was, indeed, Oswald in the grave. The coroner who'd conducted the autopsy was there, and made some bizarre statements. The casket, he said, was broken, indicating it had been lifted out of the ground after the burial. He suggested that the body in the casket did not have scars or injuries he knew Oswald to have, meaning someone must have removed the head of the body in the casket, and replaced it with the head of Oswald! The crazy mystery grew deeper with each passing year.

In early December that same year, on Pearl Harbor Day, I was on my way home from a bust in El Paso. I'd had a late start, and weariness settled through my bones, so I surrendered to it in Van Horn, where Highway 90 crosses I-10. After a nice chicken fried steak at a cafe, I stretched out on a king-sized bed in my motel and flipped on the television. Leafing through a newspaper, I wasn't even watching the screen. I heard the announcer say that a man who had already been convicted of one murder and was a suspect in another had been sentenced to forty years in prison for possession of cocaine. I glanced up to see if the prisoner was someone I'd crossed paths with in a drug raid somewhere.

When they flashed his picture on the screen, I thought he looked familiar. I listened as the newscaster told viewers that the man had been questioned in the killing of Judge John Wood, Jr., in San Antonio on May 29, 1979. Now, my interest turned to excitement. I'd been hoping for two and a half years they'd solve the case and prayed that they had arrested the killer at last. But where had I seen that face?

Over a long period of time, I'd been involved in hundreds of arrests for a wide variety of crimes. Those features on the TV screen kept nagging me. Tall guy, lots of hair, kind of a slope to the flesh over his right eye. I dug deeper into my memory and sorted through a vast clutter of images stored in dusty, long unused compartments. Then, wham! A two-by-four slugged me right between the eyes. My God!

There was no doubt in my mind that I was looking at the tall stranger who'd worn the topcoat at the Rodeo Cafe, and at Nick's hamburger stand, just prior to the assassination of John F. Kennedy! Same facial characteristics, same height, same confident expression. I'd filed away the strange encounters for years, hoping someday to make some sense of them. And there it was, right on the television screen. They said his name was Charles Voyde Harrelson, forty-three years old. That would have made him about twenty-five back then, which fit perfectly. And he was a suspect in the rifle shooting of Judge Woods. Since I knew that Lee Oswald couldn't have hit Kennedy from that distance, I had been waiting for a long time to get a lead on who actually did it. Certainly, just being in Fort Worth a couple of days before the assassination wasn't enough to convict Harrelson, but it put him high up on my list of candidates, along with that sharpshooting Cuban who had the fancy rifle and scope. Maybe both of them had participated.

I hoped that Harrelson would stand trial for the murder of Judge Wood. Justice sometimes works backwards, but that's better than not working at all.

While my professional life flourished in the first couple of years of the eighties, my personal life suffered. The marriage had floundered because my wife couldn't understand my dedication to the danger, long hours, and travel bounty hunting required. I'm not sure I could, either. It seemed that everyone I cared about had died or left me in one way or another.

I threw myself into my work with increased vigor to keep my mind off loneliness and nostalgia. The distraction caused several near misses that could have cost my life. Somehow I survived the physical threats and the emotional roller-coaster.

* * *

In March 1983, some long awaited news caught up with
me. Charles Harrelson, the man I'd seen in Fort Worth who
had later been identified as a suspect in the death of Judge
John Wood, Jr., had faced trial and been convicted of the
murder the previous December. Three other people, including Harrelson's wife, had also been found guilty of crimes
related to the homicide. Harrelson, I heard, had committed
a killing for hire in the late sixties and was sent to prison
for it, but had been released. He denied killing Judge Wood,
whined that he'd been framed, and accused rogue elements
of the DEA of ordering the jurist's death. I worked with
the DEA and couldn't believe any of them would commit
such a stupid act.

At his sentencing, Harrelson criticized the judge, saying,
"The only thing missing from your robes are the twin lightning bolts of the SS, the Gestapo. You have murdered the
Constitution." Ignoring the outburst, the judge handed
down two consecutive life terms, one for killing Wood, and
the other for plotting the murder. Five more years were
tacked on for obstructing justice during the investigation.

Mrs. Harrelson found herself facing a guilty verdict on
charges of obstruction of justice and perjury, which sent
her to the pen for twenty-five years.

Two brothers, marijuana dealers, were suspected of
plotting the killing and paying Harrelson to fire the mor-
tal rifle shot. One of the bothers cut a deal, pled guilty
to conspiring to murder, and got ten years. He testified
against Harrelson and his wife. The other brother was
acquitted of murder but imprisoned for fifteen years on
drug charges.

It didn't look like Charles Harrelson would ever get out.

* * *

By the start of the '90s, my fugitive chasing activities finally tapered down in favor of more time spent with my horse business. I had participated in over 2,000 cases successfully closed. I have an excellent memory, but some of the names had started to fade.

One name from the past popped up in March 1993. An acquaintance of mine casually mentioned that he'd read a newspaper article announcing that Carlos Marcello had died. I hadn't heard about the New Orleans Mafioso leader for years, and didn't even know he was still alive. My friend said that rumors had floated since 1963 about Marcello being linked to the Kennedy assassination. Finally, just a few months before Marcello's death, a mobster who'd been close to Santos Trafficante, the crime boss of Tampa, Florida, gave a television interviewer some inside information. He quoted Trafficante as saying that Marcello had "messed up" when he had had Kennedy killed!

"I always wondered if he had anything to do with it," I said, recalling that day I'd seen Marcello and his two thugs in the Rodeo, making poor old Tommy nervous. My suspicions that Ruby had been acting under Marcello's orders made more sense now. "Marcello must have been pretty old," I said, trying to sound no more than mildly interested.

"The old boy was 83 and he'd been in failing health for a long time. Just got out of prison about four years ago."

"Prison? He was in the slammer?" Maybe there was justice, after all.

"Yeah. I read that back in 1981 they nailed him on a sting for trying to bribe a federal judge in California. He got sentenced to seven years. Louisiana went after him the next year and convicted him of violating federal racketeering laws. The FBI was in on that one. They set up a phony insurance scam, and Marcello could hardly wait to get his hands on some of the easy money. He must have had a good lawyer, though, because the Federal Supreme Court threw out the conviction and the seven-year rap that went with it. So the Godfather did his seven years on the California beef, but he had some strokes in prison and spent a lot of the time in hospitals."

"I once heard that he ran the organized crime show in New Orleans," I said, trying to sound only politely interested.

"That's what the article in the paper said. He got started in the 1930s and did some time for pushing marijuana and for robbery. Then, during World War II, he muscled in on gambling profits. Eventually, he controlled rackets and vice along the whole Gulf Coast, and Bobby Kennedy went after him. Threw him out of the country. That must have made him hate the Kennedys."

I could feel the urge rising to tune him out, to throw the switch. I hated talking about the death of President Kennedy. But he kept talking.

"Marcello must have been something like Napoleon, 'cause he was only five-foot-two"

The mental picture of the dapper little man, reeking of power, flashed back in my mind. Tough as nails, but dressed like a bank executive. I was trying to recall what business he said he was in, when my pal laughed and said, "Marcello sure had an odd cover for his underworld activities. Always said he was nothing but a simple tomato salesman." His comment took me back to that day in the cafe, when he'd said the same thing to me. And his goons had snickered like it was really hilarious.

I didn't shed any tears over the death of Carlos Marcello.

* * *

The name Harrelson came up again not long after that, when I watched some old episodes of the television series *Cheers* and admired a young actor who played a goofy bartender. The kid had done very well, going on to make big-screen movies like *White Men Can't Jump*. I was astonished when a friend told me that the kid's father was in federal prison for murder. The father's name was Charles Harrelson!

Somehow, the fact caught up with me that a whole new generation had grown up since 1963, and people who were just little kids then were the movers and shakers of today's world. I realized that I could not keep letting the past control my life.

Time was slipping by too fast. Death had visited so many of the people I had known way back then. All the power players, on both sides of justice, were gone. Earl Warren and several members of his commission had died. John Connally joined the long list in 1995. Even as I assemble the facts for this book, I read that the actor I knew and admired, Ben Johnson, passed away in April 1996.

Jack Ruby had pulled me into a whirlpool of madness and had muffled the truth forever when he'd taken the life of Lee Harvey Oswald. LBJ had manipulated me into keeping silent. I had promised John Marshall that I wouldn't risk being killed by telling what I knew, and waited in futility for his murder to be solved. Strange phone calls had threatened me and the people I loved. And I suffered heartbreak when I lost them.

Threats still existed from behind a curtain of obscured faces. I knew they were there, but I didn't know who they were. Now, nearly all of them had faced their maker and whatever justice exists in the Great Beyond.

* * *

I've kept my bargain, with honor. There still may be some danger in revealing what happened in 1963, but that is no longer important. I think I owe a greater debt to my country and to my fellow Texans. I ask forgiveness and understanding for my long silence.

I know that the people I loved who have passed on will grant me that benevolence, and welcome me with open arms when I finally join them.

My name is Ray Tex Brown.

Epilogue

When Ray "Tex" Brown stepped forward, ready to tell his story, I accepted the opportunity to collaborate with him as coauthor, but with mixed feelings. Hundreds of books have been written on the subject, dissecting every available bit of information and speculating about the myriad of unanswered questions. I saw no need for another textbook. But when I heard that Tex Brown planned to reveal his *personal* involvement, rather than another analysis of the incomplete mosaic other writers have scrutinized ad infinitum, I agreed to meet him and hear what he planned to say.

Most Americans who are old enough to remember November 22, 1963, can say exactly where they were and what they were doing when the stunning announcement came that President John Fitzgerald Kennedy had been assassinated. The nation ground to a halt. People huddled around radios and television sets, waiting for news bulletins. We cried. Through that dismal weekend, we mourned, watched the sad funeral, and heard the muffled drums. Our hearts went out to the widow and her two children as they knelt beside the casket in the Capitol rotunda. "Hail to the Chief" sounded like a dirge and lodged in our hearts forever to be associated with the loss of JFK. We saw the caisson roll slowly over the bridge to Arlington National Cemetery, bearing the youthful president who had brought us new hope and vigor. Our souls felt as empty as the saddle on the riderless horse, Blackjack, who followed behind, carrying boots mounted backward in the stirrups, the symbol of a departed hero. We thought nothing could shock us anymore.

Then, on Sunday, we watched the most shocking event of all. Jack Ruby lunged out of a crowd of reporters and shot Lee Harvey Oswald to death while a hundred million witnesses recoiled in front of their TV screens.

A third of a century has passed, and we are still unsatisfied with the information we have been provided. Most of us are convinced that the truth lies hidden in some guarded chamber, facts obfuscated, voices of those who know the secrets hushed in fear. So many people have died who might have shed light on the case. Was there a conspiracy to murder the president, then silence Oswald forever? Do classified government files deliberately hide the facts in the name of national security? Do surviving mobsters hold the solution? Will we ever know?

For years, I have hoped that those remaining people who might be holding back helpful information would step forward and finally divulge it. Ray "Tex" Brown, I think, is in the vanguard of those who know and remember, who will shrug off fear to reveal important facts. His contribution is one of the missing pieces of the incomplete mosaic. If we are fortunate, others like Brown will follow his lead and fill in more blanks.

In undertaking this task, I wanted to know what Brown knew, and whether I could accept his story at face value. We spoke by telephone, and he gave me a brief outline of his recollections. I caught a flight to Texas, and made some stops in various locations prior to my appointed meeting with Brown. In the LBJ presidential library, in Austin, I spent hours examining records of Johnson's visits to Texas during his presidency, especially to the ranch. If Tex Brown was going to tell me that Johnson summoned him to the ranch, I wanted authentication of dates and times. The records contain hour-by-hour diaries of Johnson's activities during his visits, so I copied them for use in testing the reasonableness of Brown's assertions.

Next, I toured the LBJ ranch, between Johnson City and Fredericksburg, now open to the public. I wanted to see where Brown met the President at the Pedernales River, and the exact layout of the ranch. I stood in silent reverence at Johnson's unpretentious grave in a small family cemetery overlooking the river. I also visited Johnson City, his boyhood home, and the home of his ancestors.

A few days later, in another part of Texas, I met Ray "Tex" Brown in person. Of course, we had arranged to meet in a cafe, as was his custom. He wore a full dark brown beard, a battered old cowboy hat, Western shirt, faded jeans, and boots. We spent hours together that first evening, trading questions and answers. By midnight, I found myself adopting his slow Texas drawl and colloquialisms. I'd already purchased a black cowboy hat and had brought along my jeans, boots, and western shirt. Hot dawg—when in Texas, become a Texan, pardner.

The next morning he insisted I return my rental car; he would drive. We climbed into his pickup, naturally, and covered the hundreds of miles to Fort Worth. I listened while he picked up his CB microphone every fifteen minutes and said something like, "Breaker, breaker for a quickie. This is Texas Outlaw. Hey, northbound flatbed, how's traffic up ahead?" In that peculiar vernacular of the citizen's band crowd, he learned of road conditions, the location of "smokies," and whatever road gossip was available. He passed on similar tidbits to his radio "good buddies." At truck stops, we refueled and ate chicken fried steaks. So far, everything checked out.

Before the trip, I had spent weeks researching the available facts of the assassination and related events before and after. I watched hours of documentaries on videotape and rolled miles of microfilm in libraries. Assembling the data, I drew timelines of activities by Jack Ruby, Lee Harvey Oswald, President Johnson, and several other bit players. My plan was to draw a similar timeline for Tex Brown's movements, then compare it to the others.

By reading dozens of books, I tried to assimilate a reasonable understanding of current knowledge, theories, and records of the events, and a familiarity with the hundreds of names related to the case. I was astonished at the number of gaps, contradictions, arguments, and misinformation in print. But I was awed by the volumes reflecting herculean efforts of diligent researchers. Some of the authors have made a lifetime career of exhuming all available data and writing scholarly works. To them, my hat is respectfully tipped.

The foundation for most of the research begins with the Warren Commission Report. By Executive Order No. 11130, on November 29, 1963, President Lyndon Johnson created a commission of learned public servants, to "ascertain, evaluate and report upon the facts relating to the assassination of the late President John F. Kennedy and the subsequent violent death of the man charged with the assassination." Ten months later, on September 24, 1964, the commission officially presented its findings and conclusions to Johnson.

Almost immediately, investigative journalists used the twenty-seven-volume report as a springboard to launch independent quests for corroborating and supplementary facts, or contradictory information. What they discovered was, for many of them, a quagmire of oversights and misleading conclusions in the massive work. Charges fired off in all directions accusing the commission of biased investigation, deliberate cover-up, and incompetence. Researchers strongly suggested that the commission had deliberately concluded, in advance, that Lee Harvey Oswald acted alone to assassinate John F. Kennedy. The entire investigation, analysts complained, had been structured to support that verdict. Writers divided themselves into two groups: a heavy majority who believed a conspiracy had led to the assassination along with the associated murders, and a small minority who rejected the conspiracy theory in favor of the commission report.

"Conspiracy" became the key word, the eye of the hurricane of controversy. Most arguments revolved around it. Each researcher sought new evidence to confirm or denounce the multitude of theories advanced. Some of them hurled accusations at each other of shading the truth.

Ray "Tex" Brown agonized over the decision to reveal his knowledge that would support the existence of a conspiracy. For many valid reasons, he chose to remain mute for thirty-three years. He'd committed his silence to President Johnson, and he felt a loyalty to John Marshall, to whom he'd made a promise not to speak out. And he feared for his life—with good reason.

Mysterious deaths of people on the periphery of the assassination began soon after the events of November 1963.

Various writers, alarmed by the trend, published growing lists. By the early '80s, there were claims that over 100 witnesses or other individuals had died prematurely or been murdered. Following is a partial list:

Karen Kupcinet—*murdered* in late November 1963. Allegedly screamed into a telephone, before the assassination, that the president was going to be killed.

Jack Zangretti—*murdered* in 1963. Manager of an Oklahoma motel. Allegedly told a group of friends that three men planned to kill the president, and that Ruby would silence Oswald.

Betty McDonald—*suicide* in 1964. Ex-employee of Jack Ruby. Her male friend tried to kill a commission witness, and she provided his alibi.

Hank Killiam—*murdered* in 1964. His wife had worked for Ruby, and he may have been associated with a man who rented a room in the Beckley Street house where Oswald lived.

Bill Hunter—*shot to death* in 1964. The shooting was declared accidental. Hunter, a reporter, wrote an article for a Long Beach, California, newspaper describing his visit to Jack Ruby's apartment on November 24, 1963.

Jim Koethe—*murdered* in 1964. Also a reporter, he was with Bill Hunter on the visit to Ruby's apartment.

Eddie Benavides—*murdered* in 1964. The brother of a

witness to the killing of Officer J. D. Tippit, which was surrounded in controversy.

Gary Underhill—*suicide* in 1964. One author identified Underhill as a CIA agent who planned to blow the whistle revealing the CIA's complicity in the assassination.

Mary Meyer—*murdered* in 1964. Reportedly had sexual involvement with JFK.

Dorothy Kilgallen—*died of drug and alcohol overdose* in 1965. Famous reporter, TV quiz show panelist. Allegedly conducted confidential interview with Jack Ruby.

Rose Cheramie—*head crushed by car* on roadside near Big Sandy, Texas, 1965. She was rescued from similar near-miss two days before the assassination. On November 21, she told police she was a stripper for Jack Ruby and she'd been thrown from a car by two Latins who also worked for Ruby. Supposedly, she informed a hospital attendant the men with whom she was riding were headed to Dallas to kill the president. A few days after the assassination, she repeated her story to police and added that Ruby and Oswald knew each other.

William Whaley—*killed in car accident,* 1965. The cab driver who'd picked up Oswald at the Greyhound bus depot and taken him to Oak Cliff after JFK was shot.

Marilyn "Delilah" Walle—*murdered* in 1966. Had worked for Jack Ruby.

Lee Bowers, Jr.—*died in car accident,* 1966. Worked in

tower behind Texas Book Depository for railroad. Testified
to Warren Commission he'd seen suspicious movement of
cars behind wooden fence on top of grassy knoll at time
of assassination.

James Worrell—*died in car accident,* 1966. Was at Dealey
Plaza on day of assassination, said he saw the rifle that
fired shots from the sixth floor.

William Pitzer—*suicide,* 1966. Was allegedly present at
autopsy of JFK. One author said Pitzer took postmortem
movie films, but the film has never been found.

Clyde Johnson—*murdered* in 1969. Allegedly claimed he
could link Oswald with New Orleans businessman Clay
Shaw, who D.A. Jim Garrison pursued as a suspected par-
ticipant in assassination.

Buddy Walthers—*killed by gunshot* in 1969. Dallas deputy sheriff. Was part of team searching around Dealey
Plaza on November 22.

George McGann—*murdered* in 1970. Reputed Mafia figure and husband of Beverly Oliver, a stripper for another
Dallas club, but friends with Jack Ruby. She divulged that
she'd seen Ruby and Oswald together in the Carousel Club,
where Jack hinted Lee was with the CIA.

Joseph Milteer—*died when a heater exploded* in 1974.
In Miami, five days before assassination, he told tipster
who worked for police that Kennedy was going to be assassinated "from an office building with a high-powered

rifle," and "they will pick somebody up within hours afterward, just to throw the public off."

Sam Giancana—*murdered* in 1975. Major player in Mafia, called by many the Godfather of Chicago. His girlfriend, Judith Campbell, allegedly had affair with JFK. Ruby reportedly had links with Giancana.

Johnny Roselli—*murdered* in 1976. Mafia chieftain. Body found hacked to pieces in a floating oil drum off the Florida coast. Reportedly called Ruby "one of our boys." Said that Oswald was the patsy who may have fired a gun, but JFK was killed by a Cuban working for Trafficante, and that Ruby had silenced Oswald at mob's orders.

George de Mohrenschildt—*suicide* in 1977. One of Oswald's only friends in Dallas. He and his wife socialized with Marina and Lee. Odd, because de Morenschildt was well-to-do, sophisticated, and considerably older than the Oswalds.

Many other strange deaths have been mentioned by various authors. Some swear the murders, suicides, and odd accidents were clearly related to the assassination conspiracy. Others argue each one was coincidence. Tex Brown thinks he knows at least two more who were silenced by the conspirators: Tommy, the owner of the Rodeo Cafe, and Big John Marshall. Tex will always wonder about the auto accident that killed his ex-girlfriend, Judy, and the little girl named Rae who might have been his daughter.

One of the reputed top three most powerful men in the Mafia hierarchy, Carlos Marcello, lived eighty-three years and died in 1993 of natural causes in his Metairie, Louisiana, home. He always denied any ties with organized crime, once saying, "I wouldn't know a Mafia or a Cosa Nostra from a Congolese tribesman." He may have feared the Kennedys, though, because he contributed a half-million dollars to Richard M. Nixon's 1960 presidential campaign.

Tex Brown is certain he saw the diminutive Marcello with Jack Ruby in the Rodeo Cafe in 1963. Several investigative journalists reported possible links Marcello had with the assassination. Bobby Kennedy, as JFK's attorney general, strongly believed that Marcello was a top leader of organized crime and deported Marcello to Guatemala in 1961.

The deportation was handled in an unusual way. Federal agents nabbed Marcello on a New Orleans sidewalk, snapped cuffs on him, and hustled him to a jet passenger plane standing by at the airport. Marcello was the only passenger. In Guatemala, they dumped him at an airstrip and took off.

Just two months later, his trusted associate, a homosexual pilot who had been fired by Eastern Airlines, flew him back to the States. The pilot was David Ferrie (portrayed by actor Joe Pesci in Oliver Stone's controversial 1991 movie *JFK*). Ferrie had a disease called *alopecia praecox,* which denudes the body of hair, so he wore ill-fitting wigs and used thick paint daubed in high arches to simulate eyebrows. It is not widely known that Lee Harvey Oswald, at age fifteen in 1955, joined a student aviation organization of the Civil Air Patrol and eagerly wore his uniform at meetings and activities of the group. His unit commander was David Ferrie!

Enraged at the Kennedys, Carlos Marcello reportedly told a confidante that a plan for revenge was in operation.

"Don't worry about that little Bobby son of a bitch. He's going to be taken care of." When an underling cautioned him about going after Robert Kennedy, Marcello is quoted as saying, "If you want to kill a dog, you don't cut off the tail, you cut off the head." In reference to the president, Marcello allegedly said that he would be killed and some "nut" would take the fall for it.

Another survivor of the mob circle was lawyer Frank Ragano, who worked with Jimmy Hoffa and Trafficante, and ultimately revealed that he'd acted as Hoffa's messenger to request Marcello and Trafficante to kill Kennedy. He also quoted Trafficante as saying they should have killed Bobby instead of John.

Charles Harrelson, the man Tex Brown was positive he saw in Fort Worth just prior to the assassination, was interviewed a few years ago in a federal prison and asked if he was one of three so-called tramps who had been seen near the book depository on November 22, 1963. The trio was arrested, but released shortly afterward. Someone took a photo of them walking together. The tallest of the three men bears a remarkable resemblance to Harrelson. In prison, he examined the photo, pushed it away, then pulled it back again and agreed that it resembled him. He denied, however, being anywhere near Dallas when the assassination occurred.

The Dallas police officer, Roscoe White, who had married one of Jack Ruby's employees became the focal point of controversy years later. His own son charged White with shooting JFK from behind the grassy knoll fence. His father's diary, the son said, had recorded the event, but was unfortunately "missing." The accusation faded into obscurity, along with scores of other invalidated allegations of "shooters' " identities. White's widow, though, revealed that she had seen Oswald with Ruby in the Carousel Club.

Lee Harvey Oswald lived with relatives in New Orleans during the summer of 1963. One of his hosts was reportedly an operative in the organization headed by Carlos Marcello. Oswald was allegedly seen visiting the hotel used by Marcello as a headquarters.

Following the 1993 death of Marcello and a host of others, the number of people who might contribute any personal information about the continuing mystery continued to diminish. That, combined with personal events in the life of Ray "Tex" Brown, finally convinced him to make the decision with which he has wrestled for more than half his life. He told me that he is finally ready to reveal what he knows. Every bit of his story, though, comes from his personal recollection. The diaries, notes, photographs, and artifacts he kept were all destroyed in a disastrous fire. His memory is the last remaining record. Thirty-three years is a long time to recall so much specific detail, so I accepted the possibility that some of his information might be a bit fuzzy, even though he recalled most of it with remarkable clarity. But the important issues needed some corroboration. So it became necessary for me to apply some tests to his memory.

First, I wanted to know if he had studied published accounts of the events and details, or watched documentaries on television. Absolutely not, he insisted. On the contrary, he has meticulously avoided such material because it brings back so much emotional pain. "I know what I did, I know who I met, and I remember what happened," he firmly asserts. "I was there. I don't need to hear what somebody else says about it." He didn't want his memory clouded by distortions from other accounts. To meet Tex is to believe that he is not interested in academic research. He's bright and has photographic recall, but his interest is in horses, not textbooks. He refused to even watch the movie *JFK*. He tells his stories in the colloquialisms of pioneer Americana, with the voice inflections of Slim Pickens and Arthur Hunnicut. He is a true truck-driving cowboy who became a bounty hunter against his will, but performed his duties as well as anyone. And from those experiences, he used all the hard-learned lessons to take every precaution for personal safety. During our time together, I learned how he avoids leaving a trail. It was a fascinating experience.

Next, I interspersed some test questions among those I'd prepared for the interviews. For example, I wanted to know if he'd noticed anything physically unusual about Jack Ruby. Nothing, he said, other than a missing index fingertip on Jack's left hand. Certainly, that information is available in some books, but it's quite obscure, overlooked by most readers.

"Did Jack bring along any of his cats?" I asked.

"Nope. Ole Jack didn't have any cats. He loved dogs, though. Had some of those little weeny dogs. But I wouldn't let him bring 'em along to target practice. It'd spook 'em, and they'd either run away or make a mess in his car."

I challenged Tex's assertion that Oswald couldn't handle a rifle. After all, I pointed out, he'd qualified as a sharpshooter in the Marine Corps.

"Bullllll———. I don't know how he qualified, but that boy could not shoot, or even handle a gun right." I smiled, recalling my own experience in basic training. My buddy down in the target pits wouldn't have waved 'maggie's drawers" (red flag indicating complete miss of target) even if I'd accidentally shot a plane out of the sky. I didn't bother to tell Tex that a Marine Corps sergeant who knew Oswald quite well had stated that Oswald was a "poor shot" who drew three maggie's drawers out of ten tries and almost failed in rapid firing exercises. As in all military pursuits, there are ways to get what you need.

I compared the time frames Tex gave me to the spreadsheets I'd made and came away satisfied. His memory dovetailed consistently with known facts.

On our final morning together, because I threatened to take photographs, Tex wore his trademark black Stetson, red shirt with black vest, jeans, and black cowboy boots. We drove to each of the Fort Worth sites he'd described in his stories to me.

The Rodeo Cafe and the gas station where he'd received a call from LBJ have been razed, leaving only vacant lots. At Lake Worth, he had no trouble, after so many years, locating the exact site of the target practice sessions.

For lunch we went to the barbecue restaurant where he had eaten with Jack Ruby and John Marshall. The owner has passed on, but his elderly wife still operates the business, now located across the street from the original building. The ribs were delicious.

From there, we traveled toward Dallas and turned into the Rose Hill Burial Park, where we found the headstone marking the grave of Lee Harvey Oswald. If Tex hadn't watched the funeral in 1963, it would have been difficult to locate the stone, because the cemetery staff does not reveal that information. Vandals have plagued the site, and the original headstone, engraved with dates and his full name, was stolen some years ago. Now the grave is marked with a one word engraving: "Oswald."

Two hours later, we parked in the lot behind the red brick building that was the Texas School Book Depository in

1963. The temperature had dropped from record highs reaching 100 degrees just a few days earlier to a bone-chilling 29 degrees at midday. But it wasn't the weather bothering Tex.

His demeanor had changed drastically as we'd approached Dealey Plaza. Ordinarily loquacious and cheerful, he'd stopped talking. He seemed sullen and nervous. Out of the pickup and shivering, despite the jackets we had both donned, we walked down the grassy knoll. Tex's left leg reacted painfully to the cold, and he had difficulty descending the slope. His face was drawn and pale, and his eyes were unhappy. Furrows deepened in his forehead and around his mouth.

I wanted to go inside the brick building to see the museum on the sixth floor, where Oswald allegedly hid in the sniper's nest of book cartons and shot President Kennedy. Besides, I wanted to get in out of the cold. But Tex adamantly refused to go inside. He had no desire to see the museum. Since I planned to remain in Dallas while he returned home, I could wait for another day.

He reluctantly posed for a photograph by the brass plaque on the corner of the building, then he said he'd like to take me to my hotel, drop me off, and head on home. We trudged in silence back to the pickup and slid into the warm cab.

He sat still for a moment, then fired up the engine. I looked over at him. He tried to turn away in time, but it was too late.

I saw the stream of tears running down those weathered cheeks.

Don Lasseter
April 1996

This book is humbly dedicated to the men I have worked with and the women in my life. To live a double life is hard. Some knew who I was, but a lot never even knew my first name. No one will ever know what it's like to walk in my boots until they make a promise to the president of the United States.

I hope I haven't left any names out.

My three children are the greatest thing that ever happened to me in my life—Raine, Lindsay, and Raymond Junior.

Becky Harmon, my ex-wife, for the best years of my life. And Eunice Hall, for thirty years of friendship and someone who cared. And Elaine Nance.

Mr. Dean and Mary Alexander, for being by my side for thirty years. For the good times and the bad times.

Robert A. Griffin, who stood by me during the hard times and the good times.

Whitey and Marilyn Whiteman, the best neighbors a man could have.

Karen Gray, who helped me get my books out, and the best friend my kids could ever have.

Judge John Wood, murdered in San Antonio, Texas.

Judge Steve Jones and his wife Dorothy, for all the hard work they've done in Torrance County.

Kim Olsen.

Jim Summers, who went all the way to help me.

Jim Frost, who made sure the horses were always fed.

Bill Webb, good friend.

Orene King, for being a good friend to me and my kids.

Allen R. Manka, attorney at law, for working with me over twenty years and being a good friend.

Mr. John Spears, attorney at law, who has been a good friend and a big help in my life.

Mr. Chris Lackman, attorney at law, who walked down the road with me.

Mr. Ernest Davis Gutiersey.

Mr. Bill Mack, of WPAP radio, for all the good music he has played during the nights, and for being a good friend.

Mrs. Marie Fry and Wendell Fry.

Mr. Don Kell, for being one of the best friends I've had since I was fourteen years old.

Bob and Mabel Smith.

The late Jack Ryan.

Dan Miller.

Wallace Barbee.

Clint and Liz Haverty.

Mr. Sam Nelson..

Mr. Pete Naverra.

Mr. Ray Harmon, for being a good brother-in-law.

Pepper Martin and Don Marshall.

And the men in law enforcement I worked with and entrusted my life to:

Ben Rogers, who worked for U.S. Customs and DEA.

Henry Pozlo, U.S. Customs, who I trusted with my life.

Mr. George W. Ellington, Texas Department of Public Safety.

Mr. Terry Bowen, DEA and U.S. Customs.

Mr. Charlie Rumpfield, who I made the biggest case of my career with, of Drug Enforcement.

Bobby Porter, Texas Department of Public Safety.

Roy Barnett, Texas Department of Public Safety.

Robert Klaies, Texas Department of Public Safety.

The late Stan Guffey, Texas Ranger, who died in action, who I trusted my life with.

FULL
CIRCLE

Danielle Steel

A DELL BOOK

Published by
Dell Publishing Co., Inc.
1 Dag Hammarskjold Plaza
New York, N.Y. 10017

Dell ® TM 681510, Dell Publishing Co., Inc.

ISBN: 0-440-12689-4

Reprinted by arrangement with Delacorte Press
Printed in the United States of America
First Dell printing—June 1985

To Alex Haley,
my brother,
my friend,
with much, much love.

To Isabella Grant,
with love and admiration
and immeasurable gratitude.

And with special love
and thanks
to Lou Blau.

And always,
always,
to John,
with my heart and
soul.

D.S.

Part I

THE
EARLY
YEARS

Chapter 1

On the afternoon of Thursday, December 11, 1941, the country was still in a daze. The casualty list was complete, the names of those killed had already been released, and slowly, slowly, in the past few days, the monster of vengeance was raising its head. In almost every American breast pounded a pulse that had been unknown before. It had finally hit us at home, and it wasn't simply a matter of Congress declaring war. There was much more to it than that, much, much more. There was a nation of people filled with dread, with rage, and the sudden fear that it could happen here. Japanese fighter planes could appear overhead at any time of day or night and suddenly wreak destruction in cities like Chicago and Los Angeles, Omaha . . . Boston . . . New York . . . it was a terrifying thought. The war was no longer happening to a distant, remote "them," it was happening to *us.*

And as Andrew Roberts hurried east in the chill wind, his coat collar up, he wondered what Jean would say. He had already known for two days. When he had signed his name, there hadn't been any doubt in his mind, yet when he'd come home, he had looked into her face and the words had caught in his throat. But there was no choice now. He had to tell her tonight. Had to. He was leaving for San Diego in another three days.

The Third Avenue El roared overhead, as his feet pounded up the front steps of the narrow brownstone in which they lived. They had lived there for less than a year, and they hardly even noticed the train anymore. It had been awful at first, at night they had held each other tight and laughed as they lay in bed. Even the light fixtures shook as the elevated train careered by, but they were used to it now. And Andy had come to love the tiny flat. Jean kept it spotlessly clean, getting up sometimes at five o'clock to make him homemade blueberry muffins and leave everything immaculate before she left for work. She had turned out to be even more wonderful than he'd thought and he smiled to himself as he turned the key in the lock. There was a chill wind whistling through the hall and two of the lights were burned out, but the moment he set foot inside, everything was cheery and bright. There were starched white organdy curtains, which Jean had made, a pretty little blue rug, slipcovers she had gone to a night class to learn how to make. And the furniture they'd bought secondhand shone like new beneath her hardworking hands. He looked around now, and suddenly felt the first shaft of grief he had felt since he signed up. It was an almost visceral ache as he thought of telling her that he was leaving New York in three days, and suddenly there were tears in his eyes as he realized that he didn't know when he'd be back . . . when . . . or even if . . . but hell, that wasn't the point, he told himself. If he didn't go to fight the Japs, then who the hell would? And if they didn't, then one of these days the

bastards would be flying overhead and bombing the hell
out of New York . . . and this house . . . and Jean.

He sat down in the armchair she had upholstered
herself in a deep, cozy green, and was lost in his own
thoughts . . . San Diego . . . Japan . . . Christmas . . .
Jean . . . he didn't know how long he'd been sitting there
when suddenly, startled, he looked up. He had just heard
her key in the lock. She flung the door wide, her arms
filled with brown bags from the A&P, and she didn't see
him at first, and then jumped as she turned on the light,
and saw him smiling at her, his blond hair falling over
one eye as it always did, the green eyes looking straight at
her. He was still as handsome as he had been when they
first met. He had been seventeen then, and she had been
fifteen . . . six years . . . he was only twenty-three.

"Hi, sweetheart, what are you doing here?"

"I came home to see you." He walked towards her
and easily grabbed the bags in his powerful arms, and she
turned her big, dark brown eyes up to him with the same
look of awe she always wore when she looked up at him.
She was so impressed with him, always had been, he'd
had two years of college, going at nights, had been on the
track team in school, the football team for a few months
till he hurt his knee, and had been a basketball star when
they met during his senior year. And he seemed no less
heroic to her now. In fact, he seemed more so to her, and
she was so proud of him. He had landed a good job. He
sold Buicks in the biggest dealership in New York, and
she knew that he'd be the manager eventually . . . one
day . . . or maybe he'd go back to school. They had
talked about that. But he brought home a nice paycheck
for now, and combined with her own, they did all right.

She knew how to stretch a dollar more than a mile. She'd
been doing it for a long time. Both her parents had died
in a car accident when she was just eighteen, and she'd
been supporting herself since then. Fortunately, she had
just finished secretarial school when they died, and she
was a bright girl. She'd had a job in the same law firm
now for almost three years. And Andy was proud of her
too. She looked so cute when she went off to work in the
well-tailored suits that she made herself, and hats and
gloves she always bought so carefully, checking the styles
in the magazines, and then consulting with Andy to
make sure they looked just right. He smiled at her again
now, as she peeled off her gloves, and tossed her black felt
fedora onto the big green chair. "How was your day,
Cutie Pie?" He loved to tease her, pinch her, whisk her
into his arms, nuzzle into her neck and threaten to ravish
her as he walked in from work. It was certainly a far cry
from her constantly proper demeanor at work. He
dropped in to see her there once in a great while, and she
looked so serious and sedate that she almost frightened
him. But she had always been that kind of girl. And
actually, she'd been a lot more fun since she'd been married to him. She was finally beginning to relax. He kissed
her on the back of the neck now and she felt a shiver run
up her spine.

"Wait till I put the groceries away. . . ." She smiled
mysteriously and tried to wrest one of the bags from his
hand, but he pulled it away from her and kissed her on
the lips.

"Why wait?"

"Andy . . . come on. . . ." His hands were beginning to rove passionately over her, pulling off the heavy

coat, unbuttoning the jet buttons on the suit jacket she
wore underneath. The grocery bags had long since been
cast aside, as they suddenly stood, their lips and bodies
pressed tight against each other, until Jean finally pulled
away for air. She was giggling when they stopped, but it
didn't discourage his hands. "Andy . . . what's gotten
into you . . . ?"

He grinned mischievously at her, afraid to make a
remark that would shock her too much. "Don't ask." He
silenced her with another kiss, and relieved her of coat,
jacket, and blouse, all with one hand, and a moment
later, her skirt dropped to the floor as well, revealing the
white lace garter belt with matching pants, silk stockings
with seams, and a pair of absolutely sensational legs. He
ran his hands across her behind, and pressed hard against
her again, and she didn't object as he pulled her down on
the couch. Instead she pulled his clothes off as suddenly
the elevated train roared by and they both started to
laugh. "Damn that thing. . . ." He muttered under his
breath as he unhooked her bra with one hand and she
smiled.

"You know, I kind of like the sound of it by now.
. . ." This time it was Jean who kissed him, and a moment later their bodies were enmeshed just as their
mouths had been, and it seemed hours before either of
them spoke in the silent room. The kitchen light was still
on, near the front door, but there was no light in the
living room where they lay, or the tiny bedroom beyond.
But even in the darkness of the room, he could sense that
Jean was looking at him. "Something funny's going on,
isn't it?" There had been a small hard rock in the pit of
her stomach all week. She knew her husband too well.

"Andy . . . ?" He still didn't know what to say. It was no easier now than it would have been two days before. And it was going to be even worse by the end of the week. But he had to tell her sometime. He just wished it didn't have to be now. For the first time in three days, he suddenly wondered if he'd done the right thing.

"I don't quite know what to say."

But instinctively she knew. She felt her heart lurch as she looked up at him in the dark, her eyes wide, her face already sad, as it always was. She was very different from him. There was always laughter in his eyes, always a quick line on his tongue, a joke, a funny thought. He had happy eyes, an easy smile. Life had always been gentle with him. But it was not so with Jean. She had the tense nervousness of those who have had hard times from birth. Born to two alcoholic parents, with an epileptic sister who died in the bed next to Jean when she was thirteen and Jean nine, orphaned at eighteen, struggling almost since the day she was born, and yet in spite of it all, she had a certain kind of innate style, a joie de vivre which had never been allowed to bloom and which Andy knew would blossom in time, if nurtured enough. And he did nurture her, in every way he could. But he couldn't make it easier for her now, and the old sorrow he had seen when they first met suddenly stood out in her eyes again. "You're going, aren't you?"

He nodded his head, as tears filled the deep, dark eyes and she lay her head back on the couch where they'd just made love. "Don't look like that, baby, please. . . ." She made him feel like such a son of a bitch, and suddenly unable to face her pain, he left her side and strode across the room to fish a pack of Camels out of his coat.

He nervously tapped one out, lit it, and sat down in the green chair across from the couch. She was crying openly now, but when she looked at him, she didn't seem surprised.

"I knew you'd go."

"I have to, babe."

She nodded her head. She seemed to understand, but it didn't ease the pain. It seemed to take hours to get up the courage to ask the only thing she wanted to know, but at last she did. "When?"

Andy Roberts gulped hard. It was the hardest thing he'd ever said. "Three days."

She visibly winced and closed her eyes again, nodding her head as the tears slid down her cheeks.

And for the next three days, nothing was ever normal again. She stayed home from work, and seemed to go into a frenzy, doing everything she possibly could for him, washing underwear, rolling socks, baking him cookies for the train. Her hands seemed to fly all day long, as though by keeping them as busy as she could, she would be able to keep a grip on herself, or perhaps even on him. But it was no use, by Saturday night, he forced her to put it all down, to stop packing the clothes he didn't need, the cookies he'd never eat, the socks he could have done without, he took her in his arms and she finally broke down.

"Oh, God, Andy . . . I can't . . . how will I live without you . . . ?" He felt as though he had a hole in his guts the size of a fist when he looked into her eyes and saw what he had done to her. But he had no choice . . . no choice . . . he was a man . . . he had to fight . . . his country was at war . . . and the worst of it was that

when he didn't feel sick over what he'd done to her, he
felt a strange, unfamiliar thrill of excitement about going
to war, as though this was an opportunity he might never
have again, something he had to do almost like a mystic
rite, in order to become a man. And he felt guilty about
that too. And by late Saturday night, it had gotten to him
too. He was so torn between Jean's clinging little hands
and what he knew he had to do that he wished it was
already over with and he was on the train, heading west,
but he would be soon enough. He had to report to Grand
Central Station at five A.M. And when he finally got up in
the tiny bedroom to get dressed, he turned and looked at
her, she was quieter now, her tears were spent, her eyes
swollen and red, but she looked a little bit more resigned
than she had before. For Jean, in some terrible, desperate,
frightening way, it was like losing her sister, or her parents, again. Andy was all she had left. And she would
rather have died herself than lose him. And suddenly he
was leaving her too.

"You'll be all right, won't you, babe?" He sat on the
edge of the bed, looking at her, desperate for some reassurance from her now, and she smiled sadly and reached
a hand out for his.

"I'll have to be, I guess, won't I?" And then she
smiled again, almost mysteriously. "You know what I
wish?" They both knew that, that he weren't going to
war. She read his thoughts, and kissed his fingertips.
"Aside from that . . . I hope you got me pregnant this
week. . . ." In the emotions of the past few days, they
had thrown caution to the winds. He had been aware of
it, but there had been so much else going on. He had just
hoped that it wasn't her dangerous time. But he won-

dered now, as he looked at her. They had been so careful about that for the past year, they had agreed from the first that they didn't want babies for a while, at least not for the first few years until they both got better jobs, or maybe Andy went back to college for another two years. They were in no hurry, they were both young, but now . . . in the past week, their whole life had turned upside down.

"I kind of wondered what was happening this week. . . . Do you think you could have . . . ?" He looked worried. That hadn't been what he wanted at all. He didn't want her to be pregnant alone, with him God knows where, at war.

She shrugged. "I might. . . ." And then she smiled again and sat up. "I'll let you know."

"Great. That's all we need." He looked suddenly upset, and then glanced nervously at the bedside clock. It was ten after four. He had to go.

"Maybe it is." And then suddenly, as though she had to tell him before he left, "I meant what I said just now, Andy. I'd like that a lot."

"Now?" He looked shocked and she nodded her head, her voice a whisper in the tiny room.

"Yes."

Chapter 2

The elevated train roared past the windows of Jean Roberts' apartment, providing the only breeze she had felt in days as she sat motionless in front of the open windows. It felt as though the entire building had turned into an inferno, as the blazing August heat rose off the sidewalks, and seemed to bake right into the walls of the brownstone building. And sometimes at night, she had to leave her bed, and sit on the stoop, just to get some air as the train hurtled by. Or she would sit in her bathroom, wrapped in a wet sheet. There seemed to be no way to cool down, and the baby made it worse. She felt as though her whole body were about to explode, and the hotter it got, the more the baby would kick her, as if it knew, as if it were stifling too. Jean smiled to herself at the thought. She could hardly wait to see the baby now . . . there were only four weeks left . . . four weeks until she held their baby . . . she hoped that it would look just like Andy. He was in the Pacific now, doing just what he had wanted to do, "fighting the Japs," as he said in his letters, although somehow the words always pained her. One of the girls in the law firm she had worked in was Japanese and she had been so nice to Jean when she

found out she was pregnant. She even covered for her
when Jean was almost too sick to move in the beginning.
She would drag herself in to work, and stare into her
typewriter, praying that she wouldn't throw up before
she reached the bathroom. They had kept her for six
months, which was decent of them, it was longer than
most firms would have kept her, she knew, but they felt it
was the patriotic thing to do, because of Andy, as she
told him in one of her letters. She wrote to him almost
every day, although she rarely heard from him more than
once a month. Most of the time, he was too tired to write,
and the letters took forever to reach her. It was a long
way from selling Buicks in New York, as he said in one
letter, making her laugh about the bad food, and his buddies. Somehow he always seemed to make her laugh with
his letters. He made everything sound better than it was,
and she was never as frightened after she heard from him.
She had been terrified at first, particularly when she felt
so ill. She had gone through agonies of conflict after she
first found out she was pregnant. It had seemed like such
a good idea at first, during those last few days before he
left, but when she found out, she had panicked. It meant
she had to give up her job, she'd be alone, and how would
she support herself, and the baby? She had been desperately afraid of his reaction too, only when he finally wrote
to her, he sounded so thrilled that it all seemed fine to her
again, and by then, she was almost five months pregnant,
and she wasn't as nervous.

    And in the last few months she'd had plenty of time
to turn their bedroom into a nursery for the baby. She
had sewn everything herself in white eyelet with yellow
ribbons, sewing and knitting, and making little hats and

booties and sweaters. She had even painted pretty little
murals on the baby's walls and clouds on the ceiling,
although one of her neighbors had given her hell when he
found out that she was doing the painting herself and
standing on the ladder. But she had nothing else to do
now that she wasn't working. She had saved every penny
she could, and she wouldn't even go to a movie now, for
fear of eating into those savings, and she was receiving
part of Andy's paycheck from the army. She was going to
need everything she had for the baby, and she was going
to stay home for the first few months if she could, and
after that she'd have to find a sitter and go back to work.
She was hoping that elderly Mrs. Weissman on the fourth
floor would baby-sit for her. She was a warm, grand-
motherly woman who had lived in the building for years,
and had been excited to hear about Jean's baby. She
checked on her every day, and sometimes she would even
come down late at night, unable to sleep herself in the
heat, and tap on Jean's door, if she saw a light beneath it.

But tonight, Jean didn't turn on the lights. She just
sat in the dark, feeling breathless and stifled in the killing
heat, listening to train after train come by until they
stopped and then started again just before the dawn. Jean
even watched the sun come up. She wondered if she
would ever be able to breathe normally again, or lie down
without feeling as though she were being smothered.
There were days when it was really very trying and the
heat and the train didn't help. It was almost eight o'clock
in the morning when she heard the knock on her door,
and assumed it was Mrs. Weissman. She put her pink
bathrobe on, and with a tired sigh padded toward the
front door in bare feet. Thank God she only had four

weeks to go. She was beginning to think she couldn't take it for much longer.

"Hi. . . ." She pulled the door open with a tired smile, expecting to see her friend, and blushed to find herself looking into the face of a stranger, a stranger in a brown uniform with a cap and mustard colored braid, holding a yellow envelope toward her. She looked at him, uncomprehending, not wanting to understand because she knew only too well what that meant, and the man seemed to be leering at her. It was as though his face was distorted as she reeled from the shock and the heat, clutching the envelope and tearing it open without saying a word to him. And it was there, just as she had feared, and she looked at the messenger of death again, focusing on the words on his uniform as her mouth formed a scream, and she sank to his feet in a quiet heap on the floor, as he gaped at her in silent horror, and then suddenly called out for help. He was sixteen years old and he had never been that close to a pregnant woman before. Two doors opened across the hall, and a moment later, there was the sound of running feet on the stairs above, and Mrs. Weissman was putting damp cloths on Jean's head, as the boy backed slowly away and then hurried down the stairs. All he wanted to do was get out of the stifling little building. Jean was moaning by then, and Mrs. Weissman and two other ladies were leading her to the couch where she slept now. It was the same couch where the baby had been conceived, where she had lain and made love with Andy . . . Andy . . . Andy. . . . "We regret to inform you . . . your husband died in the service of his country . . . killed in action at Guadal-

canal . . . in action . . . in action . . ." her head was
reeling and she couldn't see the faces.

"Jean . . . ? Jean. . . ." They kept calling her
name, and there was something cold on her face, as they
looked at her and at each other. Helen Weissman had
read the telegram, and had quickly shown it to the
others. "Jean. . . ." She came around slowly, barely able
to breathe, and they helped her to sit and forced her to
drink a little water. She looked blankly at Mrs. Weissman, and then suddenly she remembered, and the sobs
strangled her more than the heat, and she couldn't catch
her breath anymore, all she could do was cry and cling to
the old woman who held her . . . he was dead . . . just
like the others . . . like Mommy and Daddy and Ruthie
. . . gone . . . he was gone . . . she would never see
him again . . . she whimpered almost like a small child,
feeling a weight in her heart that she had never felt before, even for the others. "It's all right, dear, it's all right.
. . ." But they all knew that it wasn't, and never would
be again, not for poor Andy.

The others went back to their apartments a little
while later, but Helen Weissman stayed. She didn't like
the glazed look in the girl's eyes, the way she sat and
stared and then suddenly began to sob, or the terrible
endless crying she heard that night when she finally left
Jean for a little while, and then returned to open the
unlocked door and check on her again as she had all day.
She had even called Jean's doctor before he left his office,
and he had told Mrs. Weissman to tell Jean how sorry he
was to hear the news, and warned her that Jean could go
into labor from the shock, which was exactly what she
was afraid of, and it was exactly what she suspected when

she saw Jean press her fists into her back several times later that evening, and walk restlessly around the tiny apartment, as though it had grown too small for her in the past few hours. Her entire world had shattered around her, and there was nowhere left to go. There wasn't even a body to send home . . . just the memory of a tall, handsome blond boy . . . and the baby in her belly.

"Are you all right?" Helen Weissman's accent made Jean smile. She had been in the country for forty years, but she still spoke with a heavy German accent. She was a wise, warm woman, and she was fond of Jean. She had lost her own husband thirty years before, and she had never remarried. She had three children in New York, who visited her from time to time, mostly to drop their respective children off so she could baby-sit, and a son who had a good job in Chicago. "You have pains?" Her eyes searched Jean's, and Jean started to shake her head. Her whole body ached after the day of crying, and yet inside she felt numb. She didn't know what she felt, just achy and hot and restless. She arched her back as though to stretch it.

"I'm all right. Why don't you get some sleep, Mrs. Weissman?" Her voice was hoarse after the long day of crying. She glanced at the kitchen clock and registered the fact that it had been fifteen hours since she had gotten the telegram telling her about Andy . . . fifteen hours, it felt like fifteen years . . . a thousand years . . . she walked around the room again as Helen Weissman watched her.

"You want to go for a walk outside?" The train whizzed past nearby and Jean shook her head. It was too hot to go for a walk, even at eleven o'clock at night. And suddenly Jean was even hotter than she'd been all day.

"I think I'll have something cold to drink." She fixed herself a glass of the lemonade she kept in a pitcher in the icebox, and it tasted good going down, but it came back up almost as quickly. She rushed to the bathroom, where she threw up and retched repeatedly, and then emerged wanly a little while later.

"You should lie down." Meekly, she agreed. She was more uncomfortable when she did. It was easier to sit up than lie down, so she tried the comfortable old green chair again, but after a few minutes she found that she couldn't do that either. She had gnawing pains in her lower back and an unsettled feeling in her stomach, and Helen Weissman left her alone again at midnight, but only after insisting that Jean come and get her during the night if she had a problem. But Jean was sure she wouldn't have to. She turned off the lights, and sat alone in the silent apartment, thinking of her husband . . . Andy . . . of the big green eyes and straight blond hair . . . track star . . . football hero . . . her first and only love . . . the boy she had fallen head over heels in love with the first time she saw him, and as she thought of him, she felt a shaft of pain slice through her from her belly to her back, and then again, and again, and yet again, so that she couldn't catch her breath at all now. She stood up unsteadily, nausea overwhelming her, but determined to get to the bathroom, where she clung miserably to the toilet for almost an hour, the pains pounding her body, the retching tearing at her soul, until weakly at last, barely conscious, she began calling for Andy. It was there that Helen Weissman found her at one thirty in the morning. She had decided to check on her once more before going to bed. It was too hot for anyone to sleep that night, so she was awake unusually late. And she thanked God that she was, when she found her. She went back to her own apartment just long enough to call Jean's doctor and the police, who promised to send an ambulance at once. She climbed into a cotton housedress, grabbed her purse, kept the same sandals on her feet, and hurried back to Jean, to drape a bathrobe around her shoulders, and ten minutes later, they heard the sirens. Helen did, but Jean seemed to hear nothing at all as she retched and cried, and Helen Weissman tried to soothe her. She was writhing with pain and calling Andy's name by the time they reached New York Hospital, and the baby didn't take long to come after that. The nurses whisked Jean away on a gurney, and they didn't have time to give her anything at all, before the wiry five-pound four-ounce little girl emerged with jet black hair, and tightly clenched fists, wailing loudly. Helen Weissman saw them both barely an hour later. Jean mercifully drugged at last, the baby dozing comfortably.

And she went back to the apartment house that night, thinking of the lonely years Jean Roberts had ahead, bringing up her baby girl alone, a widow at twenty-two. Helen brushed the tears from her cheek as the elevated train roared by at four thirty that morning. The older woman knew what kind of devotion it would take to bring the child up alone, a kind of religious zeal, a solitary passion to do all for this baby that would never know her father.

Jean gazed at her baby the next morning when they brought her to nurse for the first time; she looked down

at the tiny face, the dark silky hair that the nurses said
would fall out eventually, and she knew instinctively
what she would have to do for her. It didn't frighten Jean
at all. This was what she had wanted. Andy's baby. This
was his last gift to her, and she would guard her with her
life, do all she could, give her only the best. She would
live and breathe and work and do, and give her very soul
to this baby.

The tiny rosebud mouth worked as she nursed and
Jean smiled at the unfamiliar feeling. She couldn't believe
that it was twenty-four hours since she had learned of
Andy's death, as a nurse came into the room to check on
them both. They seemed to be doing fine, and the baby
was a good size, considering that she'd been almost four
weeks early.

"Looks like she has a good appetite." The woman in
the starched white uniform and cap glanced at mother
and child. "Has her daddy seen her yet?" They couldn't
know . . . no one did . . . except Jean, and Helen
Weissman. Her eyes filled with tears and she shook her
head as the nurse patted her arm, not understanding. No,
her daddy hadn't seen her yet, and he never would.
"What are you going to name her?"

They had written back and forth to each other about
that, and had finally agreed on a name for a girl, although they both thought they wanted a boy. Funny,
how after the first moment of surprise and near disappointment a girl seemed so much better now, as though
that had been their choice all along. Nature somehow
managed things well. Had she been a boy, she would
have been named after her father. But Jean had found a
girl's name that she loved, and she tried it out on the

nurse now as her eyes glowed with pride as she held her baby. "Her name is Tana Andrea Roberts. Tana. . . ." She loved the sound of it, and it seemed to suit her to perfection.

The nurse smiled as she lifted the tiny bundle from Jean's arms when she was finished nursing. She smoothed the covers expertly with one hand and looked at Jean. "Get some rest now, Mrs. Roberts. I'll bring Tana back to you when she's ready." The door closed, and Jean lay her head back against the pillow, with her eyes closed, trying not to think of Andy, but only of their baby . . . she didn't want to think of how he had died, what they had done to him . . . if he had screamed her name . . . a tiny sob broke from her as she turned in her bed, and lay on her stomach for the first time in months, her face buried in the pillows, and she lay there and sobbed for what seemed like hours, until at last she fell asleep, and dreamt of the blond boy she had loved . . . and the baby he had left her . . . Tana . . . Tana. . . .

Chapter 3

The phone rang on Jean Roberts' desk only once before she answered it. She had a brisk, efficient way about her, which came from long years of managing a mammoth job. It had fallen into her lap twelve years before. She had been twenty-eight, Tana six, and Jean thought she would scream if she had to work one more day in another law firm. There had been three jobs in six years, in law firms that were one more boring than the other. But the pay was good, and she had Tana to think of now. Tana always came first. Tana upon whom the sun rose and set, in Jean's eyes.

"For God's sake, let the kid breathe . . . ," one of her co-workers had told her once, and Jean had been cool to her after that. She knew exactly what she was doing, taking her to the theater and the ballet, museums, libraries, art galleries, and concerts when she could afford to, helping her inhale every drop of culture. Almost every dime she made went to the education and support and entertainment of Tana. And she had saved every penny of the pension from Andy. And it wasn't that the child was spoiled, she wasn't. But Jean wanted her to have the good things in life, the things she herself had seldom had,

and which she thought were so important. It was hard to
remember objectively now if they would have had that
kind of life with Andy. More likely he would have rented
a boat and taken them sailing on Long Island Sound,
taught Tana to swim at an early age, gone clam digging,
or running in the park, riding a bike . . . he would have
worshipped the pretty little blond child who looked so
exactly like him. Tall, lanky, blond, green-eyed, with the
same dazzling smile as her father. And the nurses in the
hospital had been right when she was born, the silky
black hair had fallen out and had been replaced by pale
golden peach fuzz, which as she got older, grew into
straight wheat-like shafts of golden hair. She was a lovely
looking little girl, and Jean had always been proud of her.
She had even managed to get her out of public schools
when she was nine and send her to Miss Lawson's. It
meant a lot to Jean, and was a wonderful opportunity for
Tana. Arthur Durning had helped her in, which he insisted was a small favor. He knew himself how important
good schools were for children. He had two children of
his own, although they went to the exclusive Cathedral
and Williams schools in Greenwich, and were respec-
tively two, and four years older than Tana.

The job came to Jean almost by accident when Arthur came to the law firm where she worked for a series
of lengthy conferences with Martin Pope, the senior partner. She had worked for Pope, Madison, and Watson for
two years by then, and was bored to death, but the salary
was more than she dared to hope for. She couldn't afford
to run around looking for a "fun job," she always had
Tana to think of. She thought of her night and day. Her
whole life revolved around her daughter, as she explained

to Arthur when he invited her to drinks after seeing her
for almost two months during his meetings with Martin
Pope.

Arthur and Marie were separated then, in fact, she
had been in New England, at a "private institution." He
seemed loath to discuss it and she didn't press him. She
had her own problems and responsibilities. She didn't go
around crying on other people's shoulders about the husband she had lost, the child she supported on her own,
the responsibilities, the burdens, the fears. She knew what
she wanted for Tana, the kind of life, the education, the
friends. She was going to give her security, no matter
what, the kind of life she herself had never had. And
without Jean having to say too much, Arthur Durning
had seemed to understand that. He was the head of one
of the largest conglomerates in the country, in plastics, in
glass, in food packaging, they even had enormous hold-
ings in oil in the Middle East. He was an enormously
wealthy man. But he had a quiet, unassuming way about
him that she liked.

In fact, there had been a lot about Arthur Durning
that appealed to her, enough so that when he asked her
out to dinner shortly after that first drink, she went. And
then she went again, and somehow, within a month they
were having an affair. He was the most exciting man Jean
Roberts had ever met. There was a quiet aura of power
about the man that one could almost touch, he was so
strong, and yet he was vulnerable too, and she knew that
he had suffered with his wife. Eventually he told her
about that. Marie had become an alcoholic almost immediately after their second child was born, and Jean knew
the pain of that only too well, having watched her par-

ents attempt to drink themselves to death, and in the end, they killed themselves in their car, drunk on an icy road on New Year's Eve. Marie had also cracked up the car, driving a car pool full of little girls one night. Ann and her friends were ten years old, and one of the children had almost been killed. Marie Durning had agreed to put herself away after that, but Arthur didn't have much hope. She was thirty-five and she'd been a hopeless drunk for ten years, and Arthur was desperately tired of it. Enough so to be swept off his feet by Jean. At twenty-eight, there was something unusually dignified about her that he liked, and at the same time, there was something kind and gentle in her eyes. She looked as though she cared a great deal, about everything and in particular her daughter. Her basic warmth came through, and it was precisely what he had needed just then. He hadn't known what to do with her at first, or what to make of what he felt for her. He and Marie had been married for sixteen years, and he was forty-two years old. He didn't know what to do about the children, about his house . . . his life . . . about Marie. Everything seemed to be hanging so precariously that year, and it was an unusual way of life for him, and one that he didn't like. He didn't take Jean home at first, for fear of upsetting the children, but eventually he saw Jean almost every night, and she began to take care of things for him. She hired two new maids, a gardener he didn't have time to see, she orchestrated some of the small business dinners he liked to give, a party for the children at Christmas, helped him pick out a new car. She even took a few days off to take a couple of brief trips with him. Suddenly it seemed as though she were running his whole life and he couldn't function

without her, and she began to ask herself more and more
what it meant, except that deep in her heart she knew.
She was in love with him, and he was in love with her,
and as soon as Marie was well enough to be told, they'd
get divorced, and he would marry Jean. . . .

Except that instead after six months, he offered her a
job. She wasn't sure what to do about that. She didn't
really want to work for him. She was in love with him,
and he was so wonderful to her, but the way he described
it was like throwing open a window onto a vista she had
longed for, for years. She could do exactly what she'd
done for him in the past six months, just as a friend.
Organize parties, hire help, make sure that the children
had the right clothes, the right friends, the right nurses.
He thought she had fabulous taste, and he had no idea
that she made everything she and Tana wore herself. She
had even upholstered the furniture in their tiny apartment. They still lived in the narrow brownstone, near
where the Third Avenue El had been, and Helen Weissman still baby-sat for Tana, when Jean was at work. But
with the job Arthur described, she could send Tana to a
decent school, he'd even help her get in. She could move
to a bigger place, there was even a building Arthur
owned on the Upper East Side, it wasn't Park Avenue, he
said with his slow smile, but it was far nicer than where
they were. When he told her the salary he had in mind,
she almost died. And the job would be so easy for her.

If she hadn't had Tana, she might have held out. It
would have been easier not to be indebted to him, and yet
it was such a wonderful chance to be side by side all the
time . . . and when Marie was well . . . He already
had an executive secretary at Durning International, but

there was a small secluded office just beyond the conference room which adjoined the handsome wood-panelled
office he used. She would see him every day, be right
nearby, she would be virtually essential to him, as she
was rapidly becoming now. "It would just be more of the
same," he explained, begging her to take the job, offering
her even more benefits, an even higher salary. He was
already dependent on her now, he needed her, and indirectly his children did too, although they hadn't met her
yet. But she was the first person he had relied on in years.
For almost two decades everyone else had relied on him,
and suddenly here was someone he could turn to, who
never seemed to let him down. He had given the matter a
great deal of thought and he wanted her near him always,
he said, in bed that night as he begged her again to take
the job.

In the end, although she seemed to fight so hard, it
was an easy choice to make, and her whole life seemed
like a dream now as she went to work every day, sometimes after he had spent the night with her. His children
were used to his spending a few nights in town. And the
house in Greenwich was efficiently staffed now, Arthur
was no longer as worried about them, although Ann and
Billy had had a hard time at first when Marie left, but
they seemed less anxious about it now. And once they
met Jean, it was as though they had always been old
friends. She took them to movies with Tana constantly,
bought them toys, shopped for their clothes, drove their
car pools, went to their schools, and their school plays
when Arthur was out of town, and she took even better
care of him. He was like a well-fed cat, polishing his paws
by the fire and he smiled at her one night in the apart-

ment he'd gotten her. It wasn't sumptuous, but for Tana
and Jean, it was more than enough, two bedrooms, a
living room, dining room, handsome kitchen. The building was modern and well built and clean, and they had a
view of the East River from the living room windows. It
was a far cry from the elevated train in Jean's old apartment.

"Do you know," she looked at him with a smile,
"I've never been happier in my life."

"Neither have I."

But that was only days before Marie Durning tried
to take her own life. Someone told her that Arthur was
having an affair, although they didn't say with whom,
and things were touch and go with her after that. Six
months later, the doctors began talking of letting her go
home, and by then Jean had worked for Arthur Durning
for over a year. Tana was happy in her new school, new
home, new life, as was Jean. And suddenly it was as
though everything stopped. Arthur went to see Marie
and came home looking grim.

"What did she say?" Jean looked at him with wide,
terrified eyes. She was thirty years old now. She wanted
security, stability, not a clandestine affair for the rest of
her life. But she had never objected to their life because
she knew how desperately ill Marie Durning was, and
how it worried him. But only the week before he had
been talking about marriage to Jean. He looked at her
now with a bleak expression she had never seen before, as
though he had no hope left, no dreams.

"She said that if she can't come home to us, she'll
try to commit suicide again."

"But she can't do that to you. She can't keep threatening you for the rest of your life." Jean wanted to scream, and the bitch of it was that Marie could threaten, and did. She came home three months after that, with only a tenuous grip on her own sanity. She was back at the hospital by Christmas that year, home by spring, and this time she held out until fall, and began drinking heavily over bridge lunches with her friends. All in all it went on for more than seven years.

When she came out of the hospital the first time, Arthur was so upset that he actually asked Jean to help her out. "She's so helpless, you don't understand . . . she's nothing like you, sweetheart. She can't cope . . . she can barely think." And for love of Arthur, Jean found herself in the unenviable position of being the mistress caring for the wife. She spent two or three days a week, during the day, in Greenwich with her, trying to help her run the house. Marie was desperately afraid of the help; they all knew that she drank. And so did her kids. At first they seemed to view her with despair, and eventually with scorn. It was Ann who hated her most, Billy who cried when she got drunk. It was a nightmarish scene, and just like Arthur, within a few months, Jean was trapped. She couldn't let her down, let her go . . . it would have been like deserting her parents. It was as though this time she could make things happen right. Even though, in the end, Marie came to an almost identical end as Jean's parents. She was going to meet Arthur in town for a night at the ballet, and Jean swore that she was sober when she left, at least she thought she was, but she must have had a bottle with her. She spun out on an icy patch on the Merritt Parkway halfway to New York, and died instantly.

They were both still grateful that Marie never knew of their affair, and the agony of it all was that Jean had been fond of her. She had cried at the funeral more than the children had, and it had taken her weeks to be willing to spend a night with Arthur again. Their affair had gone on for eight years, and now he was afraid of what his children would say. "In any case, I've got to wait a year." She didn't disagree with that, and anyway he spent a great deal of time with her. He was thoughtful and attentive. She had never had any complaints. But it was important to her that Tana not suspect their long-standing affair but finally a year after Marie died, she turned and accused Jean.

"I'm not stupid, you know, Mom. I know what's going on." She was as long and lanky and beautiful as Andy had been, and she had the same mischievous light in her eyes, as though she were always about to laugh, but not this time. She had hurt for too long, and her eyes almost steamed as she glared at Jean. "He treats you like dirt and he has for years. Why doesn't he marry you instead of sneaking in and out of here in the middle of the night?" Jean had slapped her for that, but Tana didn't care. There had been too many Thanksgivings they spent alone, too many Christmases with expensive boxes from fabulous stores, but no one but the two of them there, while he went to the country club with his friends. Even the year that Ann and Billy were gone with their grandparents. "He's never here when it counts! Don't you see that, Mom?" Huge tears had rolled down her cheeks as she sobbed and Jean had had to turn away. Her voice was hoarse as she tried to answer for him.

"That's not true."

"Yes, it is. He always leaves you alone. And he treats you like the maid. You run his house, drive his kids around, and he gives you diamond watches and gold bracelets and briefcases and purses and perfume, and so what? Where is *he*? That's what counts, isn't it?" What could she say? Deny the truth to her own child? It broke her heart to realize how much Tana had seen.

"He's doing what he has to do."

"No, he's not. He's doing what he wants to do." She was very perceptive for a girl of fifteen. "He wants to be in Greenwich with all his friends, go to Bal Harbour in the summer, and Palm Beach in the winter, and when he goes to Dallas on business, he takes you. But does he ever take you to Palm Beach? Does he ever invite us? Does he ever let Ann and Billy see how much you mean to him? No. He just sneaks out of here so I won't know what's going on, well I do . . . dammit . . . I do. . . ." Her whole body shook with rage. She had seen the pain in Jean's eyes too often over the years, and she was frighteningly close to the truth, as Jean knew. The truth was that their arrangement was comfortable for him, and he wasn't strong enough to swim upstream against his children. He was terrified of what his own children would think of the affair with Jean. He was a dynamo in business, but he couldn't fight the same wars at home. He had never had the courage to call Marie's bluff and simply walk out, he had catered to her alcoholic whims right till the end. And now he was doing the same with his kids. But Jean had her own worries too. She didn't like what Tana had said to her, and she tried to talk to Arthur about it that night, but he brushed her off with a tired

smile. He had had a hard day, and Ann was giving him
some trouble.

"They all have their own ideas at that age. Hell, look
at mine." Billy was seventeen, and had been picked up on
drunk driving charges twice that year, and Ann had just
gotten kicked out of her sophomore year at Wellesley, at
nineteen. She wanted to go to Europe with her friends,
while Arthur wanted her to spend some time at home.
Jean had even tried to take her to lunch to reason with
her, but she had brushed Jean off, and told her that she'd
get what she wanted out of Daddy by the end of the year.

And true to her word, she did. She spent the following summer in the South of France, and picked up a
thirty-seven-year-old French playboy, whom she married
in Rome. She got pregnant, lost the child, and returned
to New York with dark circles under her eyes and a
penchant for pills. Her marriage had made the international press, of course, and Arthur had been sick about it
when he met the "young man." It had cost him a fortune
to buy him off, but he had, and he left Ann in Palm
Beach to "recuperate" as he said to her, but she seemed
to get into plenty of trouble there, carousing all night
with boys her own age, or their fathers if she had the
chance. She was a racy one, in ways of which Jean did
not approve, but she was twenty-one now, and there was
little Arthur could do. She had gotten an enormous trust
from her mother's estate, and she had the funds she
needed now to run wild. She was back in Europe, raising
hell, before she was twenty-two. And the only thing that
cheered Arthur a little bit was that Billy had managed to
stay in Princeton that year in spite of several near fatal
scrapes he'd been in.

"I must say, they don't give one much peace of mind, do they, love?" They had quiet evenings together in Greenwich now, but most nights she insisted on driving home, no matter how late she got in. His children were no longer there, but she still had Tana at home, and Jean wouldn't dream of staying out for the night unless Tana was at a friend's, or skiing for a weekend somewhere. There were certain standards she expected to maintain, and it touched him about her. "You know, in the end they do what they want anyway, Jean. No matter how good an example you set." It was true in a way, but he didn't fight her very hard. He was used to spending his nights alone now, and it made it more of a treat when they awoke side by side. There was very little passion left in what they shared. But it was comfortable for them both, particularly for him. She didn't ask him for more than he was willing to give, and he knew how grateful she was for all that he had done for her over the years. He had given her a security she might never have had without him, a wonderful job, a good school for her child, and little extras whenever he could, trips, jewels, furs. They were minor extravagances to him, and though Jean Roberts was still a wizard with a needle and thread, she no longer had to upholster her own furniture or make their own clothes, thanks to him. There was a cleaning woman who came twice a week, a comfortable roof over their heads, and Arthur knew that she loved him. He loved her too, but he was set in his ways, and neither of them had mentioned marriage in years. There was no reason to now. Their children were almost grown, he was fifty-four years old, his empire was doing well, and Jean was still attractive and fairly young, although there had been a

matronly look to her now for the past several years. He
liked her that way, though, and it seemed hard to believe
that it had been twelve years. She had just turned forty
that spring. And he had taken her to Paris for the week.
It was almost like a dream. She brought back dozens of
tiny treasures for Tana, and enchanted her with endless
tales, including that of her birthday dinner at Maxim's. It
was always sad coming home after trips like that, waking
up in bed alone again, reaching out to him in the night
and finding no one there, but she had lived that way for
so long that it no longer bothered her, or at least she
pretended that to herself, and after her outbreak three
years before, Tana had never accused her again. She had
been ashamed of herself afterwards. Her mother had always been so good to her. "I just want the best for you
. . . that's all . . . I want you to be happy . . . not to
be alone all the time. . . ."

"I'm not, sweetheart," tears had filled Jean's eyes, "I
have you."

"That's not the same." She had clung to her mother
then, and the forbidden subject had not come up again.
But there was no warmth lost between Arthur and Tana
when they met, which always upset Jean. Actually, it
would have been harder on her if he'd insisted on marrying her after all, because of the way Tana felt about
him. She felt that he had used her mother for the past
dozen years, and given nothing in exchange.

"How can you say that? We owe him so much!" She
remembered the apartment beneath the elevated train,
which Tana did not, the meager checks, the nights she
couldn't even afford to feed the child meat, or when she

bought lamb chops or a little steak for her and ate maca-
roni herself for three or four days.

"What do we owe him? A deal on this apartment?
So what? You work, you could get us an apartment like
this, Mom. You could do a whole lot of things for us
without him." But Jean was never as sure. She would
have been frightened to leave him now, frightened not to
work for Durning International, not to be at his right
hand, not to have the apartment, the job, the security
that she always knew was there . . . the car he replaced
every two years so that she could go back and forth to
Greenwich with ease. Originally, it had been a station
wagon so that she could car pool his kids. The last two
had been smaller though, pretty little Mercedes sedans he
bought and replaced for her. And it wasn't as though she
cared about the expensive gifts, there was more to it than
that, much, much more. There was something about
knowing that Arthur was there for her, if she needed
him. It would have terrified her not to have that, and
they had been together for so long now. No matter what
Tana thought, she couldn't have given that up.

"And what happens when he dies?" Tana had been
blunt with her once. "You're all alone with no job, nothing. If he loves you, why doesn't he marry you, Mom?"

"I suppose we're comfortable like this."

Tana's eyes were big and green and hard, as Andy's
had been when he disagreed with her. "That's not good
enough. He owes you more than that, Mom. It's so damn
easy for him."

"It's easy for me, too, Tan." She hadn't been able to
argue with her that night. "I don't have to get used to
anyone's quirks. I live the way I please. I make my own

rules. And when I want, he takes me to Paris or London, or L.A. It's not such a bad life." They both knew it wasn't entirely true, but there was no changing it now. They were set in their ways, both of them. And as she tidied the papers on her desk, she suddenly sensed him in the room. Somehow, she always knew when he was there, as though years ago, someone had planted a radar in her heart, designed to locate only him. He had walked silently into her office, not far from his own, and was looking at her, as she glanced up and saw him standing there.

"Hello," she smiled the smile that only they had been sharing for more than twelve years, and it felt like sunshine in his heart as he looked at her. "How was your day?"

"Better now." He hadn't seen her since noon, which was unusual for them. They seemed to touch base half a dozen times during the afternoons, met for coffee each morning, and often he took her to lunch with him. There had been gossip on and off over the years, particularly right after Marie Durning died, but eventually it had died down, and people just assumed they were friends, or if they were lovers, it was both discreet and dead-end, so no one bothered to talk about them anymore. He sat in his favorite comfortable chair across from her desk and lit his pipe. It was a smell she had come to love as part of him for more than a decade, and it pervaded all the rooms in which he lived, including her own bedroom with the East River view. "How about spending the day in Greenwich with me tomorrow, Jean? Why don't we both play hookie for a change?" It was rare for him to do that, but he'd been pushing very hard on a merger for the past seven weeks, and she thought the day off would do him good, and wished he would do things like that more frequently. But now she smiled at him regretfully.

"I wish I could. Tomorrow's our big day." He often forgot things like that. But she didn't really expect him to remember Tana's graduation day. He looked blankly at her and she smiled as she said the single word. "Tana."

"Oh, of course," he waved the pipe and frowned as he laughed at her, "how stupid of me. It's a good thing you haven't depended on me the way I have on you, or you'd be in trouble most of the time."

"I doubt that." She smiled lovingly at him, and something very comfortable passed between them again. It was almost as though they no longer needed words. And in spite of the things Tana had said over the years, Jean Roberts needed nothing more than she had. As she sat there with the man she had loved for so long, she felt totally fulfilled.

"Is she all excited about graduation day?" He smiled at Jean, she was a very attractive woman in her own way. Her hair was peppered with gray, and she had big, beautiful dark eyes, and there was something delicate and graceful about her. Tana was longer, taller, almost colt-like, with a beauty that would surely stop men in the street in the next few years. She was going to Green Hill College in the heart of the South, and had gotten in under her own steam. Arthur had thought it a damn odd choice for a girl from the North, since it was filled mostly with Southern belles, but they had one of the finest language programs in the States, excellent laboratories, and a strong fine arts program. Tana had made up her own mind, the full scholarship had come through, based on her grades, and she was all set to go. She had a job in

New England at a summer camp, and she would be going to Green Hill in the fall. And tomorrow was going to be her big day—graduation.

"If the volume of her record player is any indication of how she feels," Jean smiled, "then she's been hysterical for the last month."

"Oh, God, don't remind me of that . . . please . . . Billy and four of his friends are coming home next week. I forgot to tell you about that. They want to stay in the pool house, and they'll probably burn the damn thing down. He called last night. Thank God they'll only be here for two weeks before moving on." Billy Durning was twenty now, and wilder than ever, from the correspondence Jean saw from school. But she knew that he was probably still reacting to his mother's death. It had been hard on all of them. Billy most of all, he had been only sixteen when she died, a difficult age at best, and things were a little smoother now. "He's giving a party next week, by the way. Saturday night, apparently. I was 'informed,' and he asked me to tell you."

She smiled. "I shall make due note. Any special requests?"

Arthur grinned. She knew them all well. "A band, and he said to be ready for two or three hundred guests. And by the way, tell Tana about that. She might enjoy it. He can have one of his friends pick her up here in town."

"I'll tell her. I'm sure she'll be pleased." But only Jean knew how big a lie that was. Tana had hated Billy Durning all her life, but Jean had forced her to be courteous whenever they met, and she would make the point to her again now. She owed it to Billy to be polite, and to go

to his party if he invited her, after all his father had done
for them. Jean never let her forget that.

". . . I will not." Tana looked stubbornly at Jean,
as the stereo blared deafeningly from her room. Paul
Anka was crooning "Put Your Head on My Shoulder"
and she had already played it at least seven times, to
Jean's dismay.

"If he's nice enough to invite you, you could at least
go for a while." It was an argument they had had before,
but Jean was determined to win this time. She didn't
want Tana to be rude.

"How can I go for a while? It takes at least an hour
to drive out there, and another hour back . . . so what
do I do, stay for ten minutes?" She tossed the long shaft
of golden wheat colored hair over her shoulder with a
look of despair. She knew how insistent her mother always was about anything that emanated from the Durnings. "Come on, Mom, we're not little kids anymore.
Why do I have to go if I don't want to? Why is it rude
just to say no? Couldn't I have other plans? I'm leaving
in two weeks anyway, and I want to see my friends. We'll
never see each other again, anyway. . . ." She looked
forlorn and her mother smiled at her.

"We'll talk about it another time, Tana." But Tana
knew just how those discussions went. She almost
groaned. She knew how stubborn her mother was going
to be about Billy Durning's party, and he was a creep, as
far as she was concerned. There were no two ways about
it, and Ann was even worse in Tana's eyes. She was
snobby, stuck up, and she looked easy, no matter how
polite she pretended to be to Jean. Tana knew she was

probably a whore, she had seen her drink too much at
some of Billy's other parties, and she treated Jean in a
condescending manner that made Tana want to slap her
face. But Tana also knew that any hint of her feelings to
her mother would lead them into a major battle again. It
had happened too often before, and she wasn't in the
mood tonight.

"I just want you to understand how I feel now,
Mother. I'm not going."

"It's still a week away. Why do you have to decide
tonight?"

"I'm just telling you. . . ." The green eyes looked
stormy and ominous and Jean knew better than to cross
her when she looked like that.

"What did you defrost for dinner tonight?"

Tana knew the tactic of avoidance, her mother was
good at that, but she decided to play the game for now,
and followed her mother into the kitchen. "I took out a
steak for you. I'm having dinner with some of my
friends." She looked sheepish then. As much as she
wanted her own life, she hated leaving Jean alone. She
knew just how much her mother had given her, how
much she had sacrificed. It was that which Tana understood all too well. She owed everything to her mother,
not to Arthur Durning, or his selfish, spoiled, overin-
dulged children. "Do you mind, Mom? I don't have to go
out." Her voice was gentle, and she looked older than her
eighteen years as Jean turned to look at her. There was
something very special between the two of them. They
had been alone together for a very long time, and had
shared bad times and good, her mother had never let her
down, and Tana was a gentle, thoughtful child.

Jean smiled at her. "I want you to go out with your friends, sweetheart. Tomorrow is a very special day for you." They were going to dinner at "21" the following night. Jean never went there except with Arthur, but Tana's graduation day was occasion enough to warrant the extravagance, and Jean didn't need to be as careful now. She made an enormous salary from Durning International, at least compared to what she had made as a legal secretary twelve years before, but she was cautious by nature, and always a little worried. She had worried a lot over the past eighteen years since Andy had died, and sometimes she told Tana that was why things had turned out so well. She had worried all her life, in sharp contrast to Andy Roberts' easy ways, and Tana seemed to be a great deal like him. There was more joy in her than in her mother, more mischief, more laughter, more ease with life, but then again life had been easier for her with Jean to love and protect her, and Tana smiled now as Jean took out a pan to cook the steak.

"I'm looking forward to tomorrow night." She had been touched to learn that Jean was taking her to "21."

"So am I. Where are you all going tonight?"

"To the Village, for a pizza."

"Be careful." Jean frowned. She always worried about her, anywhere she went.

"I always am."

"Will there be boys along to protect you?" She smiled. Sometimes it was hard to know if they were protection or a threat, and sometimes they were both. Reading her mind, Tana laughed and nodded.

"Yes. Now will you worry more?"

"Yes. Of course."

"You're silly, but I love you anyway." She threw her
arms around her neck, gave her a kiss, and disappeared
into her room to turn the music up even louder, as Jean
winced, and then found that she was singing along. She
had certainly heard it all often enough, but by the time
Tana finally turned it off and reappeared, wearing a white
dress with big black polka dots and a wide black patent
leather belt, with black and white spectator shoes, Jean
was suddenly struck by how pleasant the silence sounded.
And at the same moment she realized how quiet the
apartment would be once Tana was gone, too much so. It
would be tomblike when Tana was away.

"Have a good time."

"I will. I'll be home early."

"I won't count on it." Her mother smiled. At eighteen, she no longer had a curfew. Jean knew better than
that, and Tana was reasonable most of the time. Jean
heard her come in that night, around eleven thirty. She
knocked softly on Jean's door, whispered "I'm home,"
and went on to her own room, and Jean turned over and
went to sleep.

The next day was one that Jean Roberts would long
remember, with the long line of innocent looking young
girls strung together with garlands of daisies, the boys
coming in solemnly behind them, all of them singing in
unison, their voices raised, so young, so strong, so powerful, and all of them so new and fresh, as though they were
about to be born into the world, a world full of politics
and ruses and lies and heartbreaks, and all of it out there,
waiting to hurt them. Jean knew that life would never be
as simple for them again, as the tears rolled slowly down
her cheeks, and they filed slowly out of the auditorium,

their voices raised together for a last time. She was embarrassed that a single sob escaped her, but she was not
alone, and the fathers cried as hard as their wives, and
suddenly all was pandemonium, and the graduates were
shouting and cheering in the hallway, kissing and hugging, and making promises that couldn't possibly be fulfilled, to come back, to travel together, to never forget
. . . to always . . . forever . . . next year . . . someday . . . Quietly, Jean watched them, and most especially Tana, her face alight, her eyes almost an emerald
green, and all of them so excited, so happy, so pure.

Tana was still bubbling over with excitement that
night when they went to "21," where they ate a delicious
dinner, and Jean surprised her by ordering champagne.
Generally, she wasn't much in favor of Tana drinking.
Her own experience with her parents and Marie Durning
still frightened her, especially for someone as young as
Tana, but graduation day was an exception. And after
the champagne, she handed Tana the little box from Arthur. He had had Jean pick it out for him, like all the
presents he gave, even those to his own children. Inside
was a beautiful gold bangle which Tana slipped on her
wrist with cautious pleasure.

"That was nice of him, Mom." But she didn't look
overly excited. They both knew the reasons why, and
Tana did not discuss it now. She didn't want to upset her
mother. And by week's end, Tana had lost a major battle
to her mother. She couldn't stand hearing about it anymore, and she had finally agreed to go to Billy Durning's
party. "But this is the last time I'm going to one of their
parties. Is that a deal?"

"Why do you have to be so rigid, Tana? It's nice of them to invite you."

"Why?" Tana's eyes flashed, and her tongue was too quick to control. "Because I'm an employee's daughter? Does that make it a special favor from the almighty Durnings? Like inviting the maid?" Tears quickly filled Jean's eyes, and Tana stalked into her room, furious with herself for losing her temper. But she couldn't stand the way her mother felt about the Durnings, not just Arthur, but Ann and Billy too. It was nauseating, as though every little word or gesture were some giant favor to be grateful for. And Tana knew all too well what Billy's parties were like. She had suffered through them before, with too much drinking, too much necking, everybody getting fresh, getting drunk. She hated going to his parties. And tonight was no different.

A friend of his who lived nearby picked her up in a red Corvette he had gotten from his father, and he drove to Greenwich driving eighty miles an hour to impress her, which it didn't, and she arrived feeling as annoyed as she had when she left her apartment. She was wearing a white silk dress, with flat white shoes, and her long slim legs looked particularly graceful as she climbed out of the low slung car, tossing her hair over her shoulder, glancing around, knowing that she would know no one at all. She had particularly hated coming to their parties when she was younger, and the children had pointedly ignored her, but it was easier now. Three boys in madras jackets made a beeline for her, and offered to get her a gin and tonic, or whatever else might be her pleasure. She was noticeably vague and managed to get lost in the crowd, anxious to ditch the boy who had driven her out there. She wandered in the garden for half an hour, wishing she hadn't come, and watching clumps of giggling girls, drinking beer or gin and tonics, the boys watching them. A little while later the music started, and couples began forming, and within half an hour the lights were dim, bodies were chafing happily, and Tana even noticed several couples strolling outside. It was only then that she finally saw Billy Durning. He had been nowhere when they arrived. He walked over to her, and seemed to be giving her a cool appraisal. They had met often enough before, but he always looked her over again, as though he might buy her. It made her angry at him every time she saw him, and tonight was no exception.

"Hello, Billy."

"Hi. Shit, you're tall." As a greeting it didn't excite her, and anyway he was considerably taller than she was, what was the point? But she noticed then that he was staring at the fullness of her breasts and for a minute she wanted to kick him, and then gritting her teeth, she decided to make one stab at good manners, for her mother's sake, if nothing else.

"Thank you for inviting me tonight." But her eyes said she didn't mean it.

"We can always use more girls." Like cattle. So many head . . . so many tits . . . legs . . . crotches. . . .

"Thanks."

He laughed at her and shrugged. "Want to go outside?" She was about to turn him down, and then figured, why not? He was two years older than Tana, but he usually acted as though he were ten. Except ten years old

with drinking. He grabbed her arm, and led her through
the unfamiliar bodies until they reached the Durnings'
elaborate garden which led, eventually, to the pool house,
where Billy was camping with his friends. They had already burned a table and two chairs the night before, and
Billy had told them to cool it or his old man would kill
them. But unable to stand the torture of living in any
kind of proximity with Billy, Arthur had wisely moved to
the country club for the next week. "You should see the
mess we're making." He grinned, waving at the pool
house in the distance, and Tana felt annoyance sweep
over her, knowing that it would be her mother's job to
replace everything they damaged, to set it to rights again,
and also to calm Arthur down when he saw the mess
they left behind them when they moved on.

"Why don't you just try not to behave like animals?" She looked sweetly at him, and for a moment he
was shocked, and then suddenly, something evil and angry glinted in his eyes as he glared back at her.

"That's a dumb thing to say, but I guess you were
always dumb, weren't you? If my old man hadn't paid to
keep you at that fancy school in New York, you'd probably have wound up in some public school whorehouse on
the West Side, giving your teacher a blow job." She was
so shocked that for a moment she was breathless as she
stared at him, and then wordlessly, she turned and
walked away, as behind her, she could hear him laugh.
What an evil little bastard he was, she thought to herself,
as she fought her way back into the house, noticing that
the crowd had thickened considerably in the past half
hour, and that most of the guests were several years older
than she was, especially the girls.

She saw the boy who had driven her out from town, a little while later, his fly open, his eyes red, his shirttail out, and there was a girl frantically sliding her hands over his body as they shared a half-full bottle of scotch. Tana looked at them in despair, and knew that she had just lost her ride back to the city. There was no way she would have driven anywhere with anyone that drunk. Which left the option of the train, or finding someone sober, which did not, for the moment at least, appear likely.

"Wanna dance?" She turned, surprised to see Billy again, his eyes redder, his mouth leering at her, still gazing at her breasts, barely able to tear his eyes away, which he did at last, in time to see her shake her head.

"No, thanks."

"They're banging their asses off in the pool house. Wanna go watch?" Her stomach turned over at the prospect, and if he hadn't been so revolting she would have laughed. It was incredible how blind her mother could be to the Sacred Durnings.

"No, thanks."

"Whatsa matter? Still a virgin?" The look on his face made her sick, but she didn't want to let on that he was right. She'd rather he thought simply that he repulsed her, which was also correct. He did.

"I'm not into watching."

"Shit, why not? Best sport there is." She turned and tried to lose him in the crowd, but for some reason he was following her around tonight, and he was beginning to make her uncomfortable. She glanced around the room again, saw that he had disappeared, probably to the pool house to join his friends, and she figured that she

had been there for long enough. All she had to do was
call a cab, get to the train station, and go home. Not
pleasant, but at least not difficult, and glancing over her
shoulder to make sure that no one had followed her, she
tiptoed up a small back staircase that she knew about, to
a private phone. It was very simple, she called information, got the number, and called the cab. They promised
to be out there within the next fifteen minutes, and she
knew that she was in plenty of time for the last train.
And for the first time all night, she felt relief, having
gotten away from the drunks and creeps downstairs, and
she wandered slowly down the thickly carpeted hall,
glancing at the photographs of Arthur and Marie, Ann
and Billy as children, and somehow it seemed as though
the photographs should have included Jean. She had been
so much a part of them, so much of their well-being had
been because of her, it didn't feel fair to leave her out,
and then suddenly without thinking, Tana opened a door.
She knew it was the family room her mother often used
as a kind of office when she was there. The walls were
covered with photographs too, but she didn't see them
tonight. As the door opened slowly, she heard a nervous
squeal, a "Shit! . . . Hey!" saw two white moons leap
into the air, and heard a scuffle of embarrassment as she
quickly closed the door again, and then jumped in horror
as someone right behind her laughed.

"Ah!" She turned, and found Billy leering at her.
"For heaven's sake. . . ." She had thought he was downstairs.

"I thought you weren't into watching, Miss Lily
Pure."

"I was just wandering around, and I stumbled

across. . . ." Her face flushed to the roots of her hair as
he grinned at her.

"I'll bet . . . what'd you come up here for, Tan?"
He had heard her mother call her that over the years, but
it annoyed her hearing it from him. It was a private name
and he had never been her friend. Never.

"My mom usually works in that room."

"Nah." He shook his head, as though surprised at
her mistake. "Not in there."

"Yes, she does." Tana was sure of it, as she glanced
at her watch. She didn't want to miss her cab. But she
hadn't heard him honk yet, anyway.

"I'll show you where she does work, if you want."
He began to walk down the hall the other way, and Tana
wasn't sure whether or not to follow him. She didn't
want to argue with him, but she knew that her mother
used the family room where they stood. But it was his
house after all, and she felt awkward standing there, particularly as groans began reaching her from the couple
inside. She had a few minutes until her cab came and for
lack of something better to do, she followed Billy down
the hall. It was no big deal, and he swung open a door
into another room. "That's it." Tana walked to the doorway and stepped in and looked around, realizing instantly that this wasn't where her mother worked. The
most dominant thing in the entire room was an enormous
bed, covered with gray velvet, trimmed in silk, there was
both a gray opossum blanket and a chinchilla one draped
across a matching chaise longue. The carpeting was gray
too, and there were beautiful prints everywhere. Tana
turned to him, looking annoyed.

"Very funny. That's your father's bedroom, isn't it?"

"Yeah. And that's where your old lady works. Hell
of a lot of work she does in here, old Jean." Suddenly
Tana wanted to grab him by the hair and slap him, but
forcing herself not to say anything she started to walk out
of the room, and instead he grabbed her arm, and yanked
her back into it, kicking the door closed with his foot.

"Let go of me, you little shit!" Tana tried to pull her
arm away, but was amazed to discover the strength he
had. He grabbed her brutally by both arms and shoved
her against the wall, knocking the air out of her.

"Want to show me what kind of work your mama
does, you little bitch?" She gasped, he was hurting her
arms, and tears suddenly came to her eyes, more out of
anger than fear of him.

"I'm getting out of here, right now." She attempted
to pull herself away from him, but he slammed her hard
against the wall again, banging her head against it, and
suddenly when she looked into his eyes, she was genu-
inely afraid of him. There was the look of a madman on
his face, and he was laughing at her. "Don't be a jerk."
Her voice trembled, as she sensed his madness, and resentment of her.

His eyes glinted evilly then, as he crushed her wrists
in one powerful hand, she had never realized what
strength he had, and with the other hand, he unzipped
his fly and undid his pants, exposing himself, and then
grabbing one of her hands in his own, pulling it down
toward him. "Grab onto that, you little cunt." She was
terrified of him now, her face deathly white, pulling away
from him, as he pushed up against her, against the wall
and she pushed him away as hard as she could, getting
nowhere, as he laughed at her. And suddenly, in horror,

she realized what was happening, as she struggled against
him, the limp penis he had exposed was getting hard and
grinding against her, it felt like an evil ugly stump, as he
smashed her back against the wall again and again, pulling at her dress suddenly, tearing it along the side, to
expose the flesh he wanted to see, and suddenly his hands
were all over her, her belly, her breasts, her thighs, he
was pressing hard against her, crushing her, smearing her
face with his tongue, breathing alcohol fumes in her face,
touching her, holding her, grabbing her, he felt as though
he were tearing at her, and suddenly his fingers plunged
into her, between her legs, as she screamed, and bit him
hard on the neck, but he didn't even move back. He just
reached up and grabbed a hunk of her long blond hair
and twisted it around his hand, until she felt it would
come out by the roots and he bit her face viciously. She
flailed at him, she attempted to fight him with her legs.
She was breathless now, fighting for her life more than
her virginity, and suddenly crying, sobbing, gasping for
air, she felt him throw her down onto the thick gray
carpeting, and tear her dress from collar to hem, revealing the last of her, tearing the white lace underpants
off too, leaving her brown and bare and beautiful, and
suddenly begging him, crying, gnashing her teeth, almost
hysterical, as he pushed his pants down, and then kicked
them off somewhere onto the carpeting, pressing his full
weight on her, pinning her down, and only letting up to
tear her flesh again, almost limb from limb, his fingers
digging into her, ripping her flesh apart, tearing her, and
then sucking at her flesh with his mouth as she cried and
howled, and each time she attempted to move away from
him he would smash her down again until at last she was

barely conscious when he entered her, mounting her with
all the force he had, plunging into her, as rivers of blood
cascaded out onto the thick carpeting, until at last in final
orgiastic glory, he exploded atop the barely whining, rag-
gedly breathing girl, her eyes glazed, a trickle of blood
coming from her mouth, another from her nose, as Billy
Durning stood up and laughed at her, grabbing his own
pants off the floor as she didn't move. She looked almost
dead as she lay there and he looked down at her.

"Thanks."

And with that, the door opened, and one of Billy's
friends walked in. "Christ, what did you do to her?"
Tana still hadn't moved, although she could hear their
voices somewhere far, far away.

"No big deal." Billy shrugged. "Her old lady is my
father's hired cunt."

The other boy laughed. "Looks like one of you had a
good time at least." It was impossible not to see the sea of
blood beneath her on the gray carpeting. "She got her
period?"

"I guess." Billy seemed unconcerned as he zipped
his pants and she still lay there with her legs spread like a
rag doll's, while his friend looked down at her. Billy bent
over and slapped her face. "Come on, Tan, get up." She
didn't move, and he went into the bathroom, wet a towel
and dropped it on her, as though she would know what
to do with it, but it was another ten minutes before she
slowly rolled over in her own mire and threw up. And he
grabbed her by the hair again as the other boy watched,
and Billy yelled at her. "Shit, don't do that here, you
little pig." He pulled her roughly to her feet and dragged
her into the bathroom where she hung over the bowl, and

then finally, reached over and slammed the door. It seemed hours before she could revive herself and there were jagged sobs in her throat. Her cab was long since gone and she had missed the last train, but more than that something hideous had happened to her that she knew she would never recover from. She had been raped. She was shaking from head to foot, trembling violently, her teeth were chattering, her mouth was dry, her head ached, and she couldn't begin to figure out how she was ever going to leave the house. Her dress was torn, her shoes were smeared with blood, and as she sat in the bathroom crouching on the floor, the door opened and Billy strode into the room and threw some things at her. She saw a moment later that it was a dress and a pair of shoes that were some of Ann's things. He looked at Tana tentatively now, and she could see how drunk he was. "Get dressed. I'll take you home."

"And then what?" She suddenly screamed at him. "How do you explain to your father about this?" She was hysterical and he glanced behind him into the room.

"About the rug?" He looked nervous now and she got totally hysterical.

"About *me!*"

"That's not my fault, you little tease." The horror of what he was saying to her made her even sicker than she was before, but suddenly all she wanted to do was get out of there, and she didn't care if she had to walk back to New York. She suddenly pushed past him, clutching the clothes to her, and dashed into the room where the rape had taken place. Her eyes were wild, her hair matted and tangled, her face streaked with tears, and she bolted naked from the room and smack into his friend, who laughed at her nervously.

"You and Billy had a good time, huh?" He laughed at her and wild-eyed, she ran past him, and into a bathroom she knew was there. She pulled on the clothes he had given her, and she ran downstairs. It was too late to catch a train, no point to call a cab. She saw that the musicians were gone, and she ran down the driveway, leaving her torn dress and her handbag behind, but she didn't give a damn. She just wanted to get away from there. She could hitchhike if she had to, stop a police car . . . anything . . . the tears were caked on her face, and she was breathing hard as she began to run, and then suddenly bright headlights shone on her and she ran harder knowing instinctively that he was coming after her. She could hear his tires on the gravel road, and she began to dart in and out of the trees, crying softly, as the tears rolled into her hair, as he honked the horn and shouted at her.

"Come on, I'll take you home."

She didn't answer him. She just kept running as fast as she could, but he wouldn't go away. He just kept driving after her, zigzagging, following her course on the deserted road until finally she turned and screamed hysterically at him. "Leave me alone!" She stood bent over in the road, crying, sobbing, hugging her knees, and slowly he got out of the car and walked toward her. The night air was beginning to sober him, and he looked different than he had before, no longer crazed, but gray and grim, and he had brought his friend along, who was silently watching them from the passenger seat of Billy's long, sleek, dark green XKE.

"I'll drive you home." He stood in the road, legs spread, the car headlights behind him glaring eerily at them. "Come on, Tan."

"Don't call me that." She looked like a frightened little girl. He had never even been her friend, and now . . . and now . . . she wanted to scream each time she thought of it, but now she couldn't even scream anymore, and she no longer had the strength to run away from him. Her whole body ached, her head pounded, there was dried blood over her face and on her thighs, and now she stared blankly at him, stumbling along the road, as he reached out and tried to grab her arm, and she screamed at him and darted away again. He stood and stared at her for a moment, and then got back in the car and drove off. He had offered to take her home, if she didn't want to go, to hell with her, and she stumbled along the road, aching from head to foot. Not twenty minutes later he was back again. He screeched to a halt beside her, got out, and grabbed her by the arm. She saw that the other boy was no longer in the car, and suddenly she wondered if he was going to rape her again. A wave of terror ran through her as he pulled her toward the car, and she pulled away, but this time he jerked her hard and shouted at her, and she could smell whiskey on his breath again.

"Goddammit, I told you I'd take you home. Now get in the fuckin' car!" He almost threw her onto the seat, and she realized that there was no arguing with him. She was alone with him, and he would do whatever he wanted with her. She had already learned that. She sat bleakly beside him in the XKE, and he roared off into the night, as she waited for him to take her somewhere else to rape her again, it all seemed so hopeless now. But he got on the highway, sank his foot to the floor, and the breeze whipping through the car seemed to sober both of them. He glanced over at her several times, and waved at a box of tissues on the floor. "You'd better clean yourself up before you go home."

"Why?" She looked straight ahead at the empty road. It was after two o'clock, and even her eyes felt numb. Only a few trucks went whizzing by, driving straight through the night.

"You can't go home like that." She didn't answer him, and she didn't turn to look at his face. She still half expected him to stop and try to rape her again, and this time she was expecting it. She would run as fast as she could, across the highway if she dared and maybe one of the trucks would stop. She still couldn't believe what he had done to her, and she was wondering now if it had somehow been her fault, had she not fought him hard enough, had she done something to encourage him . . . ? they were hideous thoughts as she noticed the powerful sports car begin to weave. She turned and glanced at him, and noticed that he was falling asleep at the wheel. She jerked on his sleeve, and he started and looked at her. "Why the hell'd you do that? You could've caused an accident." She would have liked nothing better for him. She would have liked to see him lying dead by the side of the road.

"You were falling asleep. You're drunk."

"Yeah? So what?" He sounded more tired than surly now, and he seemed all right for a while, until she saw the car weave again, but this time before she had a chance to grab his arm or shake him awake, an enormous trailer truck sped by, and the sports car veered. There was a hideous, grinding shriek of brakes, as the truck jackknifed and overturned, and miraculously the XKE whizzed just past the cab and came to rest with its nose crushed by a tree. Tana hit her head hard as they stopped, and she sat staring ahead for a long time, and then suddenly she was aware of a soft moaning beside her. His face was covered with blood and she didn't move. She just sat and stared, and then suddenly the door opened and there was a strong pair of hands on her arm, and then she began to scream. Suddenly the events of the endless night had caught up with her and she totally lost control, sobbing and hysterically trying to run from the car, as two passing trucks stopped, and the drivers tried to subdue her until the cops came, but her eyes were uncomprehending and wild. They were trying to stop the bleeding on Billy's head, and he had a terrible gash over one eye. The police arrived a short time later, followed by an ambulance, and all three victims were taken to the New Rochelle Hospital Medical Center nearby. The truck driver was almost instantly released. His vehicle had suffered more damage than he had, miraculously. Billy was being stitched up. It was also noted that he had been driving under the influence of alcohol, and as his third offense, it would cost him his driver's license for the next year, which seemed to worry him more than the wounded eye. Tana's entire body seemed to be covered with blood, but oddly enough the staff noticed that most of it was dried. They couldn't seem to get her to explain what had happened to her, and she hyperventilated each time she tried. A pleasant young nurse gently wiped her off, while Tana just lay on the examining table and cried.

They administered a sedative, and by the time her mother
arrived at four o'clock she was half asleep.

"What happened . . . ? my God!" She was looking
at the bandage on Billy's eye. "Billy, will you be all
right?"

"I guess." He smiled sheepishly, and she noticed
again what a handsome boy he was, although he had
always looked less like his father and more like Marie.
And suddenly the smile faded and he looked terrified.
"Did you call Dad?"

Jean Roberts shook her head. "I didn't want to
frighten him. They told me you were all right when they
called, and I thought I'd take a good look at you both
first myself."

"Thanks." He glanced over at Tana's dozing form
and then shrugged almost nervously. "I'm sorry about
. . . that I . . . we wrecked the car. . . ."

"The important thing is that neither of you were
badly hurt." She frowned as she looked at Tana's matted
blond hair, but there was no longer any evidence of blood
anywhere, and the nurse tried to explain how hysterical
Tana had been.

"We gave her a sedative. She should sleep for a
while."

Jean Roberts frowned. "Was she drunk?" She already knew that Billy was, but there would be hell to pay
if Tana was too, but the young nurse shook her head.

"I don't think she was. Mostly frightened, I think.
She got a nasty little bump on the head, but nothing more
than that. We don't see any evidence of concussion or
whiplash, but I'd keep an eye on her." And as she said
the words, hearing them talking around her, Tana woke

up, and she looked at her mother as though she had never seen her before, and then silently began to cry, as Jean took her in her arms and made gentle cooing sounds.

"It's all right, baby . . . it's all right. . . ."

She shook her head violently, taking great gulps of air, "No, it's not . . . it's not . . . he . . ." But Billy stood there staring at her, with an evil look in his eye, and she couldn't say the words. He looked as though he would hit her again, and she turned away, choking on her sobs, still feeling his eyes on her. She couldn't look at him again . . . couldn't see him . . . never wanted to see him again

She lay on the backseat of the Mercedes her mother had driven out, and they took Billy home. And Jean was inside with him for a long time. They threw the last people out, made half a dozen others get out of the pool, tossed two couples out of Ann's bed, and told the group in the pool house to settle down, as Jean walked back to the car where Tana still was, she knew she had her week's work cut out for her. They had destroyed half the furniture, set fire to some of the plants, spoiled the upholstery, left spots on the rugs, and there was everything from plastic glasses to whole pineapples in the pool. She didn't want Arthur to even see the place until she had had it set to rights again. She got into the car with a long tired sigh, and glanced at Tana's still form. Her daughter seemed strangely calm now. The sedative had taken effect.

"Thank God they didn't go into Arthur's room." She started the car, and Tana shook her head with a silent no, but she couldn't say the words. "Are you all right?" That was really all that mattered. They could have been killed. It was a miracle they hadn't been. It was all she could think of when the phone rang at three o'clock. She had already been worried sick for several hours, and instinctively, when she had heard the phone, she had known. And she had answered it on the first ring.

"How do you feel?" All she could do was stare at her mother and shake her head. "I want to go home." The tears slid down her cheeks again, and Jean wondered again if she was drunk. It had obviously been a wild night, and Tana had been part of it. She also noticed that she wasn't wearing the same dress she'd been wearing when she left.

"Did you go for a swim?" She sat up, her head reeling, and shook her head, as her mother glanced at her in the mirror and saw the strange look in Tana's eyes. "What happened to your dress?"

She spoke in a cold hard voice that didn't even sound like her to Jean's ears. "Billy tore it off."

"He did what?" She looked surprised, and then smiled. "Did he throw you in the pool?" It was the only image she had of him, and even if he had been a little drunk, he was harmless enough. It was just damn lucky he hadn't hit the truck. It was a good lesson for them both. "I hope you learned a lesson tonight, Tan." She began to sob again at the sound of the nickname Billy had used until finally Jean pulled off the road and stared at her. "What's happening to you? Are you drunk? Did you take drugs?" There was accusation in her voice, in her eyes, and none of that had been there when she drove Billy home. How unfair life was, Tana thought to herself. But her mother just didn't understand what Precious Little Billy Durning had done. She looked straight into her mother's eyes.

"Billy raped me in his father's room."

"Tana!" Jean Roberts looked horrified. "How can you say a thing like that? He would never do such a thing!" Her anger was at her own child, not at her lover's son. She couldn't believe a thing like that about Billy, and it was written all over her face as she glared at her only child. "That's a terrible thing to say." It was a terrible thing to do. But Jean only stared at her.

Two lonely tears rolled relentlessly down Tana's cheeks. "He did." Her face crumbled at the memory. "I . . . swear . . ." She was getting hysterical again as Jean turned and started the car, and this time she did not glance into the backseat again.

"I don't ever want to hear you say a thing like that again, about anyone." Surely not someone they knew . . . a harmless boy they had known for half his life . . . she didn't even care to think about what would make Tana say a thing like that, jealousy perhaps of Billy himself, or Ann, or Arthur. . . . "I never want to hear you say that again. Is that clear?" But there was no answer from the backseat. Tana just sat there, looking glazed. She would never say it again. About anyone. Something inside her had just died.

Chapter 4

⟐⟐

The summer sped past Tana easily after that. She spent two weeks in New York, recuperating, while her mother went to work every day. And Jean was concerned about her, but in an odd, uncomfortable way. There seemed to be nothing wrong with her, but she would sit and stare into space, listening to nothing, not seeing her friends. She wouldn't answer the phone when Jean, or anyone else, called. Jean even mentioned it to Arthur at the end of the first week. She almost had the house in Greenwich put to rights again, and Billy and his friends had moved on to Malibu to visit other friends. They had all but destroyed the house at the pool, but the worst damage of all was a section of the rug in Arthur's room which looked as though it had been cut out with a knife. And Arthur had had plenty to say to his son about that.

"What kind of savages are all of you? I ought to be sending you to West Point instead of Princeton for chrissake so they can teach you a thing or two about how to behave. My God, in my day, no one I'd ever known would behave like that. Did you see that carpeting? They tore the whole damn thing up." Billy had looked both subdued and chagrined.

"I'm sorry, Dad. Things got a little out of hand."

"A little? And it's a wonder you and the Roberts girl weren't killed." But on the whole he'd been all right. His eye was still bothering him a little when he left, but the stitches on the eyebrow had already been removed. And he still seemed to be out every night right up until they left for Malibu. "Damn wild kids . . ." Arthur had growled at her. "How's Tana now?" She had mentioned to Arthur several times how oddly Tana had behaved, and she really wondered if she hadn't had a worse blow on the head than they had first thought.

"You know she was almost delirious that first night . . . in fact she was . . ." She still remembered the ridiculous tale about Billy that Tana had tried to tell. The girl really wasn't all there and Arthur looked worried too.

"Have her looked at again." But when Jean tried to insist, Tana refused. Jean almost wondered if she was well enough to go to New England for her summer job, but on the night before she was due to leave, she quietly packed her bag, and the next morning, she came to the breakfast table with a pale, wan, tired face, but for the first time in two weeks, when Jean handed her a glass of orange juice, she smiled, and Jean almost sat down and cried. The house had been like a tomb since the accident. There were no sounds, no music, no laughter, no giggles on the phone, no voices, only dead silence everywhere. And Tana's deadened eyes.

"I've missed you, Tan." At the sound of the familiar name, Tana's eyes filled with tears. She nodded her head,

unable to say anything. There was nothing left for her to
say. To anyone. She felt as if her life were over. She never
again wanted to be touched by a man, and she knew she
never would again. No one would ever do to her what
Billy Durning had done, and the tragedy was that Jean
couldn't face hearing it, or thinking it. In her mind, it
was impossible, so it didn't exist, it hadn't happened. But
the worst of it was that it had. "Do you really think
you're up to going to camp?"

Tana had wondered about that herself; she knew
that the choice was an important one. She could spend
the rest of her life hiding there, like a cripple, a victim,
someone shrivelled and broken and gone, or she could
begin to move out again, and she had decided to do that.
"I'll be all right."

"Are you sure?" She seemed so quiet, so subdued, so
suddenly grown up. It was as though the bump on her
head in the car accident had stolen her youth from her.
Perhaps the fear itself had done that. Jean had never seen
such a dramatic change in such a short time. And Arthur
kept insisting that Billy had been fine, remorseful, but
almost his old self by the time he left for his summer
holiday, which was certainly not the case here. "Look,
sweetheart, if you don't feel up to it, just come home. You
want to start college in the fall feeling strong."

"I'll be all right." It was almost all she said before
she left, clinging to her single bag. She took the bus to
Vermont as she had twice before. It was a summer job she
had loved, but it was different this year, and the others
noticed it too. She was quieter, kept to herself, and never
seemed to laugh anymore. The only time she talked to
anyone at all was with the campers themselves. It sad-

dened the others who had known her before, "something must be wrong at home. . . ." "Is she sick . . . ?" "Wow, she's like a different girl. . . ." Everyone noticed, and no one knew. And at the end of the summer, she got on the bus and went home again. She had made no friends this year, except among the kids, but even with them, she wasn't as popular as she'd been before. She was even prettier than she'd been in previous years but all of the kids agreed this time, "Tana Roberts is weird." And she knew herself that she was.

She spent two days at home with Jean, avoided all her old friends, packed her bags for school, and boarded the train with a feeling of relief. Suddenly, she wanted to get far, far from home . . . from Arthur . . . from Jean . . . from Billy . . . from all of them . . . even the friends she'd had at school. She wasn't the same carefree girl who had graduated three months before. She was someone different now, someone haunted and hurt, with scars on her soul. And as she sat on the train and rolled through the South, she slowly began to feel human again. It was as though she had to get far, far from them, from their deceptions, their lies, the things they couldn't see, or refused to believe, the games they played . . . it was as though ever since Billy Durning had forced his way into her, no one could see her anymore. She didn't exist, because they couldn't acknowledge Billy's sin . . . but that was only Jean, she told herself. But who else was there? If her own mother didn't believe her . . . she didn't want to think about it anymore. Didn't want to think about any of it. She was going as far away as she could, and maybe she'd never go home, although she

knew that too was a lie. Her mother's last words to her
had been, "You'll come home for Thanksgiving, won't
you, Tan?" It was as though her mother was afraid of her
now, as though she had seen something in her daughter's
eyes that she just couldn't face, a kind of bleeding, open,
raw pain that she couldn't help and didn't want to be
there. She didn't want to go home for Thanksgiving,
didn't want to go home ever again. She had escaped their
tiny, petty lives . . . the hypocrisy . . . Billy and his
barbaric friends . . . Arthur and the years and years he
had used Jean . . . the wife he had cheated on . . .
and the lies Jean told herself . . . suddenly Tana
couldn't stand it anymore, and she couldn't go far
enough to get away from them. Maybe she'd never go
back . . . never.

. . . She loved the sound of the train, and she was
sorry when it stopped in Yolan. Green Hill College was
two miles away and they had sent a lumbering old station
wagon for her, with an old black driver with white hair.
He greeted her with a warm smile, but she looked at him
suspiciously as he helped her load her bags.

"You been on the train long, miss?"

"Thirteen hours." She barely spoke to him on the
brief drive to the school, and had he even seemed about
to stop the car, she would have leapt out and begun to
scream. But he sensed that about her, and he didn't push
her by trying to get too friendly with her. He whistled
part of the way, and when he got tired of that he sang,
songs of the Deep South that Tana had never heard before, and in spite of herself, when they arrived, she smiled
at him.

"Thanks for the ride."

"Anytime, miss. Just come on down to the office and ask for Sam, I'll give you a ride anywhere you want to go." And then he laughed the warm black laugh, smiling at her. "There ain't too many places to go around here." He had the accent of the Deep South, and ever since she had gotten off the train she had noticed how beautiful everything was. The tall majestic looking trees, the bright flowers everywhere, the lush grass, and the air still, heavy and warm. One had a sudden urge to just stroll off somewhere quietly, and when she saw the college itself for the first time, she just stood there and smiled. It was all she had wanted it to be, she had wanted to come here to visit the winter before, but she just hadn't had time. Instead, she had interviewed with their traveling representative up North, and gone on what she'd seen in the brochures. She knew that academically they were one of the best schools, but she had actually wanted something more—their reputation, and the legends she had heard about what a fine old school it was. It was old-fashioned, she knew, but in a way that appealed to her. And now as she looked at the handsome white buildings, perfectly kept, with tall columns, and beautiful French windows looking out on a small lake, she almost felt as though she had come home.

She checked in at the reception room, filled in some cards, wrote down her name on a long list, found out what building she'd be living in, and a little while later, Sam was helping her again, loading all of her luggage on an old country cart. It was almost like a trip back in time just being there, and for the first time in months, she felt peaceful again. She wouldn't have to face her mother here, wouldn't have to explain how she felt or didn't feel, wouldn't have to hear the hated Durning name, or see

the unknowing pain Arthur inflicted on her mother's face
. . . or hear about Billy again . . . just being in the
same town with them had stifled her, and for the first
month or two after the rape, all she had wanted to do was
run away. It had taken all the courage she had to go on to
camp that summer anyway, and each day there had been
a battle too. She wanted to flinch each time someone
came too close, especially the men, but even the boys
frightened her now too. At least she didn't have to worry
about that here. It was an all-women's school, and she
didn't have to attend the dances or proms, or nearby
football games. The social life had appealed to her when
she had first applied, but she didn't care about that now.
She didn't care about anything . . . or at least she
hadn't in three months . . . but suddenly . . . suddenly . . . even the air here smelled good, and as Sam
rolled the luggage cart along, she looked at him with a
slow smile and he grinned at her.

"It's a long way from New York." His eyes seemed
to dance, and the nubby white hair looked soft.

"It sure is. It really is beautiful here." She glanced
out at the lake and then back at the buildings behind her,
fanned out, with still smaller buildings ahead of them. It
looked almost like a palatial estate, which was what it
had once been, everything was so perfectly manicured,
immaculately kept. She was almost sorry her mother
couldn't see it now, but perhaps she would eventually.

"It used to be a plantation, you know." He told hundreds of girls that every year. He loved to tell the story to
the girls. His granddaddy had been a slave right here, he
always bragged, as they looked at him with wide eyes.
They were so young and so fine, almost like his own

daughter had been, except she was a grown woman now, with children of her own. And these girls would be married and have children soon too. He knew that every year, in the spring, girls came back from everywhere to get married in the beautiful church right there on the grounds, and after graduation ceremonies, there were always at least a dozen who got married in the ensuing days. He glanced at Tana as she loped along at his side, wondering how long this one would last. She was one of the prettiest girls he had ever seen, with long shapely legs, and that face, the shaft of golden hair, and those enormous green eyes. If he'd known her for a while he would have teased her and told her she looked like a movie star, but this one was more reserved than most. He had noticed all along that she was unusually shy. "You been here before?" She shook her head, looking up at the building where he had just stopped the cart. "This is one of the nicest houses we got. Jasmine House. I've already brought five girls here today. There should be about twenty-five or so here in all, and a housemother to keep an eye on all of you," he beamed, "though I'm sure none of you will be needing that." He laughed his deep, rich burst of laughter again, which sounded almost musical, and Tana smiled, helping him with some of her bags. She followed him inside, and found herself in a pleasantly decorated living room. The furniture was almost entirely antique, English and Early American, the fabrics were flowery and bright, and there were big bouquets of flowers in large handsome crystal vases on several tables and a desk. There was a homey atmosphere as Tana stepped in and looked around, and one of the first things that struck her about the place was that it was ladylike. Everything looked proper and neat, and as though one ought to be wearing a hat and white gloves, and suddenly Tana looked down at her plaid skirt, her loafers and knee socks, and smiled at the woman coming across the room to her in a neat gray suit. She had white hair and blue eyes. She was their housemother, Tana soon learned. She had been housemother of Jasmine House for more than twenty years, she had a gentle Southern drawl, and when her jacket opened, Tana noticed a single strand of pearls. She looked like someone's aunt, and there were deep smile lines around her eyes.

"Welcome to Jasmine House, my dear." There were eleven other houses on campus much like this, "but we like to think that Jasmine is the very best." She beamed at Tana, and offered her a cup of tea as Sam took her bags upstairs. Tana accepted the flowered cup with the silver spoon, declined a plate of bland looking little cakes, and sat looking at the view of the lake, thinking of how strange life was. She felt as though she had landed in a different universe. Things were so different from New York . . . suddenly here she was, far from everyone she knew, drinking tea and talking to this woman with blue eyes and pearls . . . when only three months before she had been lying on Arthur Durning's bedroom floor being raped and beaten by his son. ". . . , don't you think, dear?" Tana stared blankly at the housemother, not sure of what she had just said, and demurely nodded her head, feeling suddenly tired. It was so much to take in all at once.

"Yes . . . yes . . . I do. . . ." She wasn't even sure what she was agreeing with, and suddenly all she wanted to do was escape to her room. At last, they finished their tea, set down their cups, and Tana had a sudden urge to laugh, wondering just how much tea the poor woman had had to drink that day, and then as though sensing Tana's impatience to settle in, she led the way to her room. It was up two handsomely curved flights of stairs, on a long hall, with flower prints and photographs of alumnae interspersed. Her room was at the very end of the hall. The walls were a pale pink, the curtains and bedspreads chintz. There were two narrow beds, two very old chests, two chairs, and a tiny corner sink. It was a funny old-fashioned room and the ceiling sloped directly over their beds. The housemother was watching her and seemed satisfied as Tana turned to her with a smile.

"This is very nice."

"Every room in Jasmine House is." She left the room shortly after that, and Tana sat staring at her trunks, not quite sure what to do, and then she lay down on her bed, looking out at the trees. She wondered if she should wait for her roommate to arrive before simply taking over one of the chests or half of the hanging space, and she didn't feel like unpacking anyway. She was thinking of taking a walk around the lake when she heard a knock on the door and suddenly Old Sam appeared. She sat up quickly on the edge of the bed, and he walked into the room carrying two bags with a strange look on his face. He glanced over at where Tana sat, seemed to shrug, and just looked at her.

"I guess this is a first for us." What is? Tana looked confused as he shrugged again and disappeared, and Tana glanced over at the bags. But there seemed nothing remarkable there, two large navy blue and green plaid bags with railroad tags, a makeup case, and a round hat-

box, just like the ones filled with Tana's junk. She wandered slowly around the room, wondering when their
owner would appear. She expected an endless wait as she
imagined the tea ritual, but in the end she was surprised
at how quickly the girl appeared. The housemother
knocked first, stared into Tana's eyes portentously as she
opened the door, and then stood aside, as Sharon Blake
seemed to float into the room. She was one of the most
striking girls Tana thought she had ever seen, with jet
black hair pulled tightly back, brilliant onyx eyes, teeth
whiter than ivory in a pale cocoa face that was so finely
etched it barely seemed real. Her beauty was so marked,
her movements so graceful, her style so definite that she
literally took Tana's breath away. She was wearing a
bright red coat, and a small hat, and she tossed both
swiftly into one of the room's two chairs, to reveal a
narrow tube of gray wool dress, the exact same color as
her well-made gray shoes. She looked more like a fashion
plate than a college girl, and Tana inwardly groaned at
the things she had brought. They were all kilts and
slacks, old wool skirts that she didn't really care about, a
lot of plain shirts, V neck sweaters, and two dresses her
mother had bought her at Saks just before she left.

"Tana," the housemother's voice said that she took
the introduction *very* seriously, "this is Sharon Blake.
She's from the North too. Although not as far North as
you. She's from Washington, D.C."

"Hello." Tana glanced shyly at her, as Sharon shot
her a dazzling smile and extended a hand.

"How do you do."

"I'll leave you two girls alone." She seemed to look
at Sharon almost with a look of pain, and Tana with

immeasurable sympathy. It cut her to the core to do this to her, but someone had to sleep with the girl, and Tana was a scholarship student after all. It was only fair. She had to be grateful for whatever she got. And the others wouldn't have put up with it. She softly closed the door, and walked downstairs with a determined step. It was the first time this had ever happened at Jasmine House, at Green Hill for that matter, and Julia Jones was wishing that she could have had something a little stronger than tea that afternoon. She needed it. It was a terrible strain, after all.

But upstairs Sharon only laughed as she threw herself into one of the room's uncomfortable chairs and looked at Tana's shining blond hair. They were an interestingly contrasted pair. The one so fair, the other dark. They eyed each other curiously as Tana smiled, wondering what she was doing there. It would have been easier for her to go to a college in the North, than to come here. But she didn't know Sharon Blake yet. The girl was beautiful, there was no doubt about that, and she was expensively dressed. Tana noticed that again, too, as Sharon kicked off her shoes.

"Well," the delicate, dark face broke into a smile again, "what do you think of Jasmine House?"

"It's pretty, don't you think?" Tana still felt shy with her, but there was something appealing about the lovely girl. There was something raw and courageous and bold that stood out on the exquisite face.

"They gave us the worst room, you know."

Tana was shocked at that. "How do you know?"

"I looked as we walked down the hall." She sighed then and carefully took off her hat. "I expected that."

And then she looked Tana over appraisingly. "And what sin did you commit to wind up rooming with me?" She smiled gently at Tana. She knew why she was there, she was the only token Negro to be accepted at Green Hill, and she was unusual, of course. Her father was an author of distinguished prose, winner of the National Book Award and the Pulitzer Prize, her mother was an attorney, currently in government, she would be different from most Negro girls. At least they expected her to be . . . although one could never be sure, of course . . . and Miriam Blake had given her oldest child a choice before sending her to Green Hill. She could have gone somewhere in the North, to Columbia in New York, her grades were good enough, or Georgetown closer to home, there was UCLA if she was serious about an acting career . . . or there was something important she could do, her mother said . . . "something that will mean something to other girls one day, Sharon." Sharon had stared at her, not sure what she meant. "You could go to Green Hill."

"In the South?" Sharon had been shocked. "They wouldn't even let me in."

Miriam had glared at her. "You don't understand yet, do you, babe? Your father is Freeman Blake. He's written books that people have read all around the world. Do you really think they'd dare to keep you out today?"

Sharon had grinned nervously. "Hell, yes. Mama, they'd tar and feather me before I ever unpacked." The thought terrified her. She knew what had happened in Little Rock three years before. She read the news. It had taken tanks and the National Guard to keep black children in a white school. And this wasn't just any little old school they were talking about. This was Green Hill. The most exclusive woman's junior college in the South, where daughters of Congressmen and Senators, and the governors of Texas and South Carolina and Georgia sent their little girls, to get two years of smarts before settling down with boys of their own kind. "Mama, that's nuts!"

"If every black girl in this country thinks like that, Sharon Blake, then a hundred years from now we'll still be sleeping in black hotels, sitting at the back of the bus, and drinking out of water fountains that reek of white boys' piss." Her mother's eyes had blazed at her as Sharon winced. Miriam Blake thought that way, she always had. She had gone to Radcliffe on a scholarship, Boalt Law School at UC, and ever since, she had fought hard for what she believed, for the underdog, the common man, and she was fighting for her people now. Even her husband admired her. She had more guts than anyone he'd ever known and she wasn't going to stop now. But it frightened Sharon sometimes. It frightened her a lot. As it had when she applied to Green Hill.

"What if I get in?" That scared her most of all and she told her father that. "I'm not like her, Daddy . . . I don't want to prove a point . . . to just get in . . . I want to have friends, to have a good time . . . what she wants me to do is too hard. . . ." Tears had filled her eyes and he understood. But he couldn't change either of them, Miriam and what she expected of them all, or the happy-go-lucky, fun-loving, beautiful girl, who was less like Miriam, and much more like him. She wanted to be an actress on the Broadway stage one day. And she wanted to go to UCLA.

"You can go there for your last two years, Shar," her mother said, "after you pay your dues."

"Why do I have to pay any dues at all?" she screamed. "Why do I owe anyone two years of my life?"

"Because you live here in your father's house, in a comfortable suburb of Washington, and you sleep in your nice, warm bed, thanks to us, and you've never known a life of pain."

"So beat me, then. Treat me like a slave, but let me do what I want to do!"

"Fine." Her mother's eyes had blazed black fire. "Do what you want. But you'll never walk proud, girl, not if all you think of is yourself. You think that's what they did in Little Rock? They walked every step of the way, with guns pointed at their heads, and the Klan itching for their necks every day. And you know who they did it for, girl? They did it for you. And who're you going to do it for, Sharon Blake?"

"Myself!" She had screamed before running up the stairs to her room and slamming the door. But the words had haunted her. Her mother's words always did. She wasn't an easy person to live with, or to know, or to love. She never made things comfortable for anyone. But in the long run, she made things good. For everyone.

Freeman Blake had tried to talk to his wife that night. He knew how Sharon felt, how badly she wanted to go to the western school. "Why don't you let her do what she wants for a change?"

"Because she has a responsibility. And so do I, and so do you."

"Don't you ever think of anything else? She's young. Give her a chance. Maybe she doesn't want to burn for a cause. Maybe you do enough of that for all of us." But they both knew that that wasn't entirely true. Sharon's brother Dick was only fifteen, but he was Miriam to the core, and he shared most of her ideas, except that his were angrier, more radical. No one was ever going to shove him down, and Freeman was proud of that, but he also recognized that Sharon was a different child. "Just let her be."

They had, and in the end, the guilt had won, as she told Tana later that night. "So here I am." They had been to dinner in the main dining hall, and were back in their room. Sharon in a pink nylon nightgown that had been a going away present from her best friend at home, and Tana in a blue flannel nightgown, her hair in a long silky ponytail as she watched her new friend. "I guess I'll go to UCLA after I finish here." She sighed and looked at the pink polish she had just applied to her toes, and then looked up at Tana again. "She expects so damn much of me." And all she wanted for herself was to be beautiful and smart and a great actress one day. That was enough. Except for Miriam Blake.

Tana smiled. "My mother expects a lot too. She's devoted her whole damn life to doing the right thing for me, and all she wants me to do is come here for a year or two, and then marry some 'nice young man.' " She made a face which suggested she found it an unappealing idea, and Sharon laughed.

"Secretly that's what all mothers think, even mine, as long as I promise to crusade even after I marry him. What does your father say? Thank God for mine, he gets me off the hook whenever he can. He thinks all that stuff is a pain in the ass too."

"Mine died before I was born. That's why she gets
so excited about everything. She's always scared to death
that everything's going to go wrong, so she clutches
whatever security we have, and she expects me to do the
same." She looked strangely at Sharon then, "You know,
actually your mother sounds more like my cup of tea."
The two girls laughed and it was another two hours before they turned off the lights, and by the end of the first
week at Green Hill, the two girls were fast friends. They
shared much of the same schedule, met for lunch, went to
the library, went for long walks around the lake, talking
about life, about boys, about parents and friends. Tana
told Sharon about her mother's relationship with Arthur
Durning, even when he was married to Marie, and how
she felt about him. The hypocrisy, the narrow views, the
stereotyped life in Greenwich with children and friends
and associates all of whom drank too much, in a house
that was all for show, while her mother slaved for him
night and day, lived for his calls, and had nothing to
show for it after twelve years. "I mean, Christ, Shar, it
really burns me up. And you know the worst thing about
it?" Her eyes smoldered like fiery green rocks as she
looked at her friend. "The worst thing is that she accepts
all that shit from him. It's all right with her. She'd never
walk out on him, and she'd never ask for more. She'll just
sit there for the rest of her life, grateful for all the menial
things she does for him, totally unaware that he does
nothing for her, while she insists that she owes everything
to him. What everything? She's worked like a dog all her
life for whatever she has, and he treats her like a piece of
furniture. . . ." . . . *a paid cunt* . . . Billy's words still
rang in her ears and she forced them from her head for

the ten thousandth time. "I don't know . . . she just sees things differently, but it makes me mad as hell. I can't go around kissing his ass for the rest of my life. I owe my mother a lot, but I don't owe Arthur Durning a damn thing, and neither does she, but she just doesn't see it that way. She's so damn scared all the time. . . . I wonder if she was like that before my father died. . . ." Her mother often told her that she was a lot like him, and her face kind of lit up.

"I like my dad better than my mom." Sharon was always honest about what she felt, especially with Tana. They had told each other countless secrets by the end of the first month, although the one thing Tana had said nothing about was the rape. Somehow she could never quite bring the words to her mouth, and she told herself that it didn't matter anyway, but a few days before the first dance was scheduled on Halloween with a neighboring boys' school, Sharon rolled her eyes and lay back on her bed. "So much for that. What do I do? Go as a black cat, or in a white sheet as a member of the Klan?" Girls were welcome to come to the dance alone, since it was to be held at Green Hill, which was fortunate since neither Sharon nor Tana had dates. Nor did they have any friends. The girls had all been careful not to get too close to her. They were polite to her, and none of them stared anymore, and all of the teachers treated her courteously, but it was almost as though they wanted to pretend that she wasn't there, as though by ignoring her, she would disappear. And the only friend she had was Tana, who went everywhere with her, and as a result, Sharon was Tana's only friend. Everyone stayed away from her too. If she wanted to play with niggers, she was going to find

herself playing alone. Sharon had shouted at her about it
more than once. "Why the hell don't you go play with
your own kind!" She had tried to sound harsh but Tana
had always seen through the ruse.

"Go to hell."

"You're a damn fool."

"Good. That makes two of us. That's why we get
along so well."

"Nah," Sharon would grin at her, "we get along
because you dress like shit and if you didn't have my
wardrobe and my expert advice at hand you'd go out
looking like a total jerk."

"Yeah," Tana grinned delightedly, "you're right.
But can you teach me to dance?" The girls would col-
lapse on their beds, and you could hear their laughter out
in the hall almost every night. Sharon had an energy and
a spunk and a fire about her that brought Tana back to
life again, and sometimes they just sat around and told
jokes and laughed until the tears ran down their cheeks
and they cried. Sharon also had a sense of style which
Tana had never seen before, and the most beautiful
clothes she had ever seen. They were both about the same
size and after a while, they just began to shove everything
into the same drawers, and wear whatever came to hand.

"So . . . what are you going to be for Halloween,
Tan?" Sharon was doing her nails a bright orange this
time, and it looked spectacular against her brown skin.
She glanced at the wet polish and then over at her friend,
but Tana looked noncommittal as she looked away.

"I don't know . . . I'll see. . . ."

"What does that mean?" She was quick to sense
something different in Tana's voice, something she had

never heard there before, except maybe once or twice
when Sharon suspected that she had hit a nerve, but she
wasn't yet sure what that nerve was, or precisely where it
lay. "You're going, aren't you?"

Tana stood up and stretched, and then looked away.
"No. I'm not."

"For heaven's sake, why not?" She looked stunned.
Tana liked having a good time. She had a great sense of
humor, she was a pretty girl, she was fun to be around,
she was bright. "Don't you like Halloween?"

"It's all right . . . for kids. . . ." It was the first
time Sharon had seen her behave like that and she was
surprised.

"Don't be a party pooper, Tan. Come on, I'll put
your costume together for you." She began digging into
the closet they shared, pulling things out and throwing
them on the bed, but Tana did not look amused, and that
night when the lights were out, Sharon questioned her
about it again. "How come you don't want to go to the
Halloween dance, Tan?" She knew that she hadn't had
any dates yet, but so far none of them had. For Sharon it
was a particularly lonely road, as the only black girl at
the school, but she had resigned herself to that when she
had agreed to come to Green Hill, and none of them
really knew anyone yet. Only a few lucky girls had already won dates, but they were sure to meet a flock of
young men at the dance, and Sharon was suddenly dying
to get out. "Do you have a steady at home?" She hadn't
mentioned it yet. Sharon thought it unlikely that she had
held back, although there were some things they still
hadn't shared. They had avoided the subject of their virginity, or lack of it, which Sharon knew was unusual at

Jasmine House. It seemed as though everyone else was anxious to discuss their status as far as that went, but Sharon had correctly sensed Tana's reticence, and she wasn't anxious to discuss the subject herself. But she propped herself up on one elbow now and looked at Tana in the moonlit room. "Tan . . . ?"

"No, nothing like that. . . . I just don't like going out."

"Any particular reason why not? You're allergic to men? . . . get dizzy in heels? . . . turn into a vampire after twelve o'clock? . . . although actually," she grinned mischievously, "that might be kind of a neat trick on Halloween."

In the other bed, Tana laughed. "Don't be a jerk. I just don't want to go out, that's all. It's no big deal. You go. Go fall in love with some white guy and drive your parents nuts." They both laughed at the prospect of that.

"Christ, they'd probably kick me out of school. If old Mrs. Jones had her choice, they'd be fixing me up with Old Sam." The housemother had several times looked patronizingly at Sharon, and then glanced at Sam, as though there were some kind of kinship between them.

"Does she know who your father is?" Freeman Blake had just won another Pulitzer, and everyone in the country knew his name, whether they had read his books or not.

"I don't think she can read."

"Give her an autographed book when you come back from the holidays." Tana grinned and Sharon roared.

"She'd die. . . ." But it still didn't solve the problem of the Halloween dance. In the end, Sharon went as an excruciatingly sexy black cat, in a black leotard, her warm cocoa face peeking out, her eyes huge, her legs seeming to stretch forever, and after an initial tense moment or two, someone asked her to dance, and she was on the floor all night long. She had a terrific time, although none of the girls talked to her, and Tana was tucked into bed and sound asleep when she got home just after one o'clock. "Tan? . . . Tana? . . . Tan . . . ?" She stirred faintly, lifted her head, and opened one eye with a groan.

"D'ya have a good time?"

"It was great! I danced all night!" She was dying to tell her all about it but Tana had already turned over in bed.

"I'm glad . . . g'night. . . ." Sharon watched the other girl's back and wondered again why she hadn't gone, but nothing more was said, and when Sharon tried to bring it up again the next day, it was obvious that Tana didn't want to talk about it. The other girls began going out after that. The phone in the downstairs hall seemed to ring all the time, and only one boy called Sharon Blake. He asked her to a movie and she went, but when they arrived, the ticket taker wouldn't let them in. "This ain't Chicago, friends"—he glared at them as the boy blushed a deep, anguished red—"you're in the South now." He addressed the young man, "Go home and find yourself a decent girl, son." Sharon was reassuring when they left.

"I didn't want to see it anyway. Honest, Tom, it's all right." But the silence was agonizing as he drove her back, and finally when they reached Jasmine House, she turned to him. Her voice was sultry and soft, her eyes kind, her hand like velvet as she touched his. "It really is all right, Tom. I understand. I'm used to this." She took a deep breath. "That's why I came to Green Hill." It seemed an odd thing to say and he looked questioningly at her. She was the first black girl he had ever asked out, and he thought her the most exotic creature he had ever seen.

"You came here to be insulted by some turd in a movie house in a one horse town?" He was still burning inside, he was angry for her even if she was not.

"No," she spoke softly, thinking of her mother's words, "I came here to change things, I guess. It starts like this, and it goes on for a long time, and eventually no one gives a damn, black girls and white guys go to movies, ride in cars, walk down streets, eat hamburgers anywhere they want. It happens in New York. Why shouldn't it happen here? People may look, but at least there they don't throw you out. And the only way to get to that point is to start small, like tonight." The boy looked at her, suddenly wondering if he'd been used but somehow he didn't think he had. Sharon Blake wasn't like that, and he had already heard who her father was. You had to be impressed by someone like that. And he admired her more after what she had just said. It confused him a little bit, but he knew that there was truth in it.

"I'm sorry we didn't get in. Why don't we try again next week?"

She laughed at that. "I didn't mean that we had to change it all at once." But she liked his spunk. He was getting the idea, and maybe her mother hadn't been so wrong. Maybe it was all right to serve a cause after all.

"Why not? Sooner or later that guy'll get tired of kicking us out. Hell, we can go to the coffee shop . . . the restaurant across town. . . ." The possibilities were limitless and Sharon was laughing at him, as he helped her out of the car and walked her into Jasmine House. She offered him a cup of tea, and they were going to sit in the living room for a while, but the looks they got from the other couples sitting there were so ominous that eventually Sharon got up. She walked him slowly to the door, and for a moment she looked sad. It would have been so much easier at Columbia UCLA . . . anywhere in the North . . . anywhere but here. . . . Tom was quick to sense her mood, and he whispered as he stood in the open door. "Remember . . . it doesn't happen overnight." He touched her cheek then and was gone, as she watched him drive away . . . he was right, of course . . . it didn't happen overnight.

And as she walked upstairs, she decided that it hadn't been a totally wasted night. She liked Tom, and wondered if he would call her again. He was a good sport.

"Well? Did he propose?" Tana was grinning at her from the bed as Sharon walked in, and groaned.

"Yeah. Twice."

"That's nice. How was the movie?"

Sharon smiled. "Ask someone else."

"You didn't go?" She was surprised.

"They didn't let us in . . . you know . . . white boy . . . brown girl . . . 'Find yourself a *decent* girl, son. . . .' " She pretended to laugh but Tana could see the pain in her eyes, and she frowned.

"The shits. What did Tom say?"

"He was nice. We sat downstairs for a while when we got back, but that was even worse. There must be seven Snow Whites sitting downstairs with their Prince Charmings, and all of them had their eyes glued on us." She sighed and sat down, looking at her friend. "Shit . . . my mother and her bright ideas . . . for about a minute outside the movie house I felt very noble and brave and pure, and by the time we got back, I decided it was really a huge pain in the ass. Hell, we can't even go out for a hamburger. I could starve to death in this town."

"Not if you went out with me, I'll bet." They hadn't gone out to eat yet, they were too comfortable where they were, and the food was surprisingly good at school. They had both already gained three or four pounds, much to Sharon's chagrin.

"Don't be so sure, Tan. I'll bet they'd raise hell if I tried to go somewhere with you too. Black is black and white is white, no matter how you look at it."

"Why don't we try?" Tana looked intrigued, and the next night they did. They walked slowly into town, and stopped for a hamburger and the waitress gave them a long, slow, ugly look and then walked away without serving them, as Tana looked at her in shock. She signaled for her again, and the woman appeared not to see, until finally Tana walked over to her, and asked if they could order their dinner now, and the waitress looked at her with chagrin.

She spoke in a low voice so that Sharon wouldn't hear. "I'm sorry, honey. I can't serve your friend. I was hoping you two'd get the idea."

"Why not? She's from Washington," as though that

would make a difference, ". . . her mother is an attorney and her father has won the Pulitzer twice. . . ."

"That don't make no difference here. This ain't Washington. It's Yolan." Yolan, South Carolina, home of Green Hill.

"Is there anywhere in town we can eat?"

The waitress looked nervously at the tall green-eyed blonde, there was a hardness in her voice that suddenly frightened her. "There's a place for her just down the street . . . and you could eat here."

"I mean together," Tana's eyes were as hard as green steel, and for the first time in her life she felt something tighten in her spine. She almost wanted to hit someone. It was a feeling she hadn't known before, an unreasoning, helpless rage. "Is there anyplace in this town where we can eat together, without taking the train to New York?" Tana glared at her, and slowly the waitress shook her head. But Tana wasn't moving an inch. "Okay, then I'll have two cheeseburgers, and two Cokes."

"No, you won't." A man appeared from the kitchen behind where they stood. "You'll go back to that damn fancy school you two come from," they were easily spotted in Yolan. Sharon's clothes alone were enough to draw attention anywhere. She was wearing a skirt and sweater her mother had bought her at Bonwit Teller in New York, "And you can eat anything you damn well please there. I don't know what's gotten into them over there, but if they let niggers into the school, then let them feed 'em over at Green Hill, we don't gotta feed 'em here." He looked pointedly at Tana, then at Sharon where she sat, and it was as though an enormous force had entered the room, and for a minute Tana thought he might physically

throw them out. She hadn't been as frightened or as angry since she'd been raped.

And then, ever so quietly, and in her graceful, long-
legged, ladylike way, Sharon stood up. "Come on, Tan."
Her voice was a sexy purr, and for an instant, Tana saw
the man's eyes almost paw at her and she wanted to slap
his face. It reminded her of something she never wanted
to think of again, and a moment later she followed
Sharon out.

"Son of a bitch. . . ." Tana was fuming as they
walked slowly back to school, but Sharon was amazingly
calm. It was the same feeling she had had the night before, with Tom, when they hadn't let them into the movie
house. For an instant, there had been a quiet surge of
power, an understanding of why she was there, and then
depression had set in. But tonight, the depression hadn't
hit her yet.

"Life is strange, isn't it? If this were in New York or
L.A., or almost anywhere else, no one would give a
damn. But down here, it's all-important that I'm black,
you're white. Maybe my mother is right. Maybe it is time
for a crusade. I don't know, I always thought that as long
as I was comfortable, it didn't matter if things like that
were happening to someone else. But all of a sudden that
someone else is me." Suddenly she knew why her mother
had insisted on her coming here, and for the first time
since she'd arrived, she wondered if she'd been right.
Maybe she did belong here after all. Maybe she owed it to
someone else for all the time that she had been comfortable. "I don't know what to think, Tan. . . ."

"Neither do I. . . ." They were walking along side
by side. "I don't think I've ever felt so helpless or been so

mad. . . ." And then suddenly Billy Durning's face
came to mind, and she visibly winced, "Well . . . maybe
once. . . ."

They suddenly felt closer than they ever had before.
Tana almost wanted to put an arm around her to protect
her from more hurt, as Sharon glanced over at her with a
gentle smile. "When was that, Tan?"

"Oh a long time ago. . . ." She tried to smile, ". . .
like five months. . . ."

"Oh yeah . . . a *real* long time ago. . . ." The two
girls exchanged a smile and walked on as a car sped by,
but no one bothered them, and Tana wasn't afraid. No
one would ever do to her again what Billy Durning did.
She would kill them first. And there was a strange ugly
look in her eyes as Sharon glanced at her. "Must've been
pretty bad."

"It was."

"Wanna talk about it?" Her voice was as soft as the
charcoal gray night, and they walked along in silence for
a time as Tana thought. She had never wanted to tell
anyone about it before, not since she'd tried to tell her
mom.

"I don't know."

Sharon nodded, as though she understood. Everyone
had something they didn't want to share. She had a secret
like that herself. "It's okay, Tan." But as she said the
words, Tana looked at her, and suddenly the words burst
from her, almost of their own.

"Yeah, I do. . . ." And then, "I don't know . . .
how do you talk about something like that?" She began
to walk faster as though to run away, and Sharon followed her easily on her long, graceful legs, unconsciously

Tana ran a hand through her hair nervously, looked
away, and began to breathe harder than she had before.
"There's nothing much to say. . . . I went to a party
after I graduated in June . . . my mother's boss's house
. . . he has this real little shit of a son . . . and I told
my mother I didn't want to go. . . ." Her breath was
coming in little short gasps and Sharon knew she wasn't
aware of it as they hurried along. She knew that whatever
it was, it was torturing the girl, and it would be better if
she got it out. "Anyway, she said I had to go anyway
. . . she always says that . . . that's the way she is,
about Arthur Durning anyway, and his kids . . . she's
blind to what they are, and . . ." the words stopped, and
they walked on, hurrying, hurrying, as though she could
still run away, and Sharon kept pace, watching her as she
struggled with the memories and then began to speak
again, ". . . anyway, this dumb boy picked me up and
we got there . . . to the party, I mean . . . and everyone got drunk . . . and the dumb guy who brought me
got drunk and disappeared and I was wandering around
the house . . . and Billy . . . Arthur's son . . . asked
me if I wanted to see the room where my mother worked,
and I knew where it was. . . ." There were tears running
down her cheeks now, but she didn't feel them in the
wind, and Sharon didn't say anything to her, "and he
took me to Arthur's bedroom instead and everything was
gray . . . gray velvet, gray satin . . . gray fur . . .
even the rug on the floor was gray," it was all she could
remember, the endless field of gray and her blood on the
floor afterwards and Billy's face, and then the accident,
she could barely breathe thinking of it, and she pulled at
the neck of her shirt as she began to run, sobbing now, as

Sharon followed her, keeping close, staying near. She wasn't alone anymore, there was a friend running through the nightmare with her and it was as though she sensed that as she went on, ". . . and Billy started to slap me and he pushed me down . . . and everything I did . . ." she remembered the helplessness again now, the desperation she felt, and suddenly in the night air she screamed and suddenly she stopped, burying her face in her hands, ". . . and I couldn't do anything to make him stop . . . I couldn't. . . ." Her whole body was shaking now as Sharon took her quietly in her arms and held her tight, ". . . and he raped me . . . and he left me there with blood all over me . . . my legs and my face . . . and then I threw up . . . and later he followed me all down the road and he made me get in his car and he almost hit this truck," the words just wouldn't stop now as she cried and Sharon began to cry with her, "and we hit a tree instead and he cut his head and there was blood all over him too and they took us to the hospital and then my mother came. . . ." And suddenly she stopped again, and with her face ravaged by the memory she had tried to flee for five months, she looked up into Sharon's eyes, "and when I tried to tell her, she wouldn't believe anything I said . . . she said Billy Durning wouldn't do a thing like that." The sobs were deep and wracking now, and quietly Sharon held her tight.

"I believe you, Tan."

Tana nodded, looking like a bereft little girl. "I never want anyone to touch me again."

She knew exactly how Tana felt, but not for the same reasons as her friend. She hadn't been raped. She had gladly given it, to the boy she loved. "My mother never believed a single word I said. And she never will. The Durnings are gods to her.''

"All that matters is that you're okay, Tan." Sharon led her to a tree stump, where they sat down and Sharon offered her a cigarette, and for once Tana took a puff. "And you are okay, you know. A lot more so than you think." She smiled gently at her friend, deeply moved by her confidence and she wiped the tears from her cheeks as Tana smiled at her.

"You don't think I'm awful because of that?"

"That's a dumb thing to ask. It's no reflection on you, Tan."

"I don't know . . . sometimes I think it is . . . as though I could have stopped him if I tried hard enough." It felt good just to say the words, just to get them out. They had haunted her for months.

"Do you really believe that, Tan? Do you really think you could have stopped him? Tell the truth."

She thought about it for a long time and then shook her head. "No."

"Then don't torture yourself. It happened. It was horrible. Worse than that. It was probably the worst thing that'll ever happen to you in your whole life, but no one will ever do that to you again. And it wasn't really you he touched. He couldn't touch the real you, no matter what, Tan. Just cut it off. Dump the memory. And move on."

"That's easy to say," Tana smiled tiredly, "but not so easily done. How do you forget something like that?"

"You make yourself. You don't let it destroy you, Tan. That's the only time a guy like that wins. He's sick. You're not. Don't make yourself sick over what he did.

As awful as it was, put it out of your mind, and move on."

"Oh Sharon . . ." She sighed and stood up, looking down at her friend. It was a beautiful night. "What makes you so smart, for a kid?"

Sharon smiled, but her eyes were serious tonight, almost sad, as Tana looked down at her. "I have my secrets too."

"Like what?" Tana felt calmer now than she ever had in her life, it was as though a raging animal had been released from her, as though Sharon had let it out of its cage and set it free, and Tana was finally at peace again. Her mother hadn't been able to do that for her five months before, but this girl had, and she knew that whatever else happened after that, they would always be friends. "What happened to you?" Tana searched her eyes, knowing now that there was something there. And she was sure of it when Sharon looked up at her. She didn't mince any words. She had never told anyone, but she had thought about it a lot, and she and her father had talked about it one night before she left for Green Hill. He had told her the same thing she had just told Tana, that she couldn't let it destroy her life. It had happened. And now it was done. And she had to let it stay that way, and move on, but she wondered if she ever could.

"I had a baby this year."

For an instant Tana's breath caught and she looked at Sharon in shock. "You did?"

"Yeah. I've been going with the same boy at home since I was fifteen and when I was sixteen he gave me his senior ring . . . I don't know, Tan . . . it kind of seemed so cute . . . he looks like an African God, and

he's smart as hell, and he dances . . ." she looked pretty
and young as she thought of him. . . . "He's at Harvard
now," her eyes grew sad, "but I haven't talked to him in
almost a year. I got pregnant, I told him, and he panicked, I guess. He wanted me to have an abortion from
this doctor his cousin knew, and I refused . . . hell, I'd
heard about girls who died. . . ." Her eyes filled with
tears at the memory, and she forgot that Tana was standing there, looking down at her. "I was going to tell my
mom, but . . . I just couldn't . . . I told my father instead . . . and then he told her . . . and everybody
went nuts . . . and they called his parents, and everyone
cried and screamed, my mother called him a nigger . . .
and his father called me a slut . . . it was the worst
night in my life, and when it was all over, my parents
gave me a choice. I could have an abortion at a doctor's
my mother had found out about, or I could have the baby
and give it up. They said," she took a deep gulp of air as
though this were the worst part, "that I couldn't keep it
. . . that it would ruin my life . . . ," her whole body
shook, "to have a baby at seventeen . . . and I don't
know why but I decided to have the baby, I think because
I thought that Danny would change his mind . . . or
my parents would . . . or a miracle would happen . . .
but nothing did. I lived in a home for five months and I
kept up with all the work for my senior year, and the
baby was born on April nineteenth . . . a little boy.
. . ." She was trembling and Tana wordlessly reached
out and took her hand, "I wasn't supposed to see him at
all . . . but I did once . . . he was so little. . . . I was
in labor for nineteen hours and it was horrible and he
only weighed six pounds. . . ." Her eyes were a thou-

sand miles away thinking of the little boy she would never see again, and she looked up at Tana now, "He's gone, Tan," she whimpered almost like a child and in many ways she still was a child. They both were. "I signed the final papers three weeks ago. My mother drew them up . . . some people adopted him in New York. . . ." She couldn't stop the sobs as she bent her head, "Oh God, Tan, I hope they're good to him . . . I never should have let him go . . . and all for what?" She looked angrily up at her friend, "for this? To come to this dumb school to prove a point, so that other colored girls can come here one day. So what?"

"That had nothing to do with this. They wanted you to have a fresh start, with a husband and a family at the right time."

"They were wrong, and so was I. You'll never know what it felt like . . . that emptiness when I went home . . . with nothing . . . with no one . . . nothing will ever replace that." She took a deep breath. "I haven't seen Danny since I went into the home in Maryland . . . and I'll never know where the baby is. . . . I graduated with my class . . . ," with a lead weight in her heart, ". . . and no one knew what I felt. . . ." Tana shook her head, watching her. They were both women now. It had been hard earned, hard won, and it was too soon to know if things would get better in time, but one thing they both knew as they walked slowly home, and that was that they each had a friend. Tana pulled Sharon off the stump, and they hugged each other tight, their tears fell on each other's cheeks, each feeling the other's pain, as much as they could.

"I love you, Shar." Tana looked at her with her gentle smile, and Sharon dried her eyes.

"Yeah . . . me too. . . ."

And they walked home arm in arm, in the silent night, went back to Jasmine House, got undressed and into their beds, each with her own thoughts.

"Tan?" It was Sharon's voice in the dark room.

"Yeah?"

"Thanks."

"For what? Listening? That's what friends are for . . . I need you too."

"My father was right, you know. You've got to move on in life."

"I guess." But how? "Did he have any suggestions about how to pull that off?"

Sharon laughed at that. "I'll have to ask him that." And then suddenly, she had an idea. "Why don't you ask him yourself? Why don't you come home for Thanksgiving with me?"

Tana mulled it over from her bed, with the beginnings of a smile. She liked the idea. "I don't know what my mother will say." But all of a sudden she wasn't sure she cared, and if she did, it wasn't as much as she would have cared six months before. Maybe it was time to try her wings and do what she wanted to do. "I'll call her tomorrow night."

"Good." Sharon smiled sleepily and turned over in her bed, with her back to her friend. "G'night, Tan. . . ." And a moment later, they were both asleep, more at ease than either of them had been in months, Tana's hands cast childlike above the blond hair, and Sharon cuddled up into a little black purring ball. Even the long legs seemed to disappear and she looked like a kitten as she slept peacefully.

Chapter 5

Jean Roberts was disappointed when her daughter called to say that she had decided not to come home for Thanksgiving.

"Are you sure?" She didn't want to insist, but she would have preferred it if Tana were coming back. "You don't know this girl very well. . . ."

"Mother, I live with her. We share the same room. I know her better than I've ever known anyone in my life."

"Are you sure her parents won't mind?"

"Positive. She called them this afternoon. They have a room for me, and she said they were delighted that she was bringing someone home." Of course they were. From what Sharon had said, it proved Miriam's point that Sharon could be happy at Green Hill, even if she was the only black girl there, and now she was bringing one of "them" home, the ultimate proof of how well they had accepted her. They didn't know that Tana was her only friend, that there wasn't a single place in Yolan where she could be served, that she hadn't been able to go to a movie since she'd arrived, and that even in the cafeteria at school, the girls avoided her. But, according to Sharon, even if they had known, Miriam would have felt it proved even more that Sharon was needed there. "They" had to accept Negroes one day, and the time was now. It was a good challenge for Sharon, particularly after last year, this would keep her from dwelling on herself, Miriam Blake thought, it would give her something else to think about, or so she had said. "Really, they said it was fine."

"All right, then be sure you invite her up sometime during the Christmas holidays," Jean smiled into the phone, "in fact, I have a little surprise for you. Arthur and I were going to tell you over Thanksgiving . . ." Tana's heart stopped. Was he finally marrying her? She was robbed of speech as her mother went on. "Arthur made it possible for you to have a little 'coming out' party of your own. There's a small cotillion here in town . . . well, not a cotillion really, but a deb party of sorts, and Arthur put up your name, I mean you did go to Miss Lawson's after all, dear, and . . . you're going to be a debutante, sweetheart. Isn't that wonderful?" For a moment, no words came to Tana's mind. It didn't seem particularly wonderful at all, and once again her mother would be kissing Arthur Durning's feet . . . marry her . . . what a joke. How could she have thought a thing like that . . . a "cotillion of sorts" . . . shit. . . . "Why don't you invite your new friend to come up then?" Tana almost choked. *Because my new friend is black, Mom.*

"I'll ask, but I think she's going away over the holidays." Shit. A debutante. And who would her escort be? Billy Durning? The son of a bitch.

"You don't sound very excited, sweetheart." There was disappointment in Jean Roberts' voice, both because Tana wouldn't be coming home, and because she didn't

sound very excited about the party Arthur had arranged.
He knew how much it meant to Jean. Ann had come out
at the International Ball four years before, of course,
though not at a small deb party like this, but nonetheless
it would be a wonderful experience for Tana to have, or
at least Jean thought it would.

"I'm sorry, Mom. I guess I'm just surprised."

"It is a beautiful surprise, isn't it?" No. She didn't
really care. Things like that didn't matter to her. They
never had. All the social nonsense of the Durnings' world
seemed irrelevant to her, but it meant so much to Jean. It
always had, ever since she had fallen in love with him.
"You'll have to think of an escort for the dance. I was
hoping Billy could," Tana felt her heart pound and her
chest get tight, "but he's going skiing in Europe with
friends. In Saint Moritz, the lucky boy," . . . lucky boy
. . . *He raped me, Mom.* . . . "You'll just have to think
of someone else. Someone suitable, of course." Of course.
How many other rapists do we know?

"It's too bad I can't go alone." Tana's voice sounded
dead at her end of the phone.

"That's a ridiculous thing to say." Jean sounded annoyed. "Well, anyway, don't forget to invite your friend
. . . the one you're going home for Thanksgiving with."

"Sure." Tana smiled. If she only knew. Jean Roberts
would have died if Tana had invited a black friend to the
little "coming out" party Arthur had arranged. It almost
amused Tana to think of it, but she would never have
taken advantage of Sharon like that. They were all a
bunch of rude pricks. She knew that even her mother
wasn't ready for that. "What'll you do for Thanksgiving,
Mom? Will you be all right?"

"I'll be fine. Arthur had already invited us to Greenwich for the day."

"Maybe now that I won't be there, you can spend the night." There was a dead silence on the phone, and Tana regretted the words. "I didn't mean it like that."

"Yes, you did."

"Well, what difference does it make? I'm eighteen years old now. It's not a secret. . . ." Tana felt sick as she thought of the endless gray room where . . . "I'm sorry, Mom."

"Take care of yourself." She drew herself up. She would miss seeing her, but she had a lot to do now, and Tana would be home in a month anyway. "And don't forget to thank your friend for having you there." Tana smiled to herself, it was like being seven years old again. Maybe it always would be.

"I will. Have a good Thanksgiving, Mom."

"I shall. And I'll thank Arthur for you." Jean said the words pointedly and Tana looked blank at her end.

"What for?"

"The ball, Tana, the ball . . . I don't know if you realize it yet, but something like that is very important for a young girl, and it's not something that I could provide for you myself." Important . . . ? Important to whom . . . ? "You have no idea what something like this means." Tears stung Jean Roberts' eyes. In some ways, it was a dream come true. Andy and Jean Roberts' little girl, the baby Andy had never seen, would be coming out in New York society, and even if it was on the fringe, it was an important event for both of them . . . for Tana . . . and especially for Jean . . . it would be the most important moment in her life. She remembered

Ann's coming out ball. She had planned every exquisite detail and had never thought that one day Tana would be coming out too.

"I'm sorry, Mom."

"You'd better be. And I think you ought to write Arthur a nice note. Tell him what it means to you." She wanted to scream into the phone. What the hell does it mean? That she'd find a rich husband some day, that they could mark it on her pedigree? Who cared? What accomplishment was that, to curtsy at a dumb ball, being gaped at by a lot of drunks? She didn't even know who she was going to take with her, and she shuddered at the thought. She had gone out with half a dozen different boys during her last two years of school, but there had never been anyone serious, and after what had happened in Greenwich in June, there was no one she wanted to go out with at all.

"I have to go, Mom." She was suddenly desperate to get off the phone, and when she returned to her room, she looked depressed and Sharon looked up. She was doing her nails again. It was an eternal process with both of them. Recently they had both tried beige, "Straw Hat" by Fabergé.

"She said no?"

"She said yes."

"So? You look like someone just burst your balloon."

"I think she did." Tana sat down on her bed with a thump. "Shit. She got her damn friend to sign me up for some dumb coming out ball. Jesus Christ, Shar, I feel like a complete fool."

Sharon looked up at her and started to laugh. "You mean you're going to be a debutante, Tan?"

"More or less." Tana looked embarrassed and groaned at her friend. "How could she do that to me?"

"It might be fun."

"For who? And what the hell's the point? It's like a big cattle drive. They shove you around in a white dress and show you off to a lot of drunks, and you're supposed to find a husband somewhere in the bunch. Pretty cute, huh?" She looked sick, and Sharon put her nail polish away.

"Who're you going to take?"

"Don't ask. She wanted Billy Durning to be my escort of course, and thank God he'll be out of town."

"Be grateful for that." Sharon looked pointedly at her.

"I am. But the whole thing sounds like a farce."

"So are a lot of things in life."

"Don't be so cynical, Shar."

"Don't be so chicken, Tan. It'll do you good."

"Says who?"

"Says I." Sharon advanced towards her and tried to stare her down. "You live like a nun around here."

"So do you. So what?"

"I don't have any choice." Tom had never called her again, it was more than he could cope with, Sharon knew, and in truth she understood. She hadn't expected more of him. But it didn't make her life very interesting at Green Hill. "You do."

"Never mind."

"You've got to start going out."

"No, I don't." Tana looked her right in the eye. "I

don't have to do a goddamn thing I don't want to do. I'm eighteen years old, and I'm free as a bird."

"A lame duck." Sharon stared her down. "Get out there again, Tan." But Tana said nothing at all. She walked into the bathroom they shared with the next room, locked the door, ran a bath, and didn't come out for an hour. "I meant what I said." Sharon's voice was husky in the darkened room, once they were both in their beds.

"About what?"

"You should start going out again."

"So should you."

"I will one of these days." Sharon sighed. "Maybe over the holidays when I'm home. There's no one for me to go out with here." And then she laughed. "Hell, Tan, I don't know what I'm complaining about. At least I've got you."

Tana smiled at her and they chatted for a few minutes and then drifted off to sleep.

The following week Tana went home to Washington with her. They were met at the train by Sharon's father, Freeman Blake, and Tana was instantly struck by how tall and handsome he was. He was a regal looking man, with a proud, beautifully carved, almost mahogany face, broad shoulders, and Sharon's same endlessly long legs. He had a warm smile, brilliantly white teeth, and he was quick to pull his daughter into his arms and hold her tight. He knew just how much she'd been through in the last year, and she'd come through it like a champ, just as he'd known she would, and he was desperately proud of her.

"Hi, baby, how's school?" She rolled her eyes, and turned quickly towards her friend.

"Tana, this is my dad, Freeman Blake. Daddy, this is Tana Roberts, my roommate at Green Hill." He gave Tana's hand a powerful shake and she was magnetized by his eyes and the sound of his voice on the way home. He was filling Sharon in on all the local news, her mother's appointment to an even more important post, her brother Dick's big new romance, the remodeling of the house, the neighbor's new child, his new book. It was a warm friendly patter that touched Tana's heart, and she felt envious of the life that Sharon obviously had. And she felt it even more at dinner that night in the handsome colonial dining room. They had a beautiful house with a huge lawn and backyard, three cars in the garage, one of which was a Cadillac Freeman drove, despite the rude things his friends said. But he admitted that he had always wanted a Cadillac convertible and he had one now after all these years. They were obviously all four closely knit, and Tana found Miriam more than a little formidable. She was so intelligent and so direct that it took one's breath away, and she seemed to constantly expect the ultimate of everyone. One was never safe from her questions, her demands, and her ever-searching gaze.

"See what I mean?" Sharon said when they were alone upstairs. "It's like being on the witness stand, just having dinner with her." She had wanted to know everything Sharon had done in the last two months, and she was interested in both the incident with Tom at the movie house, and the one at the coffee shop with Tana after that.

"It's just that she cares so much, Shar . . . about everything!"

"I know that. And it drives me nuts. Daddy is just as smart as she is for chrissake, and he's so much gentler about everything." He was that, he told exquisite tales, made everyone laugh, and he had a way of making everyone comfortable, of bringing them closer together and forming an irresistible bond. Tana had noticed it all night long and she thought him the most remarkable man she had ever met.

"He's the most incredible man, Shar."

"I know."

"I read one of his books last year. I'm going to go home now and read them all."

"I'll give them to you."

"Only if I can have an autographed set." They both laughed, and a moment later, Miriam knocked at the door, anxious to know that they were all right.

"Do you have everything you need?" Tana smiled almost shyly at her.

"I do. Thank you very much, Mrs. Blake."

"Not at all. We're so glad you could come." The smile was even more dazzling than Shar's, and the eyes were driving, omniscient, almost frightening they plunged so deep and so hard. "How do you like Green Hill?"

"I do. Very much. The professors are pretty interesting." But there was a lack of enthusiasm in her voice which Miriam picked up at once.

"But?"

Tana smiled. She was sharp. Very sharp. "The atmosphere isn't as warm as I thought it would be."

"Why is that?"

"I don't know. The girls seem to stay in cliques."

"And the two of you?"

"We're together most of the time." Sharon looked at Tana and smiled, and Miriam didn't seem displeased. She thought that Tana was a bright girl, and there was a lot of potential there. Far more than Tana herself knew. She was quick, she was bright, she was funny at times, but cautious, laced up. She would have to open up one day, and when she did, God only knew what would be there.

"Maybe that's your problem then, girls. Tana, how many other friends do you have at Green Hill?"

"Just Shar. We're in class together most of the time. We share the same room."

"And you're probably being punished for that. I'm sure you realize that. If your closest friend is the only Negro girl there they're going to penalize you, you know."

"What for?"

"Don't be naive."

"Don't be so cynical, Mom." Sharon sounded suddenly annoyed.

"Maybe it's time you both grew up."

"What the hell's that supposed to mean?" Sharon lashed out at her. "Hell, I've been home for nine hours and you're already on my back with your speeches and your crusades."

"I'm not making any speeches. I'm just telling you to face facts." She looked at them both then. "You can't hide from the truth, girls. It isn't easy being black today . . . or a black girl's friend . . . you're both going to have to realize that and be willing to pay the price if you expect the friendship to last."

"Can't you do anything without turning it into a political crusade, Mom?"

Miriam looked at her and then at her friend. "I want you to do something for me, both of you, before you go back to school on Sunday night. There's a man I know speaking this Sunday in Washington. He's one of the most extraordinary men I've ever known, Martin Luther King, and I want you to come listen to him with me."

"Why?" Sharon was still glaring at her.

"Because it's something neither of you will ever forget."

And as they rode back toward South Carolina late that night, Tana was still thinking of it. Miriam Blake had been right. He was the most visionary man Tana had ever listened to. He made everyone else seem stupid and blind, and it was hours before she could even talk about what she had heard. Simple words about being black and being a black man's friend, about civil rights and the equality of everyone, and afterwards they had sung a song, swaying together, arms crossed, holding hands. She looked at Sharon an hour after they left Washington.

"He was amazing, wasn't he?"

Sharon nodded, thinking of his words again. "You know, it feels dumb just going back to school. I feel as though I should be doing something." She leaned her head back against the seat and closed her eyes, and Tana stared out into the dark night as they rode into the South. It seemed to make his words even more important than they had been. This was where it was happening, where people were being hurt, and ignored, and abused. And as the thoughts wandered through her head, she thought of the debutante party her mother had set up, and it was as though the two thoughts were so diametrically opposed that they just wouldn't fit into her head at the same time. When Sharon opened her eyes again, Tana was looking at her.

"What are you going to do?" One had to do something after hearing him. There was no choice at all. Even Freeman Blake had agreed.

"I don't know yet." Sharon looked tired, but she had been thinking of it since they'd left Washington, of what she could do to help . . . in Yolan . . . in Green Hill . . . "What about you?"

"I don't know." Tana sighed. "Anything I can, I guess. But I'll tell you, after hearing Dr. King speak, I know one thing . . . that party my mother is forcing me into in New York is the dumbest thing I've ever done."

Sharon smiled. She couldn't really disagree now, but there was another side to it as well. A more small-scale, human one. "It'll do you good."

"I doubt that." The two girls exchanged a smile, and rode on into the South until they reached Yolan, and took one of the town's two cabs to Green Hill.

Chapter 6

The train roared into Pennsylvania Station on December twenty-first just after two o'clock in the afternoon and there was a light snow falling as Tana watched. It made everything look Christmasy and almost like a fairy tale, and yet as she gathered her things, fought her way through the station, and went outside to hail a cab, she realized again how depressed she was about coming home. It made her feel instantly guilty toward Jean, and she knew that she wasn't being fair, but she would rather have been anywhere than on her way home to her own coming out dance. And she knew how excited her mother was. For the past two weeks, she had called Tana almost every night, about the guests, the flowers, the table decor, her date, her dress. She had picked the dress out for Tana herself, an exquisite white silk with white satin trim and tiny little white beads embroidered in floral patterns around the hem. It had cost a fortune, and Arthur had told her to charge it to his account at Saks.

"He's so good to us, sweetheart. . . ." As she rode home to the apartment in the cab, Tana could close her eyes and imagine her mother's face as she said the words . . . why, why was she so everlastingly grateful to him?

What on earth did he do for her, except let her work her fingers to the bone, and wait for him all those times he never came when Marie was still alive . . . and even now, everything else always seemed to come first with him. And if he loved Jean so much, why the hell didn't he marry her? It depressed Tana to think about that too. Everything was such a goddamn farce . . . her mother and Arthur, how "good" the Durnings were to them, yeah, like the way Billy had been good to her . . . and the party she would have to go to the following night. She had invited a boy she had known for years and never liked, but he was the right type for an event like that, Chandler George III. She had gone to a couple of dances with him before, and he bored her to tears, but she knew her mother would be pleased. And she also knew that she'd have a miserable time but that couldn't be helped. Most important of all, he was harmless and polite and wouldn't do anything inappropriate.

The apartment was dark when she got in, Jean was still at work as Tana looked around. Everything looked the same except smaller somehow, and drearier than she had remembered it. And as she had the thought, it seemed somehow unfair. She knew how hard her mother tried to keep a nice home for them both, and she always had. But Tana felt as though things were different now, as though imperceptibly she had changed and no longer fit in this scene. She found herself thinking of the comfortable Blake house in Washington, and how much she had enjoyed being there. It wasn't pretentious, like the Durnings' house, but it was warm, and beautiful, and real. And she missed the Blakes as well, especially Sharon. Tana had watched her get off the train, feeling as

though she were losing her best friend, and Sharon had
turned back once to give her a big smile and a wave, and
then she was gone and the train moved north, and now
she was here, feeling as though she wanted to cry as she
set her bags down in her room.

"Is that my little girl?" The front door slammed and
Jean's voice rang out as Tana turned with a frightened
look. What if her mother could read her thoughts, could
see how uncomfortable she was just being there? But Jean
saw nothing of the sort, all she saw was the daughter she
loved, and she held her tight for an instant before step-
ping back again. "Boy, you look good!" And so did Jean.
Her cheeks were pink from the cold, there were kisses of
frost on the tips of her hair, and her eyes looked big and
dark. She was so excited that she didn't even wait to take
off her coat before running into her own room and
emerging again with Tana's dress. It was exquisite as it
hung from the padded satin hanger they had delivered it
with. It looked almost like a wedding dress, and Tana
smiled.

"Where's the veil?"

Her mother smiled back. "You never know. That'll
come next."

Tana laughed and shook her head at the thought.
"Now let's not rush into that. I'm only eighteen."

"That doesn't mean anything, sweetheart. You
might meet the man of your dreams tomorrow night, you
know. And who knows after that?" Tana stared at her in
disbelief. Something in Jean's eyes said she was serious.

"Do you mean that, Mom?"

Jean Roberts smiled again. It was wonderful to see
Tana again, and now that she saw the dress next to her,

she knew just how fabulous it was going to look on. A victory all around. "You're a beautiful girl, Tana. And some man is going to be very lucky to have you as his wife."

"But wouldn't you be upset if I met him now?"

"Why?" She didn't seem to understand and Tana looked stunned.

"But I'm eighteen years old. Don't you want me to go on with college and make something of myself?"

"You're doing that now."

"But this is just the beginning, Mom. When I finish my two years at Green Hill, I want to go on and do something else."

Jean frowned. "There's nothing wrong with getting married and having kids."

"Is that what this is all about?" Suddenly Tana felt sick. "This coming out bullshit . . . it's kind of like a slave auction, isn't it?"

Jean Roberts looked shocked. "Tana, that's a terrible thing to say."

"Well, it's true, isn't it? All these young girls lined up, curtsying like fools, and a bunch of men checking them out." She squinted her eyes as though the girls were lined up in front of her, ". . . let's see, I'll take . . . that one over there." Her eyes opened wide again, and she looked upset. "Hell, there has to be more to life than that."

"You make it sound sick somehow, and it's not. It's a beautiful tradition that means a lot to everyone." No, it doesn't, Mom, at least not to me . . . just to you . . . but she couldn't bring herself to say those words. Jean looked at her unhappily. "Why are you being so difficult about this? Ann Durning came out four years ago, and she had a wonderful time."

"Good for her. But I'm not Ann." She had also run off with some twit in Italy who had to be bought off, as Tana recalled.

Jean sighed and sat down, looking up at Tana from the chair. She hadn't seen Tana in three months and she could already feel the tension mounting between them. "Why don't you just relax and enjoy yourself, Tana? You never know, you might meet someone you like."

"I don't want to meet someone I 'like.' I don't even want to go, Mom."

Tears filled Jean's eyes as she looked at her, and Tana couldn't stand the look on her face. "I just wanted you to . . . I wanted you to have . . ." Tana knelt and hugged her close.

"I'm sorry, Mom. I'm sorry . . . I know it'll be beautiful."

Jean smiled through her tears and kissed Tana's cheek. "One thing's for sure, you will be beautiful, sweetheart."

"I'd have to be in that dress. You must have spent a fortune on it." She was touched but it seemed such a useless expense. She would have rather had clothes to wear at school. She was borrowing Sharon's all the time.

But Jean was smiling at her. "It's a gift from Arthur, sweetheart." Tana felt her stomach tie in a knot. Another reason to be "grateful" to him. She was so tired of Arthur and his gifts.

"He shouldn't have done that." Tana was visibly less than thrilled, and Jean couldn't understand why except that Tana had always been jealous of him.

"He wanted you to have a pretty dress." And indeed it was. As she stood in front of the mirror the following night, her hair teased and swept up, the way her mother had seen Jackie Kennedy's hair done in *Vogue*, with the beautiful silk dress, she looked like a fairy princess with her spun gold hair and big green eyes. It filled Jean's eyes with tears just to look at her. She looked exquisite. Moments later, Chandler George arrived to pick her up, and Jean left with them. Arthur had said that he would try to come by, but he wasn't sure. There was a dinner he had to attend that night, and he'd do his "best." Tana didn't say anything about it to Jean in the cab, but she had heard that line before, and knew that it meant nothing at all. It had applied to Christmas, Thanksgiving, and Jean's birthdays over the years. And usually doing his "best" meant that he wouldn't arrive, but a bunch of flowers, or a telegram, or a note would instead. She always remembered her mother's crestfallen face at those times, but not tonight. Jean was too excited about her to worry about Arthur very much. She hovered like a mother hen, joining a group of the other mothers at one side of a long bar. The fathers had found each other, too, and there were clumps of well wishers and old family friends, but most of the room was filled with young people about Tana's own age, girls in pink dresses, or red satin, or bright green, and only a dozen in the white dresses their parents had bought them to come out in that night. For the most part, they were a motley adolescent herd, with faces that would take years to thin out, and waistlines to match. There was something singularly undistinguished about girls that age, and because of that,

Tana especially stood out. She was tall and slim, and she held her head high.

Jean watched her proudly from across the room. When the big moment came, and the drumroll came halfway into the night, and each girl was led out on her father's arm to curtsy to the guests, there were unrestrained tears of pride on Jean's cheeks. She had hoped that Arthur Durning would be there by then, and had even dared to hope that he might lead her out. But he couldn't make it, of course. He had done enough for them, she couldn't expect him to do more. Tana came out looking nervous and flushed on the arm of Chandler George. She curtsied prettily, lowered her eyes, and disappeared into the rest of the group, and the music began again shortly after that. It had happened, it was done. Tana had officially "come out." She looked around the room afterwards, feeling like a complete fool. There was no exhilaration, no thrill, no romantic tingle up and down her spine. She had done it because her mother wanted her to and it was over now. She was grateful for the hubbub that happened afterwards, which allowed her to get lost for a while. Chandler looked as though he had fallen madly in love with a chubby redheaded girl with a sweet smile and an elaborate white velvet dress, and Tana had discreetly disappeared, allowing him to go in pursuit of his prize, as Tana wandered into an alcove and collapsed in a chair. She lay her head back, closed her eyes, and sighed, grateful to be away from it all, from the music, the people, Chandler, whom she couldn't stand, and the desperately lonely look of pride in her mother's eyes. Tana sighed again just thinking of it, and then jumped halfway off her seat as she heard a voice.

"It can't be as bad as all that." She opened her eyes to see a powerfully built dark-haired young man with eyes as green as hers. There was something rakish about him, even in black tie, a casual air about the way he stood, looking down at her, holding a glass, and smiling cynically at her, as a piece of dark hair fell over one emerald eye. "Bored, lovely one?" He managed to look both sarcastic and amused and Tana nodded her head tentatively in embarrassment and began to laugh.

"You caught me." She looked into his eyes and smiled. She had the feeling that she'd seen him somewhere, but couldn't imagine where. "What can I say? It's a drag."

"It certainly is. The cattle show. I make the rounds every year." But he didn't look as though he'd been doing it for long. Despite the air of sophistication, he didn't look very old.

"How long have you been doing this?"

He grinned boyishly. "This is my second year. Actually, this should be my first, but they invited me to the Cotillion by mistake last year. And all the rest of the coming out balls, so I went." He rolled his eyes with a grin, "What a pain in the ass." And then he looked appraisingly at her, and took a sip of his scotch. "And how did you find your way here?"

"By cab." She smiled sweetly at him and he grinned.

"Lovely date you had." The sarcasm dripped from his words again and she laughed. "Engaged to him yet?"

"No, thanks."

"That shows at least minimal good judgment on your part." He spoke in a lazy, laconic way, with the accent of the upper crust, and yet he seemed to be laugh-

ing at it all, and Tana was amused by him. There was
something outrageous about the boy, as proper as he was,
as well dressed. But at the same time there was a shocking irreverence which showed through and suited her
mood perfectly. "Do you know Chandler, then?"

The young man smiled again. "We went to the same
boarding school for two years. He plays a great game of
squash, stinks at bridge, handles himself pretty well on
the tennis court, flunked math, history, and biology, and
has absolutely nothing between his ears."

Tana laughed in spite of herself. She didn't like him
anyway, but it seemed an almost surgically accurate, albeit unkind, portrait of him. "That sounds about right.
Not nice, but right."

"They don't pay me to be nice." He looked mischievous as he sipped his drink again, and made an obvious
appraisal of her cleavage and small waist.

"Do they pay you to do anything?"

"Not yet, actually." He smiled benevolently at her.
"And with luck they never will."

"Where do you go to school?"

He frowned, as though he had just forgotten something somewhere, and then gazed blankly at her. "Do
you know . . . I can't seem to remember." He smiled
again as she wondered what that meant. Maybe he wasn't
going to college at all, although he didn't look that type
either. "What about you?"

"Green Hill."

The impish smile appeared again, with one eyebrow
raised. "How ladylike. Majoring in what? Southern plan-
tations, or pouring tea?"

"Both." She grinned and stood up. "At least I go to school."

"For two years anyway. Then what, princess? Or is that what tonight is all about? The Great Hunt for Husband Number One." He pretended to speak into a megaphone. "Will all candidates line up against the far wall. All healthy young white males with pedigrees . . . have your fathers' D&B's in hand, we will also want to know your schools, blood type, whether or not you drive, how large your personal trust is and how soon you come into it . . ." He went on as she laughed at him, and he lowered his voice. "Seen any likely ones so far, or are you too madly in love with Chandler George?"

"Much." She began to walk slowly towards the main ballroom and he followed her, just in time to see her escort kissing the chubby redhead on the other side of the room.

The tall dark handsome young man turned to Tana somberly. "I've got bad news for you. I think you're about to be jilted, princess."

She shrugged and met the green eyes so like her own. "Them's the breaks, I guess." There was laughter in her eyes. She didn't give a damn about Chandler George.

"Would you like to dance?"

"Sure."

He whirled her around the floor expertly. There was something very dashing and worldly about this boy which seemed to belie his youth. One had the feeling that he had been around, although Tana didn't know where, or even who he was, a circumstance he remedied at the end of the first dance.

"By the way, what's your name, princess?"

"Tana Roberts."

"My name's Harry." He looked at her with the boy-ish grin and she smiled, and then unexpectedly he swept her a low bow. "Harrison Winslow the Fourth, actually. But Harry will do."

"Should I be impressed?" She was, but she wouldn't give him the satisfaction of letting him know.

"Only if you read the social columns regularly. Har-rison Winslow the Third usually makes an ass of himself, in cities that circle the globe . . . Paris and London most of the time, Rome when he has time . . . Gstaad, Saint Moritz . . . Munich, Berlin. And New York when he has absolutely no choice, and needs to fight with the trustees my grandmother left in charge of her very hand-some estate. But he isn't very fond of the States, or of me, come to think of it." He spoke in a flat monotone as Tana watched, wondering what was going on inside of him, but there was no clue as yet. "My mother died when I was four. I don't remember her at all, except once in a while, something comes back in a wave . . . like a perfume . . . or a sound, her laughter on the stairs when they went out . . . a dress that reminds me of her, but that's probably impossible. She committed suicide. 'Highly un-stable,' as my grandmother used to say, 'but a pretty piece.' And poor Dad's been licking his wounds ever since . . . I forgot to mention Monaco and Cap d'An-tibes. He licks his wounds there too. With helpmates, of course. There's a regular one he parks in London for most of the year, a very pretty one in Paris . . . one with whom he likes to ski . . . a Chinese girl in Hong Kong. He used to take me along when I wasn't in school, but eventually I got too disagreeable, so he stopped. That, and . . ." the eyes grew vague, ". . . other things. Anyway," his eyes came back into focus and he smiled cynically at Tana again, "that's who Harrison Winslow is, or at least one of them."

"And you?" Her voice was soft and his eyes were sad. He had told her more than he had intended to. But it was also his fourth scotch, and although it hadn't hurt his feet when they danced, it had loosened his tongue, not that he cared. Everyone in New York knew who Harry Winslow was, both father and son. "Are you like him?" She doubted it. For one thing, he hadn't had time to develop all those skills. He couldn't have been much older than she, after all.

He shrugged carelessly. "I'm working on it." And then he smiled again. "Beware, lovely one! Beware!" And with that, he swept her into his arms and onto the dance floor again, and she saw her mother watching them. She watched them for a long time, and then inquired of someone who he was, and she didn't look displeased.

"Do you see your father very much?" She was still thinking of what he had said as he whirled her around the floor. It sounded like a lonely life . . . boarding schools . . . his mother dead by suicide when he was four . . . the father halfway around the world most of the time, and obviously a libertine.

"Actually, no. He doesn't have time." For just a minute, he sounded like a very young boy, and she was sorry for him, but he was quick to turn the tables on her. "What about you? What's your story, Tana Roberts, other than the fact that you have deplorable taste in men?" He glanced in the direction of Chandler George crushing the little redhead to him, and they both laughed.

"I'm single, eighteen years old, and I go to Green Hill."

"Jesus. How dull. What else? Any major loves?"

Her face slammed shut, and he noticed it. "No."

"Relax. I meant other than Chandler, of course." She relaxed a little again. "Although admittedly, he's hard to beat." Poor guy, they were both being rotten to him, but he was the dullest boy she had ever known, and he was an easy target for the scorn of his peers. "Let's see, what else? Parents? Illegitimate children? Dogs? Friends? Hobbies? Wait," he patted his pockets, as though he had misplaced something. "I should have a form here somewhere . . ." They both laughed. "All of the above . . . ? none of the above . . . ?"

"One mother, no dogs, no illegitimate kids."

He looked sad. "I'm disappointed in you. I thought you would have done better than that." The music was winding down and Harry looked around. "What a bunch of bores. Want to go somewhere for a hamburger or a drink?"

She smiled. "I'd like that, but do we take Chandler along?" She laughed and Harry bowed.

"Leave that to me." He vanished and returned again with an outrageous grin.

"Oh, God, what did you do?"

"I told him you were upset about the way he's behaved all night with that redheaded tart, and I'm dropping you off at your psychiatrist's. . . ."

"You didn't!"

"I did." He feigned innocence and then laughed. "Actually, I just told him that you'd seen the light and preferred me. He congratulated you on your good taste,

and ran off with his chubby little friend." But whatever
Harry had said, Chandler was waving happily at them
and leaving with the other debutante, so there was obviously no harm done.

"I have to say something to my mother before we
go. Do you mind?"

"Not at all. Well, actually, I do, but I guess I don't
have much choice." But he behaved himself when Tana
introduced him to Jean, and he looked very proper, much
to her delight, as they left the ball, and Jean went home
alone, wishing Arthur had been there to see it all. It had
been a beautiful evening, and it was obvious that Tana
had had a wonderful time. And she was leaving now with
Harry Winslow IV. Jean knew who he was, or at least she
knew the name.

"What about your old man?" He stretched his legs
out in the cab, after giving the driver the address of "21."
It was the hangout of his choice when he was in town,
and Tana had been impressed. It was certainly a lot more
fun than going out with Chandler George. And it was so
long since she'd been out on a date, she'd forgotten how
it felt, and her dates had never been like this. Usually,
they all went out for pizza in a group on Second Avenue.
And that had been before graduation . . . before Billy
Durning. . . .

"My father died before I was born, in the war."

"That was considerate of him. It's less of a wrench
that way, than if they stick around for a few years." It
made Tana wonder why his mother had committed suicide, but she would never have dared to ask. "Did your
mother remarry?"

"No," Tana shook her head hesitantly, and then,

"She has a friend." He was the sort of person you told things like that to. There was something about his eyes. Something that made you trust him and like him all at once.

He raised the mischievous eyebrow again. "Is her friend married?" He was receptive too.

She blushed beet red but he couldn't see. "What made you say that?"

"Just smart, I guess." He was so impossible, one would have wanted to slap his face if he weren't so boyish and so appealing all at once. And he was so openly impudent that it somehow made it all right. "Was I right?"

Normally, she wouldn't have admitted it to anyone, but she did now. "Yes, or at least he was for a long time. He's been a widower now for four years, and he still hasn't married her. He's a real selfish son of a bitch." It was the strongest thing she had ever said about him publicly, even to Sharon at school.

But Harry didn't look perturbed. "Most men are. You should meet my old man. He leaves them bleeding by the side of the road at least four times a week, just to keep his hand in."

"Sounds nice."

"He's not." Harry's eyes were hard. "He's only interested in one thing. Himself. It's no wonder she killed herself." He had never forgiven his father for that, and Tana's heart suddenly ached for him, as the cab pulled up in front of "21," and Harry paid and they stepped out. And a moment later, they were swept up in the excitement of the exclusive restaurant. Tana had only been there once or twice, like on graduation night, and she loved the toys hanging over the bar, the well-dressed people crowded in, there were even two movie stars she recognized at once, and the headwaiter pounced on Harry with glee, obviously ecstatic to see him again. It was clearly his favorite haunt and he went there all the time. They stayed at the bar for a while, and then went to their table, where Harry ordered steak tartare for himself, and Tana ordered eggs Benedict, but as they sipped the Louis Roederer champagne he had ordered for them, Harry saw her face go taut. She was looking across the room at a table of people who seemed to be having a good time and there was an older man with his arm around a fairly young girl. Harry watched her face, and then her eyes and a moment later he patted her hand. "Let me guess . . . an old love?" He was surprised to see that she went for older men. She didn't look the type.

"Not mine, anyway." And then he instantly knew.

"Your mother's friend?"

"He told her he had a business dinner tonight."

"Maybe it is."

"It doesn't look like it to me." Her eyes were hard as she turned to Harry again. "What irritates me more than anything is that he can do no wrong in her eyes. She always makes excuses for him. She sits and she waits and she's so goddamn grateful to him."

"How long have they been together?"

"Twelve years."

He winced. "Jesus, that's a long time."

"Yeah." Tana glanced malevolently in Arthur's direction again. "And it doesn't seem to be cramping his style." Seeing him made her think of Billy again, and she turned her head as though to avoid the thought, but Harry saw the sudden look of pain in her eyes.

"Don't take it so hard, princess." His voice was gentle in her ears and she turned to look at him.

"It's her life, not mine."

"That's right. Don't forget that. You can make your own choices with your life." He smiled, "and that reminds me, you never answered all my rude questions before. What are you going to do after Green Hill?"

"God knows. Maybe Columbia. I'm not sure. I want to go on."

"Not get married and have four little kids?" They both laughed.

"Not for a while, thanks, although it's my mother's fondest dream." And then she turned to him with a curious look. "And what about you, where do you go to school?"

He sighed as he put down his champagne. "Harvard, actually. Sounds obnoxious, doesn't it?" It was why he hadn't told her at first.

"Is it true?"

"Unfortunately, yes." He grinned. "But there's hope. I may flunk out before the end of the year. I'm working on it."

"You can't be that bad or you wouldn't have gotten in."

"A Winslow not get in? Don't be absurd, my dear. We *always* get in. We practically built the place."

"Oh . . ." She looked impressed. "I see. And you didn't want to go?"

"Not especially. I wanted to go out West somewhere. I thought Stanford or UC, but Father had a fit, and it wasn't worth arguing about it . . . so there I am, being a pain in the ass, and making them sorry they let me in."

"You must be a real treat for them." Tana laughed, and she noticed that Arthur Durning and his group had just left. He hadn't noticed her, and she wasn't sure if she was glad or not.

"You'll have to come up and see me sometime, maybe during spring break."

She laughed at that and shook her head. "I doubt that."

"Don't you trust me?" He looked amused and very debonair for a boy of eighteen.

"As a matter of fact, no." She took another sip of champagne and they both laughed. She was feeling giggly now and she was having a good time with him. He was the first boy she had liked in a long time, and she liked him as a friend. He was fun to laugh with and she could say things to him that she hadn't been able to say to anyone else recently, except Shar. And then she had an idea. "I might come up if I could bring a friend."

"What kind of friend?" He asked suspiciously.

"My roommate at Green Hill." She told him about Sharon Blake then and he looked intrigued.

"The daughter of Freeman Blake? That's something else. Is she as wonderful as you say?"

"Wonderfuler." She told him then about their being unable to get served at the coffee shop in Yolan, and the lecture given by Martin Luther King and he seemed interested in all of it.

"I'd like to meet her sometime. Do you really think you'd come up to Cambridge at spring break?"

"Maybe, I'll have to ask her."

"What are you two, joined at the hip?" He looked
Tana over appraisingly. She was one of the prettiest girls
he had ever seen, and it would be worth putting up with
someone else, just to see her.

"More or less. I visited them at Thanksgiving, and I
want to go back."

"Why don't you have her here?"

There was a long pause and then Tana looked at
him. "My mother would have a fit if she knew Sharon
was black. I've told her everything except that."

"Great." Harry smiled. "I did tell you that my ma-
ternal grandmother was black, didn't I?" For an instant
he looked so honest that she almost believed what he said
and then he started to laugh and she made a face.

"Pain in the ass . . . why don't I just tell my
mother about you?"

"Be my guest."

And she did the next day when he called to take her
to lunch in two days. They had Christmas to endure in
between.

"Isn't that the boy you met last night?" It was Saturday morning and Jean was relaxing with a book. She
hadn't heard from Arthur since the day before and she
was dying to tell him about the ball, but she didn't want
to bother him. She usually waited for him to call. It was a
habit she had picked up when he was still married to
Marie. And it was Christmas after all. He'd be busy with
Billy and Ann.

"Yes, it is." Tana explained to her mother about
Harry's call.

"He seems nice."

"He is." But not in any way Jean would approve of,

as Tana knew only too well. He was irreverent and outrageous and he drank too much, and he was obviously spoiled, but he had behaved decently when he had brought her home. He had said goodnight and there was no wrestling match. She had been nervous about that, but she hadn't needed to be. And when he came to pick her up for lunch two days later he wore a blazer and a tie and gray slacks, but as soon as they got downstairs, he put on roller skates and a crazy hat, and proceeded to behave like a complete madman as they walked downtown and Tana laughed at him. "Harry Winslow, you are completely nuts, do you know that?!"

"Yes, ma'am." He smiled and crossed his eyes, and insisted on wearing his roller skates into the Oak Room for lunch. The maître d' didn't look pleased but he knew who he was and he didn't dare throw him out. He ordered a bottle of Roederer champagne, and guzzled a glass as soon as it was uncorked, and then set down the empty glass and smiled at Tana. "I think I'm addicted to that stuff."

"You mean you're a drunk."

"Yup." He said it with pride, ordered lunch for them both, and after lunch they walked through Central Park and stopped at Wollman Rink where they watched the ice skaters for more than an hour and talked about life, and he sensed that there was a strange reticence about her. She didn't offer herself, in a romantic sense, she was careful and closed, and yet at the same time she was intelligent and warm. She cared about people and causes and things. But there was no hand held out. He knew that he had made a new friend, and no more, and she saw to it that he understood, in so many words, and it aroused his curiosity. "Are you involved with someone near Green Hill?"

She shook her head, and her eyes met his. "No, nothing like that. I don't want to get involved with anyone right now." He was surprised at her honesty. And it was a challenge, too, of course, one he couldn't completely resist.

"Why not? Afraid to get hurt the way your mother has been?" She had never thought of it that way. It was why he had told her he didn't want kids. He didn't want to hurt anyone as badly as he himself had been hurt. And she had just told him how Arthur had stood her mother up for Christmas again that year.

"I don't know. Maybe. That, and other things."

"What kind of 'other things'?"

"Nothing I want to talk about." She looked away, and he tried to imagine what had marked her that way. She kept a safe distance between them, and even when they laughed and played, she sent out messages that said "don't get too close to me." He hoped that there was nothing strange about the girl, about her sexual propensities, but he didn't think it was that. It was more that she seemed to be hiding in a protective shell, and he wasn't sure why. Someone had driven her into it and he wondered who it was.

"Was there someone important in your life before?"

"No." She looked him square in the eye. "I don't want to talk about that." The look on her face made him back off at once. It was anger and hurt and something he couldn't even define, but it was so powerful it took his breath away, and he didn't scare easily. But this time he got the point. A blind man would have.

"I'm sorry." They changed the subject then and went back to talking about easier things. He liked her a lot, and he saw her several times during that Christmas holiday. They went to dinner and lunch, went ice skating in the park, to a movie one night, and she even invited him to dinner one night with Jean. But that was a mistake, she recognized at once. Jean was grilling him as though he were a hot marriage candidate, asking about his future plans, his parents, his career goals, his grades. She could hardly wait for him to leave, and when he did, she screamed at Jean.

"Why did you do that to him? He just came here to eat, not to ask me to marry him."

"You're eighteen years old, you have to start thinking about things like that now."

"Why?" Tana was enraged. "All he is is a friend, for chrissake. Don't act like I have to get married by next week."

"Well, when do you want to get married, Tana?"

"Never, dammit! Why the hell do I have to get married at all?"

"What are you going to do for the rest of your life?" Her mother's eyes were hunting her, shoving her into corners and pushing her hard and she hated it.

"I don't know what I'm going to do. Do I have to figure that out now? Right now? Tonight? This week? Shit!"

"Don't talk to me like that!" Now her mother was angry too.

"Why not? What are you trying to do to me?"

"I want to see you have some security, Tana. Not to

be in the same boat I'm in when you're forty years old.
You deserve more than that!''

"So do you. Did you ever think of that? I hate seeing
you like this, waiting around for Arthur all the time, like
his slave. That's all you've been for all these years,
Mother. Arthur Durning's concubine.'' She was tempted
to tell her about seeing him with another girl at "21," but
she couldn't do that to her mother. She didn't want to
cause her that much pain and it would have for sure.
Tana restrained herself but Jean was irate anyway.

"That's not fair and it's not true.''

"Then why don't you want me to be like you?'' Jean
turned her back on her, so that she wouldn't see her
tears, and then suddenly she turned on Tana, and twelve
years of sorrow showed in her eyes, and a lifetime before
that.

"I want you to have all the things I didn't have. Is
that too much to ask?''

Tana's heart suddenly went out to her and she
backed down. Her voice was gentler as she spoke again.
"But maybe I don't want the same things you did.''

"What is there not to want? A husband, security, a
home, children—what's wrong with all that?'' She looked
shocked.

"Nothing. But I'm too young to think about all that.
What if I want a career?''

Jean Roberts looked shocked. "What kind of career?''

"I don't know. I just meant theoretically.''

"That's a lonely life, Tana.'' She looked worried
about her. "You'd be better off if you just settled down.''
But to Tana that felt like giving up, and she thought

about it as she rode south on the train and she and Sharon talked about it their first night back in Jasmine House, once the lights were off.

"Jesus, Tan, she sounds just like mine . . . in a different way, of course. But they all want for us what they wanted for themselves, no matter who we are, or how different we are from them, or what we think and feel and want. My dad understands, but my mom . . . all I hear about is law school, and sit-ins, and being 'responsible' about being black. I'm so goddamn tired of being 'responsible,' I could scream. That's why I came here in the first place, to Green Hill. I wanted to go somewhere where there would be other blacks. Hell, here I can't even date, and she tells me that there's plenty of time for that. When? I want to go out now, I want to have a good time, I want to go to restaurants and movies and football games." She reminded Tana then, and the pretty blonde smiled in the dark.

"Want to go to Harvard with me at spring break?"

"How come?" Sharon propped herself up on one elbow in the dark with an excited look. And Tana told her about Harry Winslow then. "He sounds neat. Did you fall for him?"

"No."

"Why not?"

There was a silence which they both understood. "You know why."

"You can't let that screw you up for the rest of your life, Tan."

"You sound like my mother now. She wants me engaged to anyone by next week, as long as he's willing to marry me, buy me a house, and give me kids."

"It beats the hell out of going to sit-ins and getting raw eggs in your hair. Doesn't that sound like fun?"

Tana smiled. "Not much."

"Your Harvard friend sounds nice."

"He is." Tana smiled to herself. "I like him a lot, as a friend. He's the most honest, straightforward person I've ever met." The call he made to her later that week underlined why she so enjoyed him. He called pretending to be the owner of a laboratory in Yolan, and they needed young ladies to perform experiments on, he explained.

"We're trying to find out if young ladies are as intelligent as young men," he said, disguising his voice. "We realize of course that they are not, however . . ." and just before she flew into a rage, she recognized his voice.

"You shit!"

"Hi, kiddo. How's life in the Deep South?"

"Not bad." She let him speak to Sharon eventually, and the two girls stood beside the phone, passing it back and forth, and eventually Sharon went upstairs and Tana talked to him for hours. There were no romantic overtones at all, he was more like a brother to her, and after two months of phone calls, aside from Sharon he was her closest friend. He was hoping to see her at spring break, and she tried to get Sharon to come along, but to no avail. She decided to brave her mother, and invite Sharon to stay with them, but Miriam Blake had been on the phone to Sharon almost every night. There was an enormous black rally scheduled in Washington with a candlelight vigil for Civil Rights over Easter weekend and she wanted Sharon to be there. She felt that it was an important part of their life, and this was no time for a vacation trip. Sharon was depressed about it when they both left Green Hill.

"All you had to do was say no, Shar." Tana looked at her and shook her head and for a moment something angry flashed in the pretty black girl's eyes.

"Just like you did about the coming out party, huh, Tan?"

There was a silence, and then slowly Tana nodded her head. Her friend wasn't far wrong. It was difficult to fight with them all the time. She shrugged, with a sheepish grin. "Okay, you win. I'm sorry. We'll miss you in New York."

"I'll miss you too." She flashed her the dazzling smile, and they chatted and played cards on the train. Sharon got off in Washington, and Tana went on to New York. It was balmy and warm when she walked out of the station and hailed a cab, and the apartment looked the same as it always had, and somehow, for no reason she could explain, it was depressing to be back. There was a sameness to it all. Nothing grew, nothing changed. There were never fresh drapes, new plants, wonderful flowers, something exciting going on. There was the same thing, the same life, the same worn-out couch, the same dreary looking plants year after year. It hadn't seemed quite so bad when she was living there every day, but now that she came and went, it looked different to her. Everything was shabbier, and the whole apartment seemed to have shrunk. Her mother was at work, and she threw her bags down in her room, just as the phone rang. She went back to the living room to pick it up, glancing around again.

"Hello?"

"Winslow here. How's it going, kid?"

She grinned. It was like a burst of fresh air in the
stale, musty room. "Hello."

"When'd you get in?"

"About four seconds ago. How about you?"

"I drove down last night with a couple of the guys.
And," he looked lazily around the apartment his father
owned at the Pierre, "here I am. Same old dump, same
old town." But he looked boyish when he smiled at his
end of the phone, and Tana was excited at the prospect of
seeing him again. They had learned so much about each
other in the last four months on the phone, it was as
though they were old friends now. "Want to come up for
a drink?"

"Sure. Where are you?"

"At the Pierre." He sounded unimpressed by his
own whereabouts and Tana grinned.

"That's nice."

"Not very. My father had the apartment redone by
some decorator last year. It looks like a fag hangout now,
but at least it's free when I'm in New York."

"Is your father there?" She was intrigued and Harry
laughed derisively.

"Don't be ridiculous. I think he's in Munich this
week. He likes spending Easter there. The Germans are
so emotional about Christian events. That and the
Oktoberfest." He was slightly over her head. "Never
mind. Come on over, and we'll drive room service nuts.
What do you want? I'll order something now, and it'll
take two hours to show up."

She was impressed. "I don't know . . . a hamburger and a Coke? Does that sound all right?" There
was something very impressive about all this, but Harry

was nonchalant about it all and when she arrived, he was
lying on the couch in jeans and bare feet watching a soc-
cer match on TV. He swept her off her feet, and gave her
a huge bear hug, and it was obvious that he was genu-
inely pleased to see her, much more than she realized.
His whole body tingled as he gave her a friendly peck on
the cheek. And there was a moment of awkwardness,
translating the intimacy they had developed on the phone
into real life, but by the end of the afternoon, they were
like old friends, and Tana hated to leave to go home.

"Then stay. I'll put some shoes on and we'll go to
'21.' "

"Like this?" She looked down at her plaid skirt and
loafers and wool socks, but she shook her head. "I have
to go home anyway. I haven't seen my mother in four
months."

"I keep forgetting rituals like that." His voice was
flat, and he looked even handsomer than he had before,
but nothing stirred in Tana's heart for him, only the
friendship that had continued to grow since they first
met, nothing more than that, and she was sure that he
had nothing other than platonic feelings for her as well.

She turned to look at him now, as she picked her
raincoat up off the chair. "Don't you ever see your father
at all, Harry?" Her voice was soft and her eyes were sad
for him. She knew how alone he was. He had spent the
holidays alone, he said he always did, or with friends, or
in empty houses or hotels, and he only mentioned his
father in the context of bad jokes about his women and
his friends and his gallivanting here and there.

"I see him once in a while. We run into each other
about once or twice a year. Usually here, or in the South

of France." It sounded very grand, but Tana easily sensed
how lonely Harry was. It was why he had opened up so
much to her. There was something inside him which was
dying to reach out and be loved. And there was something like that in her too. A part of her which had only
had Jean and had wanted more, a father, sisters and
brothers, a family . . . something more than just a
lonely woman who spent her life waiting for a man who
didn't appreciate her. And Harry didn't even have that.
Tana hated his father, just thinking about him.

"What's he like?"

Harry shrugged again. "Good-looking, I guess. At
least that's what the women say . . . smart . . . cold.
. . ." He looked Tana square in the eye. "He killed my
mother, what do you think he's like?" Something shrivelled up in her as she watched her friend's eyes, and she
didn't know what to say. She was sorry that she had
asked, but Harry put an arm around her shoulders as he
walked her to the door. "Don't let it upset you, Tan. It
happened a long time ago." But she was sad for him.
There was something so lonely about him, and he was so
funny and decent and nice, it wasn't fair . . . and he
was also spoiled and self-indulgent and mischievous. He
had put on a British accent for the first room service
waiter who'd come up, and pretended to the second one
that he was French, and afterwards he and Tana were
convulsed. She wondered if he always behaved like that
and suspected that he did. And as she took the bus back
uptown, she suddenly didn't mind the depressing little
apartment she shared with Jean. Better that than the lav-
ish, chilly decor of the Winslow suite at the Hotel Pierre.
The rooms were large, and everything was chrome and

glass and white, predictably expensive, there were two huge fabulous white fur rugs on the floor and there were priceless paintings and objects everywhere, but that's all there was. There was no one there when he arrived from school, and there wouldn't be that night or the next. There was only Harry, with an icebox filled with booze and Cokes, a wardrobe of expensive clothes, and a TV.

"Hi . . . I'm home . . . !" She called out as she got in and Jean came running to her, and held her tight with a look of delight.

"Oh baby, you look so good!" It made her think of Harry again, and all that he didn't have, in spite of his trusts, and his houses, and his fancy name . . . he didn't have this. And somehow Tana wanted to make it up to him. Jean was looking at her now and there was such obvious pleasure in her eyes that it actually felt good to be home. "I saw your bags. Where did you go?"

"I went to see a friend downtown. I didn't think you'd be home for a while."

"I left work early, in case you'd come in."

"I'm sorry, Mom."

"Who did you go to see?" Jean always liked to know what she did, who she saw. But Tana wasn't as used to the questions anymore, and she hesitated for just a moment before she smiled.

"I went to see Harry Winslow at the Pierre. I don't know if you remember him."

"Of course I do." Jean's eyes lit up. "Is he in town?"

"He has an apartment here." Tana's voice was quiet, and there were mixed reviews in Jean's eyes. It was good that he was mature enough, and solvent enough, to have his own place, but also dangerous at the same time.

"Were you alone with him?" Jean looked concerned.

This time Tana laughed. "Sure. We shared a hamburger and watched TV. All perfectly harmless, Mom."

"Still . . . I don't think you should." She watched Tana's eyes, as the pretty blonde's face began to tense.

"He's my friend, Mom."

"He's still a young man, and you never know what could happen in a situation like that."

"Yes, I do." Her eyes were instantly hard. She knew only too well. Only it had happened at precious Billy Durning's house, in his own father's bedroom, with a hundred kids right downstairs. "I know who I can trust."

"You're too young to be able to judge things like that, Tan."

"No, I'm not." Tan's face was like a rock. Billy Durning's raping her had changed her whole life. She knew everything about things like that, and if she sensed any threat from Harry at all, she would never have gone to his hotel, or stayed. But she knew instinctively that he was her friend and she would come to no harm at his hands, unlike her mother's lover's son. "Harry and I are just friends."

"You're being naive. There's no such thing between boys and girls, Tan. Men and women can't be friends."

Tana's eyes opened wide. She couldn't believe her mother was saying those words. "How can you say a thing like that, Mom?"

"Because it's true. And if he's inviting you to his hotel, he has something else in mind, whether you recognize it or not. Maybe he's just biding his time." And then she smiled. "Do you think he could be serious about you, Tan?"

"Serious?" Tana looked as though she were about to explode. *"Serious?* I just told you, all we are is friends."

"And I told you I didn't believe that." There was something almost insinuating about her smile. "You know, Tan, he would be quite a catch."

But it was too much for Tana to stand. She jumped to her feet, and looked down at her mother with scorn. "You make him sound like a fish, for chrissake. I don't want a 'catch.' I don't want to get married. I don't want to get laid. All I want is to have some friends and go to school. Can you understand that?" There were tears in her eyes, mirrored by those in Jean's.

"Why do you have to get so violent about everything? You never used to be like that, Tan." Jean's voice sounded so sad that it tore at Tana's heart, but she couldn't help how she felt or what she said anymore.

"You never used to push me all the time."

"When do I push?" She looked shocked. "I don't even see you anymore. I've seen you twice in six months. That's pushing?"

"That coming out party was pushing, and what you just said about Harry is pushing, and talking about catches, and settling down, and getting married is pushing. For chrissake, Mom, I'm eighteen years old!"

"And you're almost nineteen. And then what? When *are* you going to think about it, Tan?"

"I don't know, Mom. Maybe never, how's that? Maybe I'll never get married. So what? If I'm happy, who cares?"

"I care. I want to see you married to a nice man with nice children in a nice house. . . ." Jean was crying openly now, it was what she had always wanted for her-

self . . . yet, she was alone . . . with a couple of nights
a week with a man she loved, and a daughter who was
almost gone . . . She bent her head and sobbed, as Tana
came to her and hugged her close.

"Come on, Mom, stop . . . I know you want the
best for me . . . but just let me work things out for myself."

Her mother looked at her with big, sad, dark eyes.
"Do you realize who Harry Winslow is?"

Tana's voice was soft. "Yes. He's my friend."

"His father is one of the richest men in the United
States. He even makes Arthur Durning look poor." Ar-
thur Durning. The measuring stick for everything in
Jean's life.

"So what?"

"Do you realize what kind of life you could have
with him?"

Tana looked sad for her, and she suddenly felt sad
for herself. Her mother was missing the point, and probably had all her life. But by the same token, Jean had given
her so much. And Tana felt as though she owed her a lot
now. But in spite of that, she hardly saw Jean during the
entire two weeks she was in New York. She ran around
with Harry almost every day, although she didn't admit
it to Jean. She was still furious at what her mother had
said. *Do you realize who he is?* As though that made a
difference to her. She wondered how many people felt
that way about him. It seemed a hideous thought, to be
evaluated because of his last name.

Cautiously, she even asked Harry about it one day,
when they were having a picnic in Central Park.
"Doesn't that bug you, Harry? I mean people wanting to

get to know you because of who you are?" The thought still horrified her, but he only shrugged and munched his apple as he lay on the grass.

"That's just the way people are, I guess. It gives them some kind of a thrill. I used to see people do that to my father all the time."

"Doesn't it get to him?"

"I don't really think he cares." Harry smiled at her. "He's so insensitive, I don't think he actually feels anything at all." Tana watched Harry's eyes.

"Is he really that bad?"

"Worse."

"Then how come you're so nice?"

He laughed. "Just lucky, I guess. Or maybe it's my mother's genes."

"Do you still remember her?" It was the first time she had asked him that, and he looked away from her.

"Sometimes . . . a little bit . . . I don't know, Tan." He looked back at her again. "Sometimes, when I was a kid, I'd pretend to my friends that she was alive, that she was out shopping or whatever when they came over to play. I didn't want to be different from the rest of them. But they always found out. Their mothers would tell them or something when they went home, and then they'd think I was weird, but I didn't give a damn. It felt nice to be normal just for a few hours. I'd just talk about her like she was out . . . or upstairs . . ." Tan saw tears stand out in his eyes, and then he looked at her almost viciously. "Pretty dumb, huh, to be hung up on a mother you never even knew?"

Tana reached out to him with her heart and her

words, and the gentleness of her voice. "I'd have done the same thing in your shoes."

He shrugged and looked away, and a while later they went for a walk and talked about other things, Freeman Blake, Sharon, Tana's classes at Green Hill, and then suddenly out of the blue, Harry took her hand. "Thanks for what you said before." She knew instantly what he meant. They had that kind of rapport, had from the moment they first met.

"It's okay." She squeezed his hand, and they walked on, and she was amazed at how comfortable she was with him. He didn't push her at all, didn't ask her anymore why she didn't go out with anyone. He seemed to accept her as she was, and she was grateful to him for that. She was grateful to him for a lot of things, for the way he saw life, for the fun they had, the sense of humor that always made her laugh. It felt wonderful to have someone to share her thoughts with.

He was almost like a sounding board for everything she had in her head, and she was particularly grateful for that when she went back to Green Hill. When she saw Sharon again, it was as though her family had sent someone else instead, and all of her moderate political ideas had disappeared. She had attended a series of rallies and sit-ins with her mother and her friends, and suddenly she was as rabid as Miriam Blake was. Tana couldn't believe the change that had taken place, and finally, after listening to her for two days, Tana turned to her and screamed.

"For chrissake, Shar, what's happened to you? This room has been like a political rally ever since we got back. Get off your soapbox, girl. What the hell has happened to you?" Sharon just sat there and stared and suddenly the tears flooded her eyes and she bowed her head, the sobs choked her and her shoulders shook and it was almost half an hour before she could speak, as Tana watched her in astonishment. Something terrible had happened to the girl, but it was impossible to say what it was. She held her and rocked her, and at last Sharon spoke, as Tana's heart went out to her.

"They killed Dick on Easter Eve, Tan . . . they killed him . . . he was fifteen years old . . . and he was hanged. . . ." Tana felt instantly sick. That couldn't be. That didn't happen to people one knew . . . to blacks . . . to anyone . . . but she could see on Sharon's face that it was true, and when she called Harry that night, she cried when she told him the news.

"Oh my God . . . I heard something about it in school, that the son of an important black had been killed, but it didn't click . . . shit. . . ." He had been Sharon's brother, and barely more than a child.

"Yeah." Tana's heart felt like lead. And when her mother called her later that week, she still sounded depressed.

"What's the matter, sweetheart? Did you and Harry have a fight?" She was trying a new tack, she was going to pretend to herself and Tana that it was a romance and maybe the idea would take, but Tana didn't have any patience with her and she was instantly blunt.

"My roommate's brother died."

"Oh, how terrible . . ." Jean sounded horrified. "In an accident?"

There was a long pause as Tana weighed her words . . . *No, Mom, he was hanged, you see he's black.* . . .

"Sort of." Wasn't death always an accident? Who expected it?

"Tell her how sorry I am. Those are the people you spent Thanksgiving with, aren't they?"

"Yes." Tana's voice sounded flat and dead.

"That's just terrible."

Tana couldn't stand talking to her anymore. "I've got to go, Mom."

"Call me in a few days—"

"I'll try." She cut her off and hung up. She didn't want to talk to anyone, but she and Sharon were talking again late into the night. Suddenly everything in Sharon's life had changed. She had even contacted the local black church, and she was helping to organize sit-ins on weekends for the remainder of the spring. "Do you think you should, Shar?"

Sharon looked angrily at her. "Is there a choice anymore? I don't think there is." There was anger in her soul now, an anger that nothing would help, a fire that no love could quench. They had killed the little boy she had grown up with. ". . . and he was always such a pain in the ass. . . ." She laughed through her tears one night as they talked in the dark. ". . . He was so much like Mom, and now . . . and now . . ." She gulped her sobs down, and Tana went to sit on her bed. It went on like that every night, either talking about marches elsewhere in the South, or sit-ins in town, or Dr. Martin Luther King, it was as though she wasn't really there anymore, and by midterms she was panicking. She hadn't done any studying at all. She was a bright girl, but she was desperately afraid now that she was going to flunk. Tana helped her as much as she could, sharing notes, underlining her books for her, but she didn't have much hope, and Sharon's mind was on the sit-in she had organized in Yolan for the following week. The townspeople had already complained about her twice to the Dean of Green Hill, but because of who her father was, they had only called her in and talked to her. They understood what a strain she was under, after her brother's, er . . . unfortunate "accident," but she had to behave herself nonetheless, and they didn't want her causing trouble in town anymore.

"You better lay off, Shar. They're going to kick you out of school if you don't stop." Tana had warned her more than once, but it was something she couldn't change now. She had no choice. It was something she had to do, and the night before the big sit-in in Yolan she turned to Tana just before they turned off the lights and there was something so intense in her eyes that it almost frightened Tana as she looked at her. "Is something wrong?"

"I want to ask you a favor, and I won't be mad if you say no. I promise, so do whatever you want. Is that a deal?"

"Okay. What's up?" Tana just prayed that she didn't want her to cheat on a test.

"Reverend Clarke and I were talking today, at the church, and I think it would make a big difference if there were whites involved in the sit-in tomorrow in town. We're going to walk into the white church."

"Holy shit." Tana looked shocked, and Sharon grinned.

"That's about right." The two girls exchanged a smile. "Dr. Clarke is going to see who he can get, and I

. . . I don't know . . . maybe it's wrong, but I wanted
to ask you. But if you don't want to, Tan, don't."

"Why would they get upset if I walk into their
church? I'm white."

"Not if you walk in with us, you're not. That makes
you white trash, or worse. If you walk in holding my
hand, standing between me and Reverend Clarke or another black . . . that's different, Tan."

"Yeah," she felt a twinge of fear in her gut, but she
also wanted to help her friend, "I guess I can see that."

"What do you think?" Sharon looked her square in
the eye and Tana did the same.

"Honestly? I'm scared."

"So am I. I always am." And then very gently, "So
was Dick. But he went. And I'm going too. I'm going to
go every time I can for the rest of my life now, until
things change. But it's my fight, Tana, not yours. If you
come, you come as my friend. And if you don't come, I
love you anyway."

"Thanks. Can I think about it tonight?" She knew
that it could have repercussions if it got back to the
school, and she didn't want to jeopardize her scholarship
for the following year. She called Harry late that night,
but he was out, and she woke up the next morning at
dawn, thinking about going to church when she was a
little girl, and things her mother had said about all people
being the same in God's eyes, the rich, the poor, the
white, the black, everyone, and then she thought about
Sharon's brother Dick, a fifteen-year-old child, hanged
until he died, and when Sharon turned over in bed as the
sun came up, Tana was waiting for her.

"Sleep okay?"

"More or less." She sat up on the edge of the bed and stretched.

"You getting up?" There was a question in Sharon's eyes, and Tana smiled.

"Yeah. We're going to church today, aren't we?" And with that Sharon grinned broadly at her friend. She hopped out of bed, and gave her a hug and a kiss and a victorious smile.

"I'm so glad, Tan."

"I don't know if I am, but I think it's the right thing to do."

"I know it is." It was going to be a long, bloody fight, but Sharon would be there, and Tana, just this once. She put on a simple blue cotton shirtdress, the color of the sky, brushed her long blond hair into a sleek ponytail, put her loafers on, and they walked into town side by side.

"Going to church, girls?" the housemother had smilingly asked and both had answered yes. They both knew that she had meant different ones, but Tana went to the black church with Sharon where they met Dr. Clarke and a small crowd of ninety-five blacks and eleven whites. They were told to stay calm, to smile if it seemed appropriate, but not if it would provoke anyone, and to remain silent no matter what anyone said to them. They were to hold hands and to enter the church solemnly and respectfully, in groups of five. Sharon and Tana were to remain together. There was another white girl with them, and two black men, both burly and tall, and they told Tana on the way to the other church that they worked at the mill. They were hardly older than the girls, but both were married, one had three children, the other four, and they didn't seem to question her being there. They called her Sister, and just before they walked into the church, the five companions exchanged a nervous smile. And then quietly, they stepped inside. It was a small Presbyterian church on the residential side of town, heavily attended every Sunday, with a Sunday school that was well filled, and as the black faces began to file in, every man and woman in the church turned around. There was a look of complete shock on everyone, the organ stopped, one woman fainted, another began to scream, and within a matter of moments all hell broke loose, the minister began to shout, someone ran to call the police, and only Dr. Clarke's volunteers remained calm, standing solidly along the back wall, causing no trouble at all, as people turned and jeered, hurled insults at them, even though they were in church. Within moments the town's tiny squad of riot police had arrived. They had been recently trained for the sit-ins that had begun to occur and were mostly composed of highway patrolmen, but they began to push and shove and drag the uncooperating black bodies out, as they made themselves limp, and allowed themselves to be dragged away, and suddenly Tana realized what was happening to them. She was next, this was not happening to a remote "them," it was happening to "us" and to *her*, and suddenly two enormous policemen hovered over her, and grabbed her roughly by both arms waving their sticks in her face.

"You should be ashamed of yourself . . . white trash!" Her eyes were huge as they dragged her off, and with every ounce of her being she wanted to hit and bite and kick, thinking of Richard Blake and how he had been killed, but she didn't dare. They threw her into the back

of the truck, with much of Dr. Clarke's group, and half
an hour later, she was being fingerprinted and she was in
jail. She sat in a jail cell for the rest of the day, with
fifteen other girls, all of them black, and she could see
Sharon across the way. They had each been allowed one
phone call, the whites at least, the blacks were still being
"processed" according to the cops, and Sharon shouted
to her to call her Mom, which Tana did. She arrived in
Yolan at midnight, and released Sharon and Tana simul-
taneously, congratulating them both. Tana could see that
she looked harder and more drawn than she had six
months before, but she seemed pleased with what the
girls had done. She wasn't even upset when Sharon told
her the news the next day. She was being kicked out of
Green Hill, effective immediately. Her things had already
been packed by the housemother of Jasmine House, and
she was being asked to leave the campus before noon.
Tana was in shock when she heard, and she knew what
she could expect for herself when she was ushered into
the Dean's office. It was just as she had thought. She was
being asked to leave. There would be no scholarship the
following year. In fact, there would be no following year
at all. Like Sharon, it was all over for her. The only
difference was that if she was willing to stay on in a
probationary state, she could stay on until the end of the
year, which would at least mean that she could take her
final exams and apply to another school. But where? She
sat in her room in shock after Sharon had left. Sharon
was going back to Washington with her mother, and
there had already been talk of her spending a little time
as a volunteer for Dr. King.

"I know Daddy'll be mad because he wants me to go

to school, but you know, truthfully, Tan, I've had it up to here with school." She looked sorrowfully at Tana then. "But what about you?" She was devastated about the price of the sit-in for her friend. She had never gotten arrested before, although they had been warned before the church sit-in that it was a real possibility, yet she really hadn't expected it.

"Maybe it's all for the best." Tana tried to cheer her up, and she was still in shock when Sharon left, and she sat alone in her room until dark. Her probation meant that she had to eat alone at Jasmine House, keep to her room at night, and avoid all social activities including the freshman prom. She was a pariah of sorts, but she also knew that school would be over in three weeks.

The worst of it was that, as they had warned Tana they would, they informed Jean. She called, hysterical, that night, sobbing into the phone. "Why didn't you tell me that little bitch was black?"

"What difference does it make what color she is? She's my best friend." But tears filled Tana's eyes and the emotions of the past few days overwhelmed her suddenly. Everyone at school was looking at her as though she had killed someone, and Sharon was gone. She didn't know where she would go to school next year, and her mother was screaming at her . . . it was like being five years old and being told you had been very, very bad, but not being sure why.

"You call that a friend?" Her mother laughed through her tears. "She cost you your scholarship, and got you kicked out of school. And do you think you'll get accepted anywhere else after this?"

"Of course you will, you jerk." Harry reassured her

through her sobs the next day. "Shit, there are zillions of radicals at BU."

"I'm not a radical." She cried some more.

"I know that. All you did was go to a sit-in, for chrissake. It's your own goddamn fault for going to that prissy redneck school. I mean shit, you aren't even in the civilized world down there. Why the hell don't you come up here to school?"

"You really think I might be able to get in?"

"With your grades, are you kidding? They'd let you run the place."

"You're just trying to make me feel better." She started to cry again.

"You're giving me a mammoth pain in the ass, Tan. Why don't you just let me get you an application and see what happens?" And what happened was that she got in, much to her own astonishment and her mother's chagrin.

"Boston University? What kind of school is that?"

"One of the best in the country, and they even gave me a scholarship." Harry had taken the application over himself, put in a good word for her, which seemed like a crazy thing to do and touched her to the core, and by July first, it was settled. She was going to Boston University in the fall.

She was still numb from the events of two months before, and her mother still wanted to wrestle about it with her.

"I think you should get a job for a while, Tan. You can't hang around in school for the rest of your life."

Tana looked horrified. "How about for another three years, like until I get a degree?"

"And then what? What are you going to do then, Tana, that you couldn't do now?"

"Get a decent job."

"You could go to work for Durning International right now. I spoke to Arthur last week. . . ."

Tana seemed to be screaming at her all the time now, but she never understood. "For chrissake, don't condemn me to that for the rest of my life."

"Condemn you! *Condemn* you! How dare you say such a thing? You get arrested, kicked out of school, and you think you have a right to the world. You're lucky a man like Arthur Durning would even consider hiring you."

"He's lucky I didn't bring charges against his son last year!" The words flew out of Tana's mouth before she could stop them and Jean Roberts stared at her.

"How dare you say a thing like that?"

Her voice was quiet and sad, "It's true, Mom."

She turned her back to Tana, as though shielding herself from the look on Tana's face, not wanting to hear. "I don't want to hear you tell lies like that." Tana walked quietly out of the room, and a few days later she was gone.

She went to stay with Harry at his father's place in Cape Cod, and they played tennis and sailed, swam, and visited his friends, and she never felt threatened by him at all. The relationship was entirely platonic as far as she was concerned and therefore comfortable for her. Harry's feelings were something else but he kept them carefully veiled. She wrote to Sharon several times, but the answers she got back were brief, scrambled, and obviously written in haste. She'd never been so busy, or so happy, in her life. Her mother had been right, and she had a wonderful job working as a volunteer for Dr. Martin Luther King. It was amazing how their lives had changed in one short year.

And when Tana started school at Boston University, she was astonished at how different it was from Green Hill, how open, how interesting, how avant garde. She liked being in class with boys as well. Interesting issues were constantly raised and she did well in every class she took.

And secretly Jean was proud of her, although her rapport with Tana was no longer as good as it had once been. She told herself it was a passing phase. She had other things on her mind anyway. By the end of Tana's first year at Boston University, Ann Durning was getting married again. There was going to be an enormous wedding at Christ Episcopal Church in Greenwich, Connecticut, and a reception, organized by Jean, at the house. At the office, her desk was littered with lists, photographs, caterers' lists and Ann called her at least fourteen times a day. It was almost as though her own daughter was getting married, and after fourteen years as Arthur Durning's mistress and right arm, she felt possessive about the children anyway. And she was especially pleased at how well Ann had chosen this time. He was a lovely man of thirty-two, also previously married, and he was a partner at Sherman and Sterling, the law firm in New York, and from everything that Jean Roberts had heard, he was a very promising attorney, and he had plenty of money of his own. Arthur was also pleased about the match, and he gave Jean a beautiful gold bracelet from Cartier to thank her for all the work she did to make Ann's wedding a success.

"You're really a wonderful woman, you know." He sat in her living room, drinking a scotch, looking at her, wondering why he had never married her. Once in a while he felt like that, although most of the time now he was comfortable by himself. He was used to it.

"Thank you, Arthur." She handed him a small plate of the hors d'oeuvres he liked best, Nova Scotia salmon on little thin slices of Norwegian pumpernickel, little balls of steak tartare on white toast, the macadamia nuts she always kept in the house, in case he came by, along with his favorite scotch, favorite cookies . . . soap . . . eau de cologne . . . everything he liked. It was easier to be always ready for him now, with Tana gone. In some ways, that had helped their relationship, and in others, it had not. She was freer now, more available, always ready for him to come by at the drop of a hat, but at the same time, she was much lonelier with Tana gone, more anxious for his company. It made her hungrier, and lonelier, and less understanding when two weeks slid by without his spending a night in her bed. She realized that she should be grateful to him that he came to her at all, and he made so many things in her life easier, but she wanted so much more of him, she always had, ever since they first met.

"Tana's coming to the wedding, isn't she?" He ate another mouthful of steak tartare, and she tried to look vague. She had called Tana about it only a few days before. She hadn't responded to the invitation Ann had sent, and Jean had chided her for it, telling her it wasn't polite, and her Boston University manners didn't apply here, which of course had done nothing to warm Tana's heart.

"I'll answer as soon as I get around to it, Mom. I have exams right now. It only came last week."

"It only takes a minute to respond."

Her tone annoyed Tana as it always did now, and she was curt when she replied. "Fine. Then tell her no."

"I'll do nothing of the sort. You answer that invitation yourself. And I think you should go."

"Well, that comes as no surprise. Another command performance from the Durning clan. When do we get to say no to them?" She still cringed every time she imagined Billy's face. "I think I'm busy anyway."

"You could make the effort for my sake at least."

"Tell them that you have no control over me. That I'm impossible, that I'm climbing Mount Everest. Tell them whatever the hell you want!"

"You're really not going, then?" Jean sounded shocked, as though that weren't possible.

"I hadn't thought about it till now, but now that you mention it, I guess I'm not."

"You knew it all along."

"Oh, for chrissake . . . look, I don't like Ann or Billy. Scratch that. I don't like Ann, and I hate Billy's guts. Arthur is your affair, if you'll pardon the pun. Why do you have to drag me into this? I'm grown up now, so are they, we've never been friends."

"It's her wedding, and she wants you there."

"Bullshit. She's probably inviting everyone she knows, and she's inviting me as a favor to you."

"That's not true." But they both knew it was. And Tana was getting stronger and stronger as time went on.

In some ways, it was Harry's influence over her. He had
definite ideas about almost everything, and it brought
something similar out in her in order to respond to him.
He made her think about how she felt and what she
thought about everything, and they were as close as they
had ever been. And he'd been right about BU too. Moving to Boston had been good for her, much more so than
going to Green Hill. And in an odd way, she had grown
up more in the last year than ever before. She was almost
twenty years old.

"Tana, I just can't understand why you behave this
way." It was back to the wedding again, and her mother
was driving her nuts.

"Mom, can we talk about something else? How are
you?"

"I'm fine, but I'd like to think that you'll at least
think about this. . . ."

"All right!" She screamed into the phone at her end.
"I'll think about it. Can I bring a date?" Maybe it would
be more bearable if Harry came along.

"I was expecting that. Why don't you and the Winslow boy take a lesson from Ann and John and get engaged?"

"Because we're not in love. That's the best reason
why not."

"I find that hard to believe after all this time."

"Fact is stranger than fiction, Mom." Talking to her
mother always drove her nuts, and she tried to explain it
to Harry the next day. "It's as though she spends the
whole day planning what to say to me so that it will
irritate me the most possible, and she never fails. She hits
the nail right on the head every time."

"My father has the same knack. It's a prerequisite."

"For what?"

"For parenthood. You have to pass a test. If you're not irritating enough, they make you try again until you get it right. Then after the kid is born, they have to renew it every few years, so that after fifteen or twenty years, they've really got it down." Tana laughed at the idea as she looked at him. He was even more handsome than he had been when they first met, and the girls went crazy for him. There were always about half a dozen he was juggling at once, but he always made time for her. She came first, she was his friend, in fact she was much more than that to him, but Tana had never understood that. "You're going to be around for a long time, Tan. They'll be gone by next week." He never took any of them seriously, no matter how desperately they wanted him. He didn't fool anyone, he was careful that no one got hurt, he was sensible about birth control. "No casualties, thanks to me, Tan. Life is too short for that, and there's enough hurt out there without making more for your friends." But there was no pretense offered either. Harry Winslow wanted to have fun, and nothing more than that. No I love you's, no wedding rings, no starry eyes, just some laughs, a lot of beer, and a good time, if possible in bed. His heart was otherwise engaged, albeit secretly, but other interesting parts of him were not.

"Don't they want more than that?"

"Sure they do. They've got mothers just like you. Only most of them listen to their mothers more than you do. They all want to get married and drop out of school as soon as possible. But I tell them not to count on me to help them out. And if they don't believe me, they figure it out soon enough." He grinned boyishly and Tana laughed at him. She knew that the girls dropped like flies everytime he looked at them. She and Harry had been inseparable for the past year and she was the envy of all her friends. They found it impossible to believe that nothing was going on between them, they were as puzzled as her own mother was, but the relationship stayed chaste. Harry had come to understand her by now, and he wouldn't have dared to scale the walls she had put up around her sexuality. Once or twice he tried to fix her up with one of his friends, just as a friendly double date, but she wanted nothing to do with it. His roommate had even asked him if she was a lesbian, but he was sure that it wasn't that. He had a strong feeling that something had traumatized her, but she never wanted to talk about it, even with him, and he let it be. She went out with Harry, or her friends from BU, or by herself, but there were no men in her life, not in a romantic sense. Never. He was sure of it.

"It's a hell of a waste, you know, kid." He tried to talk to her about it teasingly, but she brushed him off, as she always did.

"You do enough of that for both of us."

"That doesn't do you much good."

She laughed. "I'm saving it for my wedding night."

"A noble cause." He swept her a low bow and they both laughed. People at Harvard and BU were used to seeing them, raising hell, cavorting, playing pranks on each other and their friends. Harry bought a bicycle for two at a garage sale one weekend, and they rode around Cambridge on it, with Harry in a huge raccoon hat in the winter months, and a straw boater when the weather got warm.

"Want to go to Ann Durning's wedding with me?" They were wandering across the Harvard Quad, the day after her mother had harassed her about it on the phone.

"Not particularly. Is it liable to be fun?"

"Not a chance." Tana smiled angelically. "My mother thinks I should go."

"I'm sure you expected that."

"She also thinks we should get engaged."

"I'll second that."

"Good. Then let's make it a double ceremony. Seriously, do you want to go?"

"Why?" There was something nervous in her eyes and he was trying to figure out what it was. He knew her well, but every now and then she hid from him, albeit not too successfully.

"I don't want to go alone. I don't like any of them. Ann's a real spoiled brat, and she's already been married once, but her daddy seems to be making a big fuss about this. I guess she did it right this time."

"What does that mean?"

"What do you think? It means the guy she's marrying has bucks."

"How sensitive." Harry smiled angelically and Tana laughed.

"It's nice to know where people's values are, isn't it? Anyway, the wedding's right after we get out of school, in Connecticut."

"I was going to the South of France that week, Tan, but I could put it off for a few days, if it'll help you out."

"That wouldn't be too big a pain in the ass for you?"

"It would." He smiled at her honestly. "But for you, anything." He bowed low, and she laughed, and he slapped her behind and they got back on the bicycle built for two, and he dropped her off at her dorm at BU. He had a big date that night. He had already invested four dinners in the girl, and he expected her to come through for him tonight.

"How can you talk like that!" Tana laughed and scolded him as they stood outside her dorm.

"I can't feed her forever, for chrissake, without getting something for it. Besides, she eats those huge steaks with the lobster tails. My income is suffering from this broad, but . . ." he smiled, thinking of her mammaries, ". . . I'll let you know how it works out."

"I don't think I want to know."

"That's right . . . virgin ears . . . oh, well. . . ." He waved as he rode off on their bicycle.

That night, she wrote a letter to Sharon, washed her hair, and had brunch with Harry the next day. He had gotten nowhere with the girl, "The Eater" as he called her now. She had devoured not only her own steak, but most of his as well, her lobster as well as his once more, and then told him that she didn't feel well and had to go home and study for exams. He got nothing whatsoever for his pains except a large check at the restaurant and a night of good, restful sleep, alone in his bed. "That's the end of her. Christ, the trouble you have to go to, to get laid these days." But she knew from all she heard that he did fine most of the time, and she teased him about it all the way to New York in June. He dropped her off at her apartment and went on to the Pierre. When he picked her up the next day to go to the wedding, she had to admit that he looked spectacular. He was wearing white flannel slacks, a blue cashmere blazer, a creamy silk shirt his father had made for him in London the year before, and a navy and red Hermès tie.

"Christ, Harry, if the bride had any sense, she'd ditch this guy and run off with you."

"That headache I don't need. And you don't look bad yourself, Tan." She was wearing a green silk dress almost the exact same color as her eyes, her hair hung long and straight down her back, and she had brushed it until it shone, just like her eyes, which sparkled as she looked at him.

"Thanks for coming with me. I know it's going to be a bore, but I appreciate it."

"Don't be silly. I didn't have anything else to do anyway. I'm not leaving for Nice until tomorrow night." And from there he was driving to Monaco, where his father was picking him up on a friend's yacht. Harry was going to spend two weeks with him, and then his father was dropping him off and going on with friends, leaving Harry alone in the house on Cap Ferrat. "I can think of worse fates, Tan." He was hinting at the hell he would raise, chasing girls in the South of France, and living in the house alone, but it sounded lonely to her. He would have no one to talk to most of the time, no one who really cared about him. On the other hand, she was going to spend the summer being smothered by Jean. In a moment of weakness, feeling guilty for the independence that had been so hard won, she had agreed to take a summer job, working for Durning International. And her mother was thrilled.

"I could kill myself every time I think about it." She

groaned to Harry every time the subject came up. "I was
nuts. But I feel so sorry for her sometimes. She's so alone
now that I'm gone. And I thought it would be a nice
thing to do for her, but Christ, Harry . . . what have I
done?"

"It won't be that bad, Tan."

"Want to make a bet?" Her scholarship had come
through for the following year, and she wanted to make
some pocket money to spend. At least this would help.
But it depressed her beyond words to think of spending
the whole summer in New York, living with Jean, and
watching her kiss Arthur's feet at work every day. The
very thought made her sick.

"We'll go to the Cape for a week when I come
back."

"Thank God for that." They exchanged a smile as
he drove her to Connecticut, and a little while later, they
were standing in Christ Episcopal Church with the rest of
the guests, painfully hot in the stifling June air, and then
mercifully they were released and they drove to the
Durning house, passing through the enormous gates, as
Harry watched her face. It was the first time she had been
back since the nightmare night two years before. Exactly
two years in fact. And there was a thin veil of sweat on
her upper lip as she thought of it.

"You really don't like it here, do you, Tan?"

"Not much." She glanced out the window and
looked vague as he watched the back of her head. But he
could sense something inside her go tense, and it was
worse once they parked the car and got out. They wandered down the receiving line saying the appropriate
things. Tana introduced Harry to Arthur and the bride

and groom, and then as she ordered a drink, she saw Billy staring at her. He was watching her intently, and Harry was watching him, as he wandered away, and Tana seemed to be in a stupor after that. She danced with Harry several times, with several people she didn't know, chatted with her mother once or twice, and then suddenly in a lull, she found herself face to face with Billy.

"Hello there. I wondered if you'd come." She had an overwhelming urge to slap his face, but instead she turned away. She couldn't breathe just looking at him. She hadn't seen him since that night, and he looked as malevolent as he had then, as weak and evil and spoiled. She could remember his hitting her, and then . . .

"Get away from me." She spoke in a barely audible voice.

"Don't be so uptight. Hell, this is my sister's wedding day. It's a romantic event." She could see that he was more than slightly drunk. She knew that he had graduated from Princeton a few days before and he had probably been drinking nonstop since then. He was going into the family firm, so he could screw around and chase secretaries. She wanted to ask him who he'd raped recently, but instead she just started to walk away and he grabbed her arm. "That was a pretty rude thing to do."

She turned back to him, her teeth clenched, her eyes wild. "Get your hand off of me or I'm going to throw this drink in your face." She hissed like a snake, and suddenly Harry materialized at her side, watching her, seeing something he had never seen before, and also noting the look in Billy Durning's eyes.

Billy Durning whispered one word, "whore," with a vicious look in his eyes, and with a single gesture, Harry grabbed his arm and twisted it back painfully until Billy groaned and tried to fight back but he didn't want to make a scene and Harry whispered in his ear, as he gripped his tie with his free hand, nearly choking him.

"Got the picture, pal? Good, then why don't you just take yourself off right now?" Billy wrenched his arm free, and without saying a word, he walked away as Harry looked at Tana. She was shaking from head to foot. "You all right?" She nodded, but he wasn't convinced. She was deathly pale, and her teeth were chattering despite the heat. "What was that all about? An old friend?"

"Mr. Durning's adorable son."

"I take it you two have met before."

She nodded. "Not very pleasantly." They stayed for a little while after that, and it was obvious that Tana was anxious to leave so Harry suggested it first. He didn't say anything for a while as they drove back to town, and he could see her visibly unwind as they put some distance between them and the Durning house. He had to ask her then. Something so powerful had been in the air, it frightened him for her.

"What was that all about, Tan?"

"Nothing much. An old hatred, that's all."

"Based on what?"

"He's a complete prick, that's what." They were strong words for her and Harry was surprised, and there was no humor in her voice. "A rotten little son of a bitch." Tears burned her eyes and her hands shook as she lit a cigarette, which she almost never did.

"I figured you two weren't the best of friends." Harry smiled but she didn't respond. "What did he do to you, to make you hate him so much, Tan?" Somehow, he had to know. For her sake and his own.

"It's not important now."

"Yes, it is."

"No, it's not!" She was shouting at him, and there were suddenly tears rolling down her cheeks. None of it had healed in the past two years, because she hadn't allowed the air to get to it. She hadn't told anyone except Sharon, hadn't fallen in love, hadn't gone on any dates. "It doesn't matter anymore."

He waited for her words to die down. "Are you trying to convince me or yourself?" He handed her his pocket handkerchief and she blew her nose, as the tears rolled down her cheeks.

"I'm sorry, Harry."

"Don't be. Remember me? I'm your friend." She smiled through her tears and patted his cheek, but something terrible had come back to haunt her again.

"You're the best friend I've got."

"I want you to tell me what happened with him."

"Why?"

He smiled. "So I can go back and kill him if you want."

"Okay. Go ahead." She laughed for the first time in hours.

"Seriously, I think you need to get it off your chest."

"No, I don't." That frightened her more than living with it. She didn't even want to talk about it now.

"He made a pass at you, didn't he?"

"More or less." She was looking out the window again.

"Tana . . . talk to me. . . ."

She turned to him with a wintry smile. "Why?"

"Because I give a damn." He pulled the car off the road, turned off the ignition, and looked at her. He knew suddenly that he was about to open a door that had been sealed tight, but he knew that for her sake he had to open it. "Tell me what he did to you."

She stared into Harry's eyes and spoke expressionlessly. She tried to shake her head, but Harry wouldn't let her off the hook, and he gently took her hand as she finally said the words. "He raped me two years ago. Two years ago tomorrow night, in fact. Happy Anniversary." Harry felt sick.

"What do you mean he raped you? Did you go out with him?"

She shook her head. "No." Her voice was a whisper at first. "My mother insisted that I go to a party here in Greenwich, at the house. His party. I went with one of his friends, who got drunk and disappeared, and Billy found me wandering around the house. He asked me if I wanted to see the room where my mother worked. And like a complete fool, I said yes, and the next thing I knew he dragged me into his father's bedroom, threw me down on the floor, and beat me up. He raped me and beat me for hours, and then he took me home and cracked up the car." She slowly began to sob, choking on her own words, feeling them rush out, almost physically, "I had hysterics at the hospital . . . after the police came . . . my mother came out . . . and she wouldn't believe me, she thought I was drunk . . . and little Billy could do no wrong in her eyes . . . I tried to tell her another time . . ." She buried her face in her hands, and Harry pulled her into his arms, and cooed to her the way no one had ever done to him, but listening to her almost broke his heart. It was why she had never gone out with anyone since they'd met, nor with him, why she was so locked up and frightened inside.

"Poor baby . . . poor Tan. . . ." He drove her back to the city then, took her to dinner at a quiet place, and then they went back and talked for hours at the Pierre. She knew her mother would be staying in Greenwich again that night. She had been staying there all week, to make sure that everything went all right. And after Harry dropped her off at her house, he wondered if things would change for Tana now, or even if possibly things might change between them. She was the most remarkable girl he had ever met, and if he had let himself, he would have fallen head over heels in love with her. But he had known better for the past two years, and he reminded himself of that now. He didn't want to spoil what they had, for what? A piece of ass? He had plenty of that, and she meant more than that to him. It was still going to take her a long time to heal, if she ever did, and he could help her more as her friend, than trying to meet his own needs by jumping into bed and playing therapist with her.

He called her the next day before he left for the South of France, and he had flowers sent to her the day after that, with a note that read, "Screw the past. You're okay now. Love, H." And he called her from Europe whenever he thought of it and had the time. His summer was a lot more interesting than hers, and they compared notes when he came back a week before Labor Day, and she finished her job and drove to Cape Cod with him. She was relieved to be out of Durning International at last. It had been a mistake, but she had lived up to her end.

"Any big romances while I was gone?"

"Nope. Remember me? I'm saving it for my wedding night." But they both knew why now. She was still traumatized by the rape, and they both also knew that she had to get over that. And after talking to him before he left, it seemed a little less painful now. It was finally beginning to heal.

"There won't be a wedding night if you never go out, you jerk."

"You sound like my mother again." She smiled. It was so good to see him again.

"How is your mother, by the way?"

"The same. Arthur Durning's devoted slave. It makes me sick. I never want to be like that with anyone."

He snapped his fingers with a look of despair. "Shit . . . and I was hoping that . . ." They both laughed, and the week sped by as it always did when they had a good time, and there was something magical about being together on Cape Cod. But in spite of Harry's hidden feelings for her, they kept the relationship as it had been. And they both went back to their respective schools for their junior year, which seemed to fly by. The following summer Tana stayed in Boston to work, and Harry went to Europe again, and when he came back they went back to Cape Cod, and the easy days were almost over with. They had only one year left before real life set in. And each in his own way, they were trying to keep reality at bay.

"What are you going to do?" she asked him somberly one night. She had finally agreed to date one of his friends, but things were going very slowly and Tana wasn't really interested in him. Secretly, Harry was glad. But he thought that a few superficial dates would do her good.

"He's just not my type."

"How the hell do you know? You haven't gone out with anyone in three years."

"From what I can see, that's no loss."

"Bitch." He grinned.

"I'm serious. What the hell are we going to do next year? Have you thought about graduate school?"

"God, no! That's all I need. I've had enough of this place to last me the rest of my life. I'm getting the hell out."

"And doing what?" She had been tormenting herself for the past two months.

"I don't know. I guess I'll stay in the house in London for a while. My father seems to be in South Africa all the time these days so it wouldn't bother him. Maybe Paris . . . Rome, then I'll come back here. I just want to play, Tan." And he was running away from something he wanted and knew he couldn't have. Not yet.

"Don't you want to work?" She looked shocked and he roared.

"Why?"

"That's disgusting!"

"What's disgusting about it? The men in my family haven't worked in years. How can I spoil a tradition like that? It would be sacrilege."

"How can you admit that?"

"Because it's true. They're a bunch of rich, lazy

bums. Just like my old man." But there was more to them than that, especially him. Much, much more.

"Is that what you want your children to say about you?" She looked horrified.

"Sure, if I'm dumb enough to have any, which I doubt."

"You sound like me now."

"God forbid." They both smiled.

"Seriously, aren't you at least going to pretend to work?"

"Why?"

"Stop saying that."

"Who cares if I work, Tan? You? Me? My old man? The columnists?"

"Then why did you go to school?"

"I had nothing else to do with myself, and Harvard was fun."

"Bullshit. You studied your ass off for exams." She tossed the gold mane over her shoulder with an earnest look. "You've been a good student. What for?"

"Myself. What about you? What are you doing it for?"

"Same thing. But now I don't know what the hell to do." But two weeks before Christmas, the choice was made for her. Sharon Blake called, and asked her if she would be willing to go on a march with Dr. King. Tana thought about it for a night, and called Sharon back the next day, with a tired smile. "You got me again, kid."

"Hurray! I knew you would!" She filled Tana in on the details. It was to take place three days before Christmas in Alabama, and it was relatively low risk. It all sounded fine to her, and the two girls chatted like old times. Sharon had never gone back to school, much to her father's chagrin, and she was in love with a young black attorney now. They were talking about getting married in the spring. And Tana was excited for her when she hung up, and she told Harry about the march the following afternoon.

"Your mother's going to have a fit."

"I don't have to tell her about it for chrissake. She doesn't have to know everything I do."

"She will when you get arrested again."

"I'll call you and you can come bail me out." She was serious and he shook his head.

"I can't. I'll be in Gstaad."

"Shit."

"I don't think you should go."

"I didn't ask you."

But when the time came, she was in bed with a fever of 102 degrees and a virulent flu. She tried to get up and pack the night before, but she was just too sick, and she called Sharon at the Blakes' home in Washington, and Freeman Blake answered the phone.

"You've heard the news, then. . . ." His voice sounded as though it came from the bottom of a well, and it was filled with gloom.

"What news?"

He couldn't even say the words. He just sat there and cried, and without knowing why, Tana began to cry too. "She's dead . . . they killed her last night . . . they shot her . . . my baby . . . my little girl. . . ." He was totally unglued and Tana was sobbing along with him, feeling frightened and hysterical, until Miriam Blake came to the phone. She sounded distraught but she was calmer than her husband had been. She told Tana when the funeral was. And Tana flew to Washington, fever and all, on the morning of Christmas Eve. It had taken that long to get the body home, and Martin Luther King had made arrangements to come and speak about her.

There was national news coverage, press pushing their way into the church, flashbulbs going off in everyone's face, and Freeman Blake was completely undone. He had lost both of his children now, to the same cause, and afterwards, Tana spent a little quiet time with them, with close friends, at their home.

"Do something useful with your life, child." Freeman Blake looked bleakly at her. "Get married, have kids. Don't do what Sharon did." He began to cry again, and eventually Dr. King and another friend led him upstairs and it was Miriam who came to sit beside Tana then. Everyone had been crying all day, and for days before, and Tana felt wrung out both from the emotions and the flu.

"I'm so sorry, Mrs. Blake."

"So am I. . . ." Her eyes looked like rivers of pain. She had seen it all, but she was still on her feet and always would be. She was that kind of woman, and in some ways Tana admired her. "What are you going to do now, Tana?"

She wasn't sure what Miriam meant. "Go home, I guess." She was going to catch a late flight that night to spend Christmas with Jean. As usual, Arthur had gone away with friends, and Jean was going to be alone.

"I mean when you finish school."

"I don't know."

"Have you ever thought about going into government? That's what this country needs." Tana smiled, she could almost hear Sharon speaking to her. Here, her daughter had just died, and she was already back at her crusades. It was frightening in some ways, and yet admirable too. "You could go into law. You could change things, Tana. You're that kind of girl."

"I'm not sure I am."

"You are. You've got guts. Sharon did too, but she didn't have your kind of mind. In some ways, you're like me." It was a frightening thought because Tana had always found her cold, and she didn't want to be like that.

"I am?" She looked a little stunned.

"You know what you want, and you go for it."

Tana smiled. "Sometimes."

"You didn't even skip a beat when you got kicked out of Green Hill."

"That was just lucky a friend suggested BU."

"If he hadn't, you'd have landed on your feet anyway." She stood up with a small sigh. "Anyway, think about it. There aren't enough lawyers like you, Tan. You're what this country needs." It was a heady thing to say to a twenty-one-year-old girl, and on the plane home the words echoed in her head, but more than that, she kept seeing Freeman's face, hearing him cry . . . hearing things Sharon had said to her at Green Hill . . . the times they had walked into Yolan . . . the memories flooded her, and she dried her eyes again and again to no avail, and she found herself thinking constantly of the baby Sharon had given up four years before, wondering where he was, what had happened to him. And she won-

dered if Freeman had been thinking of him too. They had
no one left now.

And at the same time, she kept thinking of Miriam's
words. This country needs you . . . she tried the
thought on her mother before she went back to school,
and Jean Roberts looked horrified.

"Law school? Haven't you been in school for long
enough? Are you going to stay there for the rest of your
life?"

"Only if it does me some good."

"Why don't you get a job? You might meet someone
that way."

"Oh for chrissake, never mind. . . ." It was all she
thought about . . . meet someone . . . settle down
. . . get married . . . have kids. . . . But Harry
wasn't much warmer to the idea when she tried it out on
him the following week.

"Jesus Christ, why?"

"Why not? It might be interesting, and I might be
good at it." She was getting more excited about it every
day, and suddenly it seemed like the right thing to do. It
made some sense, gave some purpose to her life. "I'm
going to apply to Boalt, at UC Berkeley." She had already made up her mind. There were two other schools
she was going to apply to also, but Boalt was her first
choice.

Harry stared at her. "You're serious?"

"Yes."

"I think you're nuts."

"Want to come?"

"Hell, no!" He grinned. "I told you. I'm going to
play . . . just kick up my heels."

"That's a waste of time."

"I can hardly wait."

And neither could she. In May she got the word. She'd been accepted at Boalt. They would give her a partial scholarship, and she had already saved the rest.

"I'm on my way." She grinned at Harry as they sat on the lawn outside her dorm.

"Tan, are you sure?"

"Never more so in my whole life." The two exchanged a long smile. The road would part for them soon. She went to his graduation at Harvard in June, and cried copiously for him, for herself, for Sharon Blake who was no more, for John F. Kennedy who had been killed seven months before, for the people they had met, and those they never would. An era had come to an end, for them both. And she cried at her own graduation too. As Jean Roberts did, and Arthur Durning had come along. And Harry sat in the back row, pretending to make conquests among the freshman girls.

But it was Tana his eyes were rivetted to, his heart leapt with pride for her and then sank as he thought of their going separate ways. He knew that inevitably their paths would cross again. He would see to that. But for her, it was still too soon. And with all his heart, he wished her godspeed and, that she would be safe and well in California. It made him nervous to think of her so far from him. But he had to let her go for now . . . for now . . . tears filled his eyes as he watched her come down the steps with her diploma in hand. She looked so fresh and young, the big green eyes, the bright shining hair . . . and the lips he so desperately longed to kiss and had for almost four years . . . the same lips brushed his cheek as he congratulated her again, and for an instant, just an instant, he felt her hold him close, and it almost took his breath away.

"Thanks, Harry." There were tears in her eyes.

"What for?" He had to fight back tears of his own.

"For everything." And then the others pressed in on them and the moment was gone. Their separate lives had begun and Harry almost felt her physically torn from him.

Part II

LIFE
BEGINS

Chapter 7

The ride to the airport seemed endless this time. Tana took a cab, and Jean insisted on coming with her. There were endless silences, pauses, staccato bursts of words, like machine gun fire at the enemy as it disappeared into the brush, and then finally they were there. Jean insisted on paying for the cab, as though it were her last chance to do something for her little girl, the only chance she'd ever have, and it was easy to see she was fighting back tears as they checked Tana's bags in.

"That's all you had, dear?" She turned to Tana nervously, as Tana nodded and smiled. It had been a difficult morning for her too. There was no pretending anymore. She wouldn't be coming home again, not for a long, long time. For a few days, a week, a brief trip. But if she managed to hang in at Boalt, she would probably never live at home again. She hadn't had to face that before when she went to Green Hill, or BU, and she was ready to go now. But it was easy to see the panic on Jean's face. It was the same expression she had worn twenty-three years before when Andy Roberts had gone to war. That look that comes of knowing that nothing will ever be the

189

same again. "You won't forget to call me tonight, will you, dear?"

"No, Mother, I won't. But I can't promise after this." Tana smiled. "If everything I hear is true, I won't come up for air for the next six months." And she had already warned her that she wouldn't be coming home for Christmas that year. The trip was too expensive anyway. And Jean had resigned herself to that. She was hoping that Arthur might give her a ticket out, but then there would be no hope of spending Christmas with him. Life wasn't easy sometimes. For some, it never was.

They both had a cup of tea, and watched the planes take off as Tana waited for her plane to be called, and she saw her mother staring at her more than once. Twenty-two years of caring for her were officially coming to an end, and it was difficult for both of them. And then suddenly Jean took her hand and looked into her eyes. "Is this what you really want, Tan?"

Tana answered her quietly. "Yes, Mom, it is."

"You're sure?"

Tana smiled. "I am. I know it seems strange to you, but it really is what I want. I've never been so sure of anything, no matter how hard it is."

Jean frowned and slowly shook her head before looking at Tana again. It was a strange time to be talking about it, just before she took off, and a strange place, with thousands of people all around, but this was where they were and what was in Jean's heart as she looked into her daughter's eyes again. "It seems more like a career for a man. I just never thought. . . ."

"I know." Tana looked sad. "You wanted me to be like Ann." She was living in Greenwich, near her Dad, and had just had her first child. Her husband was a full partner of Sherman and Sterling now. He drove a Porsche, and she a Mercedes sedan. It was every mother's dream. "That just isn't me. It never was, Mom."

"But why not?" She didn't understand. Maybe she had gone wrong somewhere. Maybe it was her fault. But Tana was shaking her head quietly.

"Maybe I need more than that. Maybe I need it to be my accomplishment, instead of my husband's. I don't know, but I don't think I could be happy like that."

"I think Harry Winslow is in love with you, Tan." Her voice was gentle, but Tana didn't want to hear the words.

"You're wrong, Mom." It was back to that again. "We love each other dearly, as friends, but he's not in love with me, and I'm not in love with him." That wasn't what she wanted. She wanted him as her brother, her friend. Jean nodded and said nothing as they called Tana's plane. It was as though she were making a last attempt to change Tana's mind, but there was nothing to change it with, no lifestyle, no man, no overwhelming gift, and nothing would have changed it anyway. She looked into her mother's eyes, and then held her close in a long hug as she whispered in her ear. "Mom, this is what I want. I'm sure. I swear it to you." It was like leaving for Africa as she said goodbye. As though she were leaving for a different world, a different life, and in a way she was. Her mother looked so grief stricken that it broke her heart, and Jean's tears flowed unchecked down her cheeks as she waved goodbye and Tana boarded the plane, shouting back, "I'll call you tonight!"

"But it'll never be the same again," Jean whispered

to herself, as she watched the doors close, the gangway
pull back, and the giant bird head down the runway at
last, and finally take off. And then at long, long last, it
was only a speck in the sky, and feeling very small and
very alone, she went outside, hailed a cab, and went back
to the office where Arthur Durning needed her. At least
someone still did, but she dreaded going home that night.
And for the next years.

Chapter 8

Tana had taken a plane which landed at Oakland airport, and it seemed a small and friendly place when she arrived. Smaller than both Boston and New York, and much, much larger than Yolan, which didn't have an airport at all. She took a cab to the Berkeley campus with her conglomeration of things, checked into the room that had been rented for her as part of her scholarship, unpacked her bags, and looked around. Everything felt different and strange and new. It was a beautiful, warm, sunny day, and people looked relaxed in everything from blue jeans to cords to flowing robes. There was more than one caftan in sight, lots of shorts and T-shirts, sandals, sneakers, loafers, bare feet. Unlike Boston University, the Jewish princesses from New York were not in evidence here, wearing expensive wools and cashmeres from Bergdorf's. This was strictly "come as you are," and it was anything but neat. But there was an excitement about it, too, and she felt exhilarated as she looked around. It was an exhilaration which stayed with her once classes began, and into the next month, as she ran from one class to the other every day, and then dashed home to study all afternoon and all night. The only other place she ever saw was the library, and whenever possible she ate in her room or on the run. She had lost six pounds which she didn't need to lose by the end of the first month. And the only good thing about the schedule she kept was that she didn't miss Harry quite as much as she had feared she would. For three years, they had been almost joined at the hip, even though they attended different schools, and now suddenly he wasn't there, although he would call her at off-hours. And on October fifth, she was in her room, when someone knocked on her door and told her that there was a call on the pay phone for her. She figured it was her mother again, and she really didn't want to go downstairs. She had a quiz the next day on contract law, and she had a paper due in another course.

"Find out who it is. Can I call back?"

"Okay, just a sec." And then she came back again. "It's from New York."

Her mother again. "I'll call back."

"He says you can't." He? Harry? Tana smiled. For him, she would even interrupt her work.

"I'll be right out." She grabbed a pair of rumpled jeans off the back of a chair, and pulled them on as she ran to the phone. "Hello?"

"What the hell are you doing? Making it with some guy on the fourteenth floor? I've been sitting here for an hour, Tan." He sounded annoyed and he also sounded drunk, to her practiced ear. She knew him well.

"I'm sorry, I was in my room, studying, and I thought it was my Mom."

"No such luck." He sounded strangely serious.

"Are you in New York?" She was smiling, happy to hear from him again.

"Yeah."

"I thought you weren't coming back till next month."

"I wasn't. I came back to see my uncle. Apparently, he thinks he needs my help."

"What uncle?" Tana looked confused. Harry had never mentioned an uncle before.

"My Uncle Sam. Remember him, the guy on the posters in the ridiculous red and blue suit with the long white beard?" He was definitely drunk and she started to laugh, but the laughter faded on her lips. He was serious. *Oh, my God. . . .*

"What the hell do you mean?"

"I got drafted, Tan."

"Oh, shit." She closed her eyes. That was all they heard about. Vietnam . . . Vietnam . . . Vietnam . . . everyone had something to say about it . . . kick the shit out of them . . . stay out of it . . . remember what happened to the French . . . go to it . . . stay home . . . police action . . . war . . . it was impossible to know what was going on, but whatever it was, it wasn't good. "Why the hell did you come back? Why didn't you stay over there?"

"I didn't want to do that. My father even offered to buy me out if he could, which I doubt. There are some things which even his Winslow money won't buy. But that's not my style, Tan. I don't know, maybe secretly I've wanted to go over there and make myself useful for a while."

"You're nuts. My God. . . . You're worse than

that. You could be killed. Don't you realize that? Harry,
go back to France." She was shouting at him now, standing in an open corridor, shouting at Harry in New York.
"Why the hell don't you go to Canada, or shoot yourself
in the foot . . . do something, resist the draft. This is
1964, not 1941. Don't be so noble, there's nothing to be
noble about, asshole. Go back." There were suddenly
tears in her eyes and she was afraid to ask what she
wanted to know. But she had to. She had to know.
"Where are they sending you?"

"San Francisco." Her heart soared. "First. For
about five hours. Want to meet me at the airport, Tan?
We could have lunch or something. I have to go to some
place called Fort Ord by ten o'clock that night, and I
arrive at three. And somebody told me it was about a
two-hour drive from San Francisco. . . ." His voice
trailed off, they were both thinking the same thing.

"And then what?" Her voice was suddenly hoarse.

"Vietnam, I guess. Cute, huh?"

She suddenly sounded pissed. "No, not cute, you
dumb son of a bitch. You should have come to law school
with me. Instead, you wanted to play and get yourself
laid in every whorehouse in France, and now look at you,
you're going to Vietnam to get your balls shot off. . . ."
There were tears rolling down her face, and no one dared
walk past her in the hall.

"You make it sound intriguing, anyway."

"You're a jerk."

"So what else is new? You fallen in love yet?"

"Who has time, all I do is read. What time does
your plane come in?"

"Three o'clock tomorrow."

"I'll be there."

"Thanks." He sounded so young again, on the last word, and when she saw him the next day, she thought he looked pale and tired. He didn't look as well as when she had seen him in June, and their brief visit was nervous and strained. She didn't know what to do with him. Five hours wasn't very long. She took him to her Berkeley room, and then they drove into town for lunch in Chinatown, wandered around, and Harry kept looking at his watch. He had a bus to catch. He had decided not to rent a car to get to Fort Ord after all, but that shortened the time he had with her. They didn't laugh as much as usual, and they were both upset all afternoon.

"Harry, why are you doing this? You could have bought your way out."

"That's not my style, Tan. You must know that by now. And maybe, secretly, I think I'm doing the right thing. There's a patriotic part of me I didn't know I had."

Tana felt her heart sink. "That's not patriotism for chrissake. It isn't our war." It horrified her that he had an out he wouldn't use. It was a side of him she had never seen. Easygoing Harry had grown up, and she saw a man in him she had never known before. He was stubborn and strong, and although what he was doing frightened him, it was clearly what he wanted to do.

"I think it will be our war soon, Tan."

"But why you?" They sat silently for a long time and the day went too fast. She held him tight when they said goodbye, and she made him promise to call whenever he could. But that wasn't for another six weeks, and by then basic training was over. He had been planning to

come back to San Francisco to see her, but instead of
going north, he was being sent south. "I leave for San
Diego tonight." It was Saturday. "And Honolulu, the
beginning of the week." And she had midterm exams, so
she couldn't just run down to San Diego for a day or two.

"Damn. Will you stay in Honolulu for a while?"

"Apparently not." She sensed instantly that he
wasn't telling her what she wanted to know.

"What does that mean?"

"It means I'm being sent to Saigon by the end of
next week." His voice sounded cold and hard, almost like
steel, and it didn't sound like Harry at all. She wondered
how this had happened to him, and it was something he
had wondered himself every day for six weeks. "Just
lucky, I guess," he had said jokingly to his friends, but
there was nothing to joke about, and you could have cut
the air with a knife when they handed the assignments
out. No one dared say anything to anyone, least of all
those who had fared well, for fear that others had not.
And Harry was one of the unlucky ones. "It's a bitch,
Tan, but there it is."

"Does your father know?"

"I called last night. No one knows where he is. In
Paris, they think he's in Rome. In Rome, they think he's
in New York. I tried South Africa, and then I figured
fuck the son of a bitch. He'll find out sooner or later
where I am." Why the hell didn't he have a father one
could reach? Tana would even have called for him, but he
had always sounded like the kind of man she didn't want
to know anyway. "I wrote to him at the London address,
and I left a message at the Pierre in New York. That's the
best I can do."

"It's probably more than he deserves anyway. Harry, is there anything I can do?"

"Say a prayer." He sounded as though he were serious, and she was shocked. This wasn't possible. Harry was her best friend, her brother, practically her twin, and they were sending him to Vietnam. She had a sense of panic she had never known before and there was absolutely nothing she could do.

"Will you call me again before you leave? . . . and from Honolulu . . . ?" There were tears in her eyes . . . what if something happened to him? But nothing would, she gritted her teeth, she wouldn't even let herself think like that. Harry Winslow was invincible, and he belonged to her. He owned a piece of her heart. But she felt lost for the next few days, waiting constantly for his calls. There were two from San Diego before he left, "Sorry I took so long, I was busy getting laid, probably got the clap, but what the hell." He was drunk most of the time, and even more so in Hawaii, and he called her twice from there too, and after that he was gone, into the silence, the jungles and the abyss of Vietnam. She constantly imagined him in danger, and then began to get outrageous letters describing life in Saigon, the hookers, the drugs, the once lovely hotels, the exquisite girls, the constant use he had for his French, and she began to relax. Good old Harry, nothing ever changed, from Cambridge to Saigon, he was the same. She managed to get through her exams, Thanksgiving, and the first two days of the Christmas holiday, which she was spending in her room with a two-foot-tall stack of books, when someone came and pounded on her door at seven o'clock one night.

"Call for you." Her mother had been calling her a lot, but Tana knew why, although neither of them ever admitted it. The holidays were difficult for Jean. Arthur never spent much time with her, and somehow she always hoped that he would. There were excuses and reasons and parties where he just couldn't take her along, and Tana suspected that there were probably other women too, and now there was Ann and her husband and her baby, and maybe Billy was there too, and Jean just wasn't family, no matter how many years she'd been around.

"I'll be right there," Tana called out, pulled on her bathrobe, and went to the phone. The hall was cold, and she knew it was foggy outside. It was rare for the fog to come this far east, but sometimes it did on particularly bad nights. "Hello?" She expected her mother's voice and was shocked when she heard Harry's instead. He sounded hoarse and very tired, as though he'd been up all night, which was understandable, if he was in town. His voice sounded exquisitely close. "Harry? . . ." Tears instantly filled her eyes, "Harry! Is that you?"

"Hell, yes, Tan." He almost growled at her, and she could almost feel the beard stubble on his face.

"Where are you?"

There was only a fraction of a pause. "Here. San Francisco."

"When did you arrive? Christ, I'd have picked you up if I'd known." What a Christmas gift, having Harry back!

"I just got in." It was a lie, but it was easier to say that than to explain why it had taken so long to call.

"You sure didn't stay long, thank God." She was so

grateful to hear his voice that she couldn't stop the tears. She was smiling and crying all at once, and at his end, so was he. He had never thought he would hear her voice again, and he loved her more than he ever had before. He wasn't even sure that he could hide it now. But he would have to, for her sake, and his own. "Why'd they let you come back so soon?"

"I guess I gave them a bad time. The food stank, the girls had lice. Shit, I caught crabs twice, and the worst case of the clap I ever had. . . ." He tried to laugh but it hurt too much.

"You creep. Don't you ever behave yourself?"

"Not if I have a choice."

"So where are you now?"

There was that pause again. "They're cleaning me up at Letterman."

"Hospital?"

"Yeah."

"For the clap?" She said it so loud that two girls turned halfway down the hall and she started to laugh. "You know, you're impossible. You're the worst person I know, Harry Winslow the Fourth, or whoever the hell you are. Can I come and visit you or will I get it too?" She was still laughing, and he still sounded tired and hoarse.

"Just don't use my toilet seat."

"Don't worry, I won't. I may not shake your hand either unless I see it boiled. God only knows where it's been." He smiled. It was so goddamn good to hear her voice. She looked at her watch. "Can I come over now?"

"Don't you have anything better to do on a Saturday night?"

"I was planning to make love to a stack of law books."

"You're about as amusing as you used to be, I see."

"Yeah, but I'm a lot smarter than you are, asshole, and nobody sent me to Vietnam." There was a strange silent pause, and Harry wasn't smiling when he answered her.

"Thank God, Tan." She felt strange as she heard his voice, and an odd feeling crept over her, that sent chills up her spine. "Do you really want to come over tonight?"

"Hell, yes, do you think I wouldn't come? I just don't want to catch the clap, that's all."

He smiled. "I'll behave myself." But he had to say something to her . . . before she came . . . it wasn't fair. "Tan . . ." His voice caught on the words. He hadn't said anything to anyone yet. He hadn't even talked to his father yet. They hadn't been able to locate him anywhere although Harry knew he'd be in Gstaad by the end of the week. He always spent Christmas there, whether Harry was there or not. Switzerland meant Christmas to him. "Tan . . . I've got a little more than the clap. . . ." An odd chill raced up her spine and she closed her eyes.

"Yeah, asshole? Like what?" She wanted to fight back the words, to make him laugh, to make him all right in case he was not, but it was too late . . . to stop either the truth or the words. . . .

"I got a little bit shot up. . . ." She heard his voice crack, and felt a sudden pain in her chest as she fought back a sob.

"Oh yeah? Why'd you go do a thing like that?" She was fighting back tears and so was he.

"Nothing better to do, I guess. The girls were really all dogs. . . ." His voice grew sad and soft, ". . . compared to you, Tan."

"Jesus, they must have shot you in the brain." They both laughed a little bit, and she stood in her bare feet feeling as though her whole body had turned to ice. "Letterman. Right?"

"Yeah."

"I'll be there in half an hour."

"Take your time. I'm not going anywhere." And he wouldn't be for quite a while. But Tana didn't know any of that as she pulled on her jeans, shoved her feet into shoes, she didn't even know which ones, pulled a black turtleneck over her head, dragged a comb through her hair, and yanked her pea jacket off the foot of her bed. She had to get to him now, had to see what had happened to him. . . . *I got a little bit shot up.* . . . It was all she could hear again and again in her head as she took the bus into town, and then found a cab to take her to Letterman Hospital in the Presidio. It was twice as long as she had said it would be, but she had run like hell, and fifty-five minutes after she hung up, she walked into the hospital and asked for Harry's room. The woman at the reception desk asked Tana what department he was in, and she had a strong urge to say "the department for the clap," but she wasn't feeling funny now, and she felt even less so as she ran down the halls labelled *Neurosurgery,* praying that he was all right. Her face was so pale it was almost gray, but so was his when she walked into the room. There was a respirator standing by, and he was lying flat on a bed with a mirror overhead. There were racks and tubes, and a nurse watching over him. She thought he was paralyzed at first. Absolutely nothing moved, and then she saw him move a hand and tears filled her eyes, but she had been half right anyway. He was paralyzed from the waist down. He had been shot in the spine as he explained to her that night, as tears filled his eyes. He could finally talk to her, cry with her, tell her how he felt. He felt like shit. He wanted to die. He had wanted to die ever since they brought him back.

"So this is it. . . ." He could hardly speak, and the tears ran down the sides of his face, down his neck, onto the sheets. "I'll be in a wheelchair from now on. . . ." He was sobbing openly. He had thought he would never see her again, and suddenly there she was, so beautiful and so good and so blond . . . just as she had always been. Everything was the same as it always had been here. No one knew about Vietnam here. About Saigon or Da Nang or the Viet Cong, whom you never even saw. They just shot you in the ass from their hiding place in a tree, and maybe they were only nine years old, or just looked that way. But no one gave a damn about that here.

Tana was watching him, trying not to cry. She was grateful he was alive. From the story he had told, of lying face down in the mud, in the driving rains, in the jungle for five days, it was obviously a miracle that he was alive at all. So what if he could never walk again? He was alive, wasn't he? And the thing Miriam Blake had seen in her so long before began to surface now. "That's what you get for screwing cheap whores, ya jerk. Now, you can lie there if you want to, for a while, but I want you to know right now that I'm not going to put up with much of this. Got that?" She stood up, and they were both unable to stop their tears, but she took his hand and she held it fast. "You're going to get off your ass and do something with yourself. Is that clear?" He stared at her in disbelief, and the crazy thing was that she was serious. "Is that clear?" Her voice was shaking as her heart swelled.

"You know you're a crazy girl. Do you know that, Tan?"

"And you're a lazy son of a bitch, so don't get too excited about this lie-on-your-ass life of yours, because it's not going to last long. Got that, asshole?"

"Yes, ma'am." He saluted her, and a few minutes later, a nurse came in and gave him a shot for the pain, and Tana watched him drift off to sleep, holding his hand, as the tears coursed down her face and she cried silently whispering her prayers and her thanks. She watched him for hours, just holding his hand, and at last she kissed his cheek, and his eyes, and she left the hospital. It was after midnight by then, and all she could think of as she took a bus back to Berkeley that night was "Thank God." Thank God he was alive. Thank God he hadn't died in that godforsaken jungle, wherever the hell it was. Vietnam had a new meaning to her now. It was a place where people went to be killed. It wasn't just someplace one read about, something to talk about between classes, with professors or friends. It was real to her now. She knew exactly what it meant. It meant Harry Winslow would never walk again. And as she stepped off the bus in Berkeley that night, the tears still running down her cheeks, she jammed her hands in her pockets, and walked back to her rented room, knowing that neither of them would ever be the same again.

Chapter 9

Tana sat at his side for the next two days, and never moved, except to go home and get a few hours' sleep, bathe, change her clothes and come back again, to hold his hand, talk to him when he was awake, about the years when he was at Harvard and she was at BU, the tandem bicycle they had, the vacations on Cape Cod. They kept him pretty doped up most of the time, but there were times when he was so lucid it hurt to look at him, and to realize the thoughts going through his mind. He didn't want to spend the rest of his life paralyzed. He wanted to die, he told Tana again and again. And she screamed at him and called him a son of a bitch. But she was also afraid to leave him at night, for fear he would do something about it himself. She warned the nurses about how he felt, but they were used to it and it didn't impress them much. They kept a close eye on him, and there were others who were worse off, like the boy down the hall who had lost both arms and his entire face when a six-year-old boy had handed a hand grenade to him.

On the morning of Christmas Eve, her mother called just before she left for the hospital. It was ten o'clock in New York, and she had gone into the office for a few hours, and she thought she'd call Tana to see how she was. She had hoped right up until the last minute that Tana would change her mind and come home to spend Christmas with her, but Tana had insisted for months that there was no chance of that. She had stacks and stacks of work to do. And she said there wasn't even any point in Jean coming out. But it seemed a depressing way to spend the Christmas holidays, almost as depressing as the way she was spending them herself. Arthur was having a family Christmas in Palm Beach with Ann and Billy and his son-in-law, and the baby, and he hadn't included Jean. She understood of course that it would have been awkward for him.

"So what are you up to, sweetheart?" Jean hadn't called her in two weeks. She was too depressed to call, and she didn't want Tana to hear it on the phone. At least when Arthur was in New York over the holidays, there was some hope that he might stop by for a few hours, but this year she didn't even have that hope held out to her, and Tana was gone. . . . "Studying as hard as you thought?"

"Yes . . . I . . . no . . ." She was still half asleep. She had stayed with Harry until four o'clock. His fever had suddenly shot up the night before and she was afraid to leave him again, but at four in the morning, the nurses had insisted she go home and get some sleep. It was going to be a long, hard climb for him, and if she burned herself out now, she wouldn't do him any good later on, when he needed her most. "I haven't been. At least not for the past three days." She almost groaned with fatigue, as she sat down in the straight-backed chair they left near the phone. "Harry got back from Vietnam." Her eyes glazed as she thought of it. This would be the first time she had told anyone, and the thought of what there was to say made her sick.

"You've been seeing him?" Jean sounded instantly annoyed. "I thought you had studying to do. If I'd thought you could take time off to play, Tana, I wouldn't be sitting here spending the Christmas holidays by myself . . . if you have time to play around with him, the least you could have—"

"Stop it!" Tana suddenly shrieked in the empty hall. *"Stop it!* He's in Letterman. No one's playing around, for God's sake." There was silence at Jean's end. She had never heard Tana sound like that. There was a kind of hysterical desperation in her voice, and a frightening despair.

"What's Letterman?" She imagined it was a hotel, but something instantly told her she was wrong.

"The military hospital here. He was shot in the spine. . . ." She began to take in great gulps of air so she wouldn't cry, but it didn't work. Nothing worked. She cried all the time when she wasn't with him. She couldn't believe what had happened to him. And she nearly collapsed now on the chair, like a little child. "He's a paraplegic now, Mom . . . he may not even live . . . he got this terrible fever last night . . ." She just sat there, crying, shaking from head to foot and unable to stop, but she had to let it out, as Jean stared at her office wall in shock, thinking about the boy she had seen so many times. He was so confident, almost debonair, if one could say that about a boy his age, he laughed all the time, he was funny and bright and irreverent and he had annoyed her most of the time, and now she thanked God Tana hadn't married him . . . imagine the life that would have been for her.

"Oh sweetheart . . . I'm so sorry. . . ."

"So am I." She sounded exactly as she had as a child when her puppy died, and it broke Jean's heart to listen to her. "And there's nothing I can do, except sit there and watch."

"You shouldn't be there. It puts too much strain on you."

"I *have* to be there. Don't you understand?" Her voice was harsh. "I'm all he has."

"What about his family?"

"His father hasn't shown up yet, and he probably never will, the son of a bitch, and Harry's just lying there, barely hanging on."

"Well, there's nothing you can do. And I don't think you should see something like that, Tan."

"Oh, no?" She was belligerent now. "What should I see, Mom? Dinner parties on the East Side, evenings in Greenwich with the Durning clan? That's the worst crock of crap I've ever heard. My best friend has just had his ass shot off in Vietnam, and you don't think I should do something like that. Just what do you think should happen to him, Mom? Should I cross him off my list because he can't dance anymore?"

"Don't be so cynical, Tana." Jean Roberts sounded firm.

"Why the hell not? What kind of world do we live in anyway? What's wrong with everyone? Why don't they see what we're getting into in Vietnam?" Not to mention Sharon and Richard Blake and John Kennedy and everything else that was wrong with the world.

"That's not in your hands or mine."

"Why doesn't anyone care what we think . . . ? what I think . . . what Harry thinks. . . . Why didn't anybody ask him before he went?" She was sobbing again and she couldn't go on.

"Get hold of yourself." Jean waited for a moment, and then said, "I think you should come home for the holidays, Tan, especially if you're going to spend them around the hospital with that boy."

"I can't come home now." Her voice was sharp and suddenly there were tears in Jean's eyes.

"Why not?" Now she sounded like the child.

"I don't want to leave Harry now."

"How can he mean that much to you . . . ?" *more than I do. . . .*

"He just does. Aren't you spending Christmas with Arthur anyway, or at least part of it?" Tana blew her nose and wiped her eyes, but Jean shook her head at her end.

"Not this year, Tan. He's going to Palm Beach with the kids."

"And he didn't invite you?" Tana sounded shocked. He was really the consummate selfish son of a bitch, second only to Harry's dad, perhaps.

"It would be awkward for him."

"Why? His wife's been dead for eight years, and you're no secret anymore. Why couldn't he invite you?"

"It doesn't matter. I have work to do here anyway."

"Yeah," it drove her nuts thinking about her mother's subservience and devotion to him, "work for him. Why don't you just tell him to jump in the lake one of these days, Mom? You're forty-five years old, you could still find someone else, and no one could treat you worse than Arthur does."

"Tana, that's not true!" She was instantly outraged.

"No? Then how come you're spending Christmas alone?"

Jean's tongue was quick and sharp. "Because my daughter won't come home."

Tana wanted to hang up in her face. "Don't lay that trip on me, Mom."

"Don't talk to me like that. And it's true, isn't it? You want him around so there isn't any responsibility on you. Well, it doesn't always work like that. You may not choose to come home, but you can't pretend it's the right thing to do."

"I'm in law school, Mom. I'm twenty-two years old. I'm grown up. I can't be there for you all the time anymore."

"Well, neither can he. And his responsibilities are far more important than yours." She was crying softly now and Tana shook her head. Her voice was calm when she spoke again.

"He's the one you should be mad at, Mom, not me. I'm sorry I can't be there for you, but I just can't."

"I understand."

"No, you don't. And I'm sorry about that, too."

Jean sighed into the phone. "I guess there's nothing we can do about it now. And I suppose you are doing the right thing." She sniffed, "But please, sweetheart, don't spend all your time at the hospital. It's too depressing, and you can't do the boy any good. He'll pull out of it on his own." Her attitude made Tana sick, but she didn't say anything to her.

"Sure, Mom." They each had their own ideas, and neither of them was going to change anymore. It was hopeless now. They had gone their own ways, and Jean knew it too. She thought of how lucky Arthur was to still have his children around so much of the time. Ann always wanted his help, financially and otherwise, and her husband practically kissed Arthur's feet, and even Billy was living at home. It was wonderful for him, she thought as she hung up. It meant he never really had enough time for her. Between his business obligations, his old friends who had been too close to Marie to accept Jean, according to him anyway, and Billy and Ann, there was scarcely ever any time for her. And yet, there was still something so special between them, and she knew there always would be.

It was worth all the hours she spent alone, waiting for him. At least that was what she told herself, as she straightened her desk and went home to her apartment to stare into Tana's empty room. It looked so painfully neat, so empty and deserted now. So unlike the room she was living in, in Berkeley, where her things were spread all over the floor, as she rapidly gathered her things, desperate to get back to Harry again. She had called the hospital after she and her mother hung up, and they said his fever was up again. He was asleep, and he had just had a shot, but she wanted to get back to him before he woke up again. And as she pulled a comb through her hair, and climbed into her jeans, she thought of the things her mother had said. It was unfair of Jean to blame her loneliness on her. What right did she have to expect Tana to always be there for her? It was her mother's way of absolving Arthur of his responsibilities. For sixteen years she had made excuses for him, to Tana, to herself, to her friends, to the girls at work. How many excuses could one make for the man?

Tana grabbed her jacket off a hook and ran downstairs. It took her half an hour to cross the Bay Bridge on the bus, and another twenty minutes to get to Letterman, peacefully nestled in the Presidio. The traffic was worse than it had been in the past few days, but it was the morning of Christmas Eve, and she had expected it. She tried not to think of her mother as she got off the bus. She could take care of herself at least, better than Harry could right now. That was all she could think about as she went up to his room on the third floor and walked softly inside. He was still asleep, and the curtains were drawn. It was a brilliantly sunny winter day outside, but none of the bright light and cheer entered here. Everything was darkness and silence and gloom. She slipped quietly into a chair next to the bed, and watched his face. He was deep in a heavy, drugged sleep, and he didn't stir for the next two hours, and finally just to move around a little bit, she walked out into the hall, and wandered up and down, trying not to look into rooms, or see the hideous machinery everywhere, the stricken faces of parents coming to see their sons, or what was left of them, the bandages, the half faces, severed limbs. It was almost more than one could stand, and she reached the end of the hall, and took a deep breath, as suddenly she saw a man who literally took her breath away. He was the tallest, most handsome man she had ever seen. Tall, dark-haired, with brilliant blue eyes, a deep tan, broad shoulders, long, almost endless legs, an impeccably cut dark blue suit, and a camel's hair coat tossed over his arm. His

shirt was so perfect and creamy white that it looked like
something in an ad. Everything about him was beautiful
and immaculate and magnificently groomed. He wore a
crest ring on his left hand, and a troubled look in his
eyes, and he stood watching her for a fraction of an instant, just as she stood watching him.

"Do you know where the neurosurgical area is?"
She nodded, feeling childlike and stupid at first, and then
shyly smiled at him.

"Yes, it's down this hall." She pointed in the direction she had come, and he smiled, but only with his
mouth, not with his eyes. There was something desperately sad about the man, as though he had just lost the
one thing he cared about, and he had, or almost.

But Tana found herself wondering why he was
there. He looked about fifty years old, although he
seemed youthful for his age and he was certainly the most
striking man she had ever seen. The dark hair peppered
with gray made him look even more handsome as he
walked swiftly past her and down the hall, and she followed slowly back the way she had come, and saw him
turn left in the direction of the nurses' station that they
were all so dependent on. Her thoughts turned back to
Harry then, and she realized that she had better get back.
She hadn't been gone long, but he might have woken up,
and there were a lot of things she wanted to say to him,
things she had thought about all night, ideas that she had
about what they could do now. She had meant what
she'd said, she wasn't going to just let him lie on his ass.
He had his whole life ahead of him. Two of the nurses
smiled at her as she walked past where they stood, and
she walked on tiptoe into Harry's room. The room was

still dim, and the sun was going down outside anyway, and she instantly saw that Harry was awake. He looked groggy, but he recognized her, and he didn't smile. Their eyes met and held, and she felt suddenly strange as she entered the room, as though something was wrong, something more than had been wrong before, as though that could even be. Her eyes swept the room as though searching for a clue, and she found him standing there, in a corner, looking grim, the handsome man with the gray hair, in the dark blue suit, and she almost jumped. It had never occurred to her . . . and now suddenly she knew . . . Harrison Winslow III . . . Harry's father . . . he had finally come.

"Hi, Tan." Harry looked unhappy and uncomfortable. It was easier before his father had come. Now he had to deal with him, and his grief too. Tana was so much easier to have around, she always understood how he felt. His father never had.

"How do you feel?" For an instant, they both ignored the older man, as though deriving strength from each other first. Tana didn't even know what to say to him.

"I'm okay." But he looked a lot less than that, and then he looked from her to the well-dressed man. "Father, this is Tana Roberts, my friend." The elder Winslow said very little, but he held out his hand. He almost looked at her as though she were an intrusion. He wanted the details of how Harry had gotten there. He had reached London from South Africa the day before, had gotten the telegrams that were waiting for him, and had flown to San Francisco at once, but he hadn't realized until he arrived what the full implications were. He was still reeling from the shock. Harry had just told him that he would be confined to a wheelchair for life, before Tana walked into the room. He hadn't wasted much time in telling him, and he hadn't been gentle or kind. But he didn't have to be, as far as he was concerned. They were his legs, and if they weren't going to work anymore, that was his problem, no one else's, and he could talk about it any way he wanted to. And he wasn't mincing words just then. "Tan, this is my father, Harrison Winslow," a sarcastic tone came into his voice, "the Third." Nothing between them had changed. Not even now. And his father looked chagrined.

"Would you like to be alone?" Tana's eyes went back and forth between the two men and it was easy to read that Harry would not, and his father would prefer that they were. "I'll go get a cup of tea." She glanced at his father with a cautious glance. "Would you like some, too?"

He hesitated, and then nodded his head. "Yes, thanks. Very much." He smiled, and it was impossible not to notice how devastatingly handsome he was, even here, in a hospital, in his son's room, listening to bad news. There was an incredible depth to the blue eyes, a strength about the chiselled jaw line, something both gentle and decisive about his hands. It was difficult to see him as the villain Harry had described, but she had to take Harry's word for it. Yet sudden doubts began to come to mind, as she took her time going to the cafeteria to get their tea. She returned in slightly less than half an hour, wondering if she should leave and come back the following day, or later that night. She had all that studying to do anyway, but there was a dogged look in Harry's eyes when she returned, as though he wanted to be rescued from his father, and the nurse saw it too when she came in, and not knowing what was causing Harry's distress, or who, in a little while she asked them both to leave. Tana bent to kiss Harry goodbye and he whispered in her ear.

"Come back tonight . . . if you can. . . ."

"Okay." She kissed his cheek, and made a mental note to call the nurses first. But it was Christmas Eve, after all, and she thought maybe he didn't want to be alone. She wondered too if he and his father had just had an argument. His father glanced back over his shoulder at him, sighed unhappily as they left the room, and walked down the hall. His head was bowed, as he stared at his highly polished shoes, and Tana was afraid to say anything. And she felt like a total slob in her scuffed loafers and jeans, but she hadn't expected to meet anyone there, least of all the legendary Harrison Winslow III. She was even more startled when he suddenly turned to her.

"How does he seem to you?"

Tana took a sharp breath. "I don't know yet . . . it's too soon . . . I think he's still in shock." Harrison Winslow nodded. So was he. He had spoken to the doctor before coming upstairs, and there was absolutely nothing they could do. Harry's spinal cord had been so badly damaged, the neurosurgeon had explained, that he would never walk again. They had made some repairs, and there would be more surgery in the next six months, and there were some things about which he was very pleased. They had told Harry as much, but it was too soon for it all to have set in. The best news of all was that he would be

able to make love, with some instruction, but that part of
his nervous system still functioned, to a degree, and although he wouldn't have complete feeling or total control, he still had a considerable amount of sensation
there. "He could even have a family," the doctor told his
father as he stared, but there were other things that he
would never do, like walk or dance, or run or ski . . .
tears filled the father's eyes as he thought of it, and then
he remembered the girl walking along at his side. She was
pretty, he had noticed her when he first saw her walking
down the hall, and had been struck by the lovely face, the
big green eyes, the graceful way she moved, and had been
surprised to see her walk into Harry's room.

"I take it you and Harry are close friends?" It was
odd, Harry had never mentioned the girl to him, but
Harry never mentioned anything to him anyway.

"We are. We've been friends for four years."

He decided not to beat around the bush as they
stood in the lobby of Letterman hospital. But he wanted
to know what he was up against, and maybe this was the
time to find out. Just how involved was Harry with this
girl, another casual affair, a hidden love, maybe even hidden wife? He had Harry's financial affairs to think of, too,
even if the boy wasn't sophisticated enough yet to protect
himself. "Are you in love with him?" His eyes bore into
hers and she was momentarily stunned.

"I . . . no . . . I . . . that is," she wasn't sure
why he had asked, "I love him very much . . . but we
. . . I'm not 'involved with him' physically, if that's
what you mean." She flushed to the roots of her hair to
be explaining that to him and he smiled apologetically.

"I'm sorry to even ask you a thing like that, but if

you know Harry well, you know how he is. I never know what the hell is going on and I assume that one of these days I'll arrive and find out that he has a wife and three kids." Tana laughed. It was unlikely but not impossible. More likely three mistresses. And she suddenly realized that she was finding it difficult to dislike him as much as Harry would want her to, in fact, she wasn't sure she disliked him at all.

He was obviously powerful, and not afraid to ask what he wanted to know. He looked her over now, glanced at his watch, and at the limousine waiting at the curb outside for him. "Would you come to have a cup of coffee with me somewhere? At my hotel perhaps? I'm staying at the Stanford Court, but I could have the driver take you back to wherever you like afterwards. Does that sound all right?" Actually, it sounded faintly traitorous to her, but she didn't know what to say to him. The poor man had been through a lot, too, and he had come an awfully long way.

"I . . . I really should get back . . . I have an awful lot of studying to do. . . ." She blushed and he looked hurt, and suddenly she was sorry for him. As elegant and dashing as he was, there was at the same time something vulnerable about him. "I'm sorry, I didn't mean to sound rude. It's just . . ."

"I know." He looked at her with a rueful smile that melted her heart. "He's told you what a bastard I am. But it's Christmas Eve, you know. It might do us both good to go and talk for a while. I've had a hell of a shock, and you must have too." She nodded sadly and followed him to the car. The driver opened the door and she got in, and Harrison Winslow sat next to her on the gray

velvet seat. He looked pensive as the city slid by and it
seemed moments later when they reached Nob Hill, and
drove down the east face of it, turning sharply into the
courtyard of the Stanford Court. "Harry and I have had
a rough time of it over the years. Somehow we never
managed to hit it off. . . ." He almost seemed to be talking to himself as she watched his face. He didn't look as
ruthless as Harry had described. In fact, he didn't look
ruthless at all. He looked lonely and sad, and he seemed
very much alone. Harrison looked pointedly at Tana
then. "You're a beautiful girl . . . inside as well, I suspect. Harry is lucky to have you as a friend."

And the oddest thing about her was something
Harry couldn't really have known. She looked so much
like his mother at the same age. It was uncanny as Harrison watched her step lightly out of the car, and he followed her into the hotel. They went to the Potpourri
restaurant and slid into a booth. He seemed to be constantly watching her, as though trying to understand who
she was, and what she meant to his son. He found it
difficult to believe that she was only his "friend," as she
claimed, and yet she was insistent about that as they
talked and she had no reason to lie to him.

Tana smiled as she watched his eyes. "My mother
feels the same way about it that you do, Mr. Winslow.
She keeps telling me that 'boys and girls can't be friends,'
and I tell her she's wrong. That's exactly what Harry and
I are . . . he's my best friend in the whole world . . .
he's like a brother to me. . . ." Her eyes filled with tears
and she looked away thinking of what had happened to
him. ". . . I'll do anything I can to help make him all
right again." She looked at Harrison Winslow defiantly,

not angry at him, but at the fate which had crippled his son. "I will, you'll see . . . I won't just let him lie there on his ass," she blushed at the word, but went on, "I'm going to get him up and moving and giving a damn again." She looked at him strangely then. "I have an idea, but I have to talk to Harry about it first." He was intrigued. Maybe she had designs on the boy after all, but he didn't think that would be so bad now. Aside from being pretty, she was obviously bright and the girl had a hell of a lot of spunk. When she spoke, her eyes lit up like green fire, and he knew that she meant everything she said.

"What kind of idea?" He was intrigued by her, and if he hadn't been so worried about his son, he would have been amused.

She hesitated. He'd probably think she was crazy, particularly if he was as unambitious as Harry said. "I don't know . . . it probably sounds crazy to you, but I thought . . . I don't know. . . ." It was embarrassing, admitting it to him. "I thought that maybe I could get him to go to law school with me. Even if he never uses it, it would be good for him, especially now."

"Are you serious?" There were laugh lines coming to light beside Harrison Winslow's eyes. "Law school? My son?" He patted her hand with a grin, she was an amazing child, a little ball of fire, but he wouldn't put anything past this girl, including that. "If you can talk him into that, especially now," his face sobered rapidly, "you really would be even more remarkable than I think you are."

"I'm going to give it a try when he's well enough to listen to me."

"That'll be a while, I'm afraid." They both nodded silently, and in the silence heard someone singing carols outside, and then suddenly Tana looked at him.

"Why do you see so little of him?" She had to ask, she had nothing to lose, and if he got angry with her, she could always leave. He couldn't do anything to her, but he didn't actually look upset as he gazed into her eyes.

"Honestly? Because Harry and I have been a lost cause until now. I tried for a long, long time, but I never got anywhere. He's hated me ever since he was a small boy, and it's only gotten worse over the years. There was no point inflicting new wounds after a while. It's a big world, I have a lot to do, he has his own life to lead," tears flooded his eyes and he looked away, ". . . or at least he did, until now. . . ."

She reached across the table and touched his hand. "He will again. I promise you . . . if he lives . . . oh, God . . . if he lives . . . please God, don't let him die." Tears flooded her eyes, too, and she brushed them from her cheeks. "He's so wonderful, Mr. Winslow, he's the best friend I've ever had."

"I wish I could say the same." He looked sad. "We're almost strangers by now. I felt like an intruder in his room today."

"Maybe that's because I was there. I should have left you two alone."

"It wouldn't make any difference anymore. It's gone too far, for too long. We're strangers now."

"You don't have to be." She was talking to him as though she knew the man, and somehow he didn't seem so impressive any more, no matter how worldly or debonair or handsome or sophisticated he was. He was only another human being, with a devastating problem on his hands, a very sick son. "You could make friends with him now."

Harrison Winslow shook his head, and after a moment he smiled at her. He thought Tana a remarkably beautiful girl, and he suddenly wondered again exactly what the story was between Harry and this girl. His son was too much of a libertine, in his own way, to let an opportunity like this pass him by, unless he cared about her even more than she knew . . . maybe that was it . . . maybe Harry was in love with her . . . he had to be. It couldn't be what she said it was between them. It seemed impossible to him.

"It's too late, my friend. Much, much too late. And in his eyes, my sins are unforgivable." He sighed. "I suppose I'd feel the same way in his shoes." He looked unwaveringly at her now. "He thinks I killed his mother, you know. She committed suicide when he was four."

She almost choked on her words. "I know." And the look in his eyes was devastating, raw pain that still lived in his soul. His love for her had never died, nor had his love for their son. "She was dying of cancer and she didn't want anyone to know. In the end, it would have disfigured her, and she couldn't have tolerated that. She'd already had two operations before she died . . . and . . ." he almost stopped, but went on, ". . . it was terrible for her . . . for all of us   Harry knew she was sick then, but he doesn't remember it now. It doesn't matter anyway. She couldn't live with the operations, the pain, and I couldn't bear to watch her suffer. What she did was a terrible thing, but I always understood. She was so young, so beautiful. She was very much like you, in

fact, and almost a child herself. . . ." He wasn't
ashamed of the tears in his eyes, and Tana looked at him,
horrified.

"Why doesn't Harry know?"

"She made me promise I'd never tell." He sat back
against the banquette as though he'd been punched. The
feeling of despair over her death never really went away.
He had tried to run away from it for years, with Harry at
first, with women, with girls, with anyone, and finally by
himself. He was fifty-two years old and he had discovered
that there was only so far he could run, and he couldn't
run that far anymore. The memories were there, the sorrow, the loss . . . and now Harry might go too . . . he
couldn't bear the thought as he looked at this lovely
young girl, so full of life, so filled with hope. It was almost impossible to explain it all to her, it was all so long
ago. "People felt differently about cancer then . . . it
was almost as though one had to be ashamed of it. I
didn't agree with her at the time, but she was adamant
that Harry not know. She left me a very long letter at the
time. She took an overdose of pills when I went to Boston
overnight to see my great aunt. She wanted Harry to
think her flighty and beautiful, and romantic, but not
riddled with disease, and so she went . . . she's a hero-
ine to him." He smiled sadly at Tana. "And she was to
me. It was a sad way to die, but the other way would
have been so much worse. I never blamed her for what
she did."

"And you let him think it was your fault." She was
horrified, and her green eyes were huge in her face.

"I never realized he would, and by the time I understood, it was already too late. I ran around a great deal

when he was a child, as though I could flee from the pain
of losing her. But it doesn't really work that way. It fol-
lows you, like a mangy dog, always waiting outside your
room when you wake up, pawing at the door, whining at
your feet, no matter how dressed up and charming and
busy you are, how many friends you surround yourself
with, it's always there, nipping at your heels, gnawing at
your cuffs . . . and so it was . . . but by the time
Harry was eight or nine, he had come to his own conclusions about me, and he got so hateful for a while that I
put him into boarding school, and he decided to stay, and
then I had nothing at all, so I ran even harder than before
. . . and," he shrugged philosophically, "she died almost
twenty years ago, and here we are . . . she died in January. . . ." His eyes looked vague for a moment and then
focused on Tana again, but that didn't help. She looked
too much like her anyway, it was like looking into the
past, just seeing her. "And now Harry is in this awful
mess . . . life is so rotten and so strange, isn't it?" She
nodded, there wasn't much she could say. He had given
her a great deal to think about.

"I think you should say something to him."

"About what?"

"About how his mother died."

"I couldn't do that. I made a promise to her   to
myself . . . it would be self-serving to tell him now.
. . ."

"Then why tell me?" She was shocked at herself, at
the anger in her voice, at what she felt, at the waste
people allowed in their lives, lost moments in which they
could have loved each other, like this man and his son.

They had wasted so many years they could have shared.
And Harry needed him now. He needed everyone.

Harrison looked apologetically at her. "I suppose I
shouldn't have told you all that. But I needed to talk to
someone . . . and you're . . . so close to him." He
looked at her point blank. "I wanted you to know that I
love my son." There was a lump in her throat the size of
a fist and she wasn't sure if she wanted to slap him or kiss
him, or perhaps both. She had never felt that way about
any man before.

"Why the hell don't you tell him yourself?"

"It wouldn't do any good."

"It might. Maybe this is the time."

He looked at her pensively, and then down at his
hands, and then finally into her green eyes again. "Perhaps it is. I don't know him, though . . . I wouldn't
know where to begin. . . ."

"Just like that, Mr. Winslow. Just the way you said
it to me."

He smiled at her, and he suddenly looked very tired.
"What makes you so wise, little girl?"

She smiled at him, and she felt an incredible warmth
emanating from him. He was a lot like Harry in some
ways, and yet he was more, and she realized with a pang
of embarrassment that she was attracted to him. It was as
though all the senses that had been deadened for years,
ever since the rape, had suddenly come alive again.

"What were you thinking just then?"

She flushed pink and shook her head. "Something
that had nothing to do with all this . . . I'm sorry . . .
I'm tired . . . I haven't slept for a few days. . . ."

"I'll get you home, so you can get some rest." He

signalled for the check, and when it came he looked at her with a gentle smile, and she felt a longing for the father she had never had, or even known. This was the kind of man she would have wanted Andy Roberts to have been, not Arthur Durning who breezed in and out of her mother's life when it suited him. This man was a great deal less selfish than Harry had wanted her to believe, or insisted on believing himself. He had put a lot of energy into hating this man over the years and Tana knew instinctively now that he had been wrong, very wrong, and she wondered if Harrison was right, if it was too late. "Thank you for talking to me, Tana. Harry is lucky to have you as his friend."

"I've been lucky to have him."

He put a twenty dollar bill under the check and looked at her again. "Are you an only child?" He suspected that about her, and she nodded with a smile.

"Yes. And I never knew my father, he died before I was born, in the war." It was something she had said ten thousand times in her life, but it seemed to have new meaning now. Everything did, and she didn't understand what that meant or why. Something strange was happening to her as she sat with this man, and she wondered if it was just because she was so tired. She let him walk her back to his car, and he surprised her by getting in with her, rather than letting the driver take her home.

"I'll ride with you."

"You really don't need to do that."

"I have nothing else to do. I'm here to see Harry, and I think he's better off resting for the next few hours." She agreed with him and they chatted on the drive across the bridge. He mentioned that he had never been to San

Francisco before. He found it an attractive place, but he
seemed distracted as they drove along. She assumed he
was thinking about his son, but he was actually thinking
about her, and he shook her hand when they arrived. "I'll
see you at the hospital again. If you need a ride, just call
the hotel and I'll send the car for you." She had mentioned that she'd been taking the bus back and forth and
that worried him. She was young, after all, and pretty
and anything could have happened to her.

"Thank you for everything, Mr. Winslow."

"Harrison." He smiled at her, and he looked exactly
like Harry when he smiled, not quite as mischievous, but
there was a sparkle there too. "I'll see you soon. Get
some rest now!" He waved, and the limousine drove off,
as she slowly climbed the stairs, thinking of all he had
said. How unfair life was at times. She fell asleep thinking
of Harrison . . . and Harry . . . and Vietnam . . .
and the woman who had killed herself, and in Tana's
dream she had no face, and when she awoke it was dark,
and she sat up with a start and couldn't catch her breath
in the tiny room. She glanced at the clock and it was nine
o'clock, and she wondered how Harry was. She went to
the pay phone and called and discovered that the fever
was down, he had been awake for a while, and now he
was dozing again, but he hadn't gone to bed for the night.
They hadn't given him his sleeping medicine yet, and
they probably wouldn't for a while, and suddenly, as
Tana heard caroling outside, she realized that it was
Christmas Eve, and Harry needed her. She showered
quickly and decided to dress for him. She wore a pretty
white knit dress, high heeled shoes, and put on a red coat
and a scarf that she hadn't worn since the winter before

in New York, and thought she would never wear here. But somehow it all looked and felt Christmasy, and she thought that might be important to him. She put on some perfume, brushed her hair, and rode back into town on the bus, thinking of his father again. It was ten thirty at night when she arrived at Letterman, and there was a sleepy holiday air about it all. Little trees with blinking lights, plastic Santa Clauses here and there. But no one seemed to be in a particularly holiday mood, there were too many desperately serious things going on, and when she reached his room, she knocked softly and tiptoed in, expecting him to be asleep, and instead, he was lying there, staring at the wall, with tears in his eyes. He started when he saw her, and he didn't even smile.

"I'm dying, aren't I?" She was shocked at his words, at his tone, at the lifeless look in his eyes, and she suddenly frowned and approached the bed.

"Not unless you want to die." She knew she had to be blunt with him. "It's pretty much up to you." She stood very close to him, looking into his eyes, and he did not reach for her hand.

"That's a dumb thing to say. It wasn't my idea to get shot in the ass."

"Sure it was." She sounded nonchalant and for a moment he looked pissed.

"What the hell is that supposed to mean?"

"That you could have gone to school. And you decided to play instead. So you got the short end of the stick. You gambled and you lost."

"Yeah. Only I didn't lose ten bucks, I lost my legs. Not exactly small stakes."

"Looks like they're still there to me." She glanced down at the useless limbs and he almost snarled at her.

"Don't be an ass. What good are they now?"

"You've got them, and you're alive, and there's plenty you can still do. And according to the nurses, you can still get it up," she had never been so blunt with him and it was a hell of a speech for Christmas Eve, but she knew it was time to start pushing him, especially if he thought he was going to die. "Hell, look at the bright side, you might even get the clap again."

"You make me sick." He turned away, and without thinking she grabbed at his arm, and he turned to look at her again.

"Look, dammit, you make *me* sick. Half the boys in your platoon were killed, and you're alive, so don't lie there whining at what you don't have. Think of what you do. Your life isn't over, unless you want it to be, and I don't want it to be," tears stung her eyes, "I want you to get off that dead ass of yours, if I have to drag you by the hair for the next ten years to make you get up and live again. Is that clear?" The tears were pouring down her cheeks. "I'm not going to let go of you. Ever! Do you understand that?" And slowly, slowly . . . she saw a smile dawn in his eyes.

"You're a crazy broad, do you know that, Tan?"

"Yeah, well maybe I am, but you'll find out just how crazy I am until you start making life easier for both of us by doing something with yourself." She wiped the tears from her cheeks and he grinned at her, and for the first time in days, he looked like the Harry she knew.

"You know what it is?"

"What?" She looked confused. It was the most emotional few days of her life and she had never felt so over-wrought as she did now.

"It's all that sexual energy you've got pent up, that's what gives you all this oomph to put into everything else. It makes you a real pain in the neck sometimes."

"Thanks."

"Anytime." He grinned, and closed his eyes for a minute and then he opened them again. "What are you all dressed up for? Going someplace?"

"Yes. Here. To see you. It's Christmas Eve." Her eyes softened and she smiled at him. "Welcome back to the human race."

"I liked what you said before." He was still smiling and Tana could see that the tides had turned. If he hung on to the will to live, he'd be all right, relatively. That was what the neurosurgeon had said.

"What did I say . . . ? you mean about booting you in the ass and making something of yourself . . . it's about time." She looked pleased.

"No, about getting it up, and getting the clap again."

"Shit." She looked at him with total contempt and one of the nurses walked in and they started to laugh, and suddenly, for just a minute it was just like old times, and then Harry's father walked into the room, and they both looked like nervous kids, and the laughter stopped, and Harrison Winslow smiled. He wanted so desperately to make friends with his son, and he already knew how much he liked the girl.

"Don't let me spoil your fun. What was that all about?"

Tana blushed. It was difficult talking to someone as

cosmopolitan as he was, but she had talked to him all
afternoon, after all.

"Your son was being as rude as he usually is."

"That's nothing new." Harrison sat down in one of
the room's two chairs, and glanced at them both. "Although you'd think on Christmas Eve, he could make an
effort to be a little more polite."

"Actually, he was talking about the nurses and.
. . ." Harry blushed and began to object, Tana laughed,
and suddenly Harry's father was laughing too. There was
something very tenuous in the room, and none of them
looked totally at ease, but they chatted for half an hour
and then Harry began to look tired, and Tana stood up.
"I just came to give you a Christmas kiss, I didn't even
think you'd be awake."

"Neither did I." Harrison Winslow stood up too.
"We'll come back tomorrow, Son." He was watching
Harry look at her, and he thought he understood. She
was innocent of what Harry felt for her, and for some
reason he was keeping it a secret from her, and Harrison
couldn't understand why. There was a mystery here
which made no sense to him. He looked at his son again.
"Do you need anything before we leave?"

Harry looked sad for a long moment and then shook
his head. He needed something, but it was nothing they
had to give. The gift of his legs. And his father understood and gently touched his arm.

"See you tomorrow, Son."

"Good night." Harry's greeting to his father wasn't
warm, but his eyes lit up when he looked at the beautiful
blonde. "Behave yourself, Tan."

"Why should I? You don't." She grinned and blew

him a kiss, as she whispered, "Merry Christmas, asshole." He laughed and she followed his father out into the hall.

"I thought he looked better, didn't you?" They were becoming friends over the disaster that had befallen his son.

"I did. I think he's over the worst. Now it's just going to be a long, slow climb back uphill." Harrison nodded, and they took the elevator downstairs again. There was a familiarity to it now, as if they had done this dozens of times before, when actually it had only been once. But their talk that afternoon had brought them much closer, and Harrison held the door open for her now, as she saw that the same silver limousine was there.

"Would you like something to eat?"

She started to say no and then realized that she hadn't had dinner yet. She had been thinking about going to midnight mass, but she didn't really want to go alone. She looked at him, wondering if it would mean something to him, too, particularly now.

"I might. Could I interest you in midnight mass afterwards?"

He looked very serious as he nodded his head, and Tana was struck once again by how handsome he was. They went out for a quick hamburger, and chatted about Harry, and their Cambridge days. She told Harrison some of the more outrageous things they'd done and he laughed with her, still puzzled by the odd relationship they shared. Like Jean, he couldn't quite figure them out. And then they went off to midnight mass, and tears streamed down Tana's cheeks as they sang Silent Night, she was thinking of Sharon, her beloved friend, and

Harry and how lucky he was to be alive, and when she glanced over at his father, standing tall and proud at her side, she saw that he was crying too. He discreetly blew his nose when they sat down, and as he took her back to Berkeley afterwards, she noticed how comfortable it was just being with him. She was almost dozing as they rode along. She was desperately tired.

"What are you doing tomorrow?"

"Seeing Harry, I guess. And one of these days I've got a lot of studying to do." She had all but forgotten it in the past few days.

"Could I take you to lunch before you go to the hospital?" She was touched that he would ask, and she accepted, worrying instantly what she should wear as soon as she stepped out of the car, but she didn't even have time to think of it when she got back to her room. She was so exhausted that she peeled off her clothes, dropped them on the floor, climbed into bed, and was instantly dead to the world. Unlike her mother in New York, who had been awake, sitting lonely in a chair and crying all night. Tana had not called, nor had Arthur in Palm Beach, and she had spent the entire night wrestling with the darker side of her soul, contemplating something she would never have thought she would do.

She had gone to midnight mass, as she and Tana used to do, and at one thirty she came home, and watched a little late night TV.

By two o'clock the most desperate loneliness she had ever felt in her life had set in. She was riveted to her seat, unable to move, almost unable to breathe. And for the first time in her life, she began to think of committing suicide, and by three o'clock it was an almost impossible

urge to resist. Half an hour later, she went into her bathroom and got out a bottle of sleeping pills she never used,
and trembling, she forced herself to put them down. She
wanted to take them more than she had ever wanted to
do anything in her life, and at the same time she did not.
She wanted someone to stop her, to tell her everything
would be all right. But who could tell her that now? Tana
was gone, and would probably never live at home again,
and Arthur had his own life, he only included her when it
suited him, and never when she needed him. Tana was
right about that, but it hurt her too much to admit it to
her. Instead she defended everything he did, and his miserable selfish kids, that bitch Ann, who was always so
rude to her, and Billy, he had been so sweet as a boy, but
now . . . he seemed to be drunk all the time, and Jean
wondered if Tana was right, if he wasn't the kind of
young man she had always thought he was, but if that
was true . . . the memory of what Tana had said four
years before came crashing down on her now. What if it
were true . . . ? if he had . . . if she hadn't believed
. . . it was almost more than she could bear . . . it was
as if her whole life were crashing in on her tonight and
she couldn't bear it, as she sat staring longingly at the
pills she held in her hand. It seemed the only thing left to
do, and she wondered what Tana would think when they
called her in California to tell her the news. She wondered who would find her body . . . the superintendent
maybe . . . one of her co-workers . . . if they waited
for Arthur to find her it could take weeks. It was even
more depressing to realize that there wasn't even anyone
left who would discover her soon. She thought of writing
Tana a note, but that seemed so melodramatic and there

was nothing left to say, except how much she had loved
her child, how hard she had tried. She cried as she
thought of Tana growing up, the tiny apartment they had
shared, meeting Arthur, hoping that he would marry her
. . . her whole life seemed to be flashing before her eyes
as she clutched the vial of sleeping pills, and the night
ground agonizingly by. She didn't even know what time
it was when the phone finally rang. It was five A.M., and
Jean was shocked when she saw the clock. She wondered
if it was Tana, maybe her friend had died . . . with a
shaking hand, she lifted the phone, and at first she didn't
recognize the voice that identified itself as John.

"John?"

"John York. Ann's husband. We're in Palm Beach."

"Oh. Of course." But she was still stunned, and the
emotions of the night had left her drained. She quietly set
down the bottle of pills, she could attend to them afterwards. She couldn't understand why they would be calling her, but John York was quick to explain.

"It's Arthur. Ann thought I should call. He's had a
heart attack."

"Oh, my God." She could feel her heart pound in
her breast, and she was suddenly crying into the phone.
"Is he all right? Is he . . . did . . ."

"He's all right now. But it was pretty bad for a
while. It happened a few hours ago, and it's still touch
and go, which is why Ann thought I should call."

"Oh, my God . . . oh, my God . . ." Here she
had been thinking of taking her own life, and Arthur had
almost died. What if she had . . . she almost shuddered
at the thought. "Where is he now?"

"At Mercy Hospital. Ann thought you might want to come down."

"Of course." She jumped to her feet, still holding the phone, grabbed a pencil, a pad, knocking over the vial of pills, and as they fell to the floor, she stood looking at them. She was herself again. It was incredible to think what she might have done, and he needed her now. Thank God she hadn't done it after all. "Give me the details, John. I'll catch the next plane." She scribbled the name and address of the hospital, jotted his room number down, asked if there was anything they would need, and a moment later set down the phone, closed her eyes, thinking of him, and when she opened them there were tears on her cheeks, thinking of Arthur, and what might have been.

Chapter 10

Harrison Winslow sent the car to Berkeley to pick Tana up at noon the next day, and they went to Trader Vic's for lunch. The atmosphere was festive and the food was good; he had been told at the hotel that it would be an appropriate place to go. And he enjoyed her company almost too much as they chatted again, about Harry, but other things as well. He was impressed by how bright she was, and she told him about Freeman Blake, and her friend who had died, and Miriam who had influenced her to go to law school. "I just hope I survive. It's even harder than I thought it would be." She smiled.

"And you really think Harry could do something like that?"

"He can do anything he wants to do. The trouble is he'd rather fool around." She blushed and he laughed.

"I agree with you. He does like to fool around. He thinks it's congenital. But actually, I was a lot more serious than he in my youth, and my father was a very scholarly man. He even wrote two books on philosophy." They chatted on for a while, and it was the most pleasant interlude Tana had spent in a long, long time. She looked guiltily at her watch eventually, and they hurried off to the hospital, bringing Harry a bag of fortune cookies. Tana had insisted on bringing him a drink. They brought him a huge Scorpion with a gardenia floating in it, and he took a long sip and grinned.

"Merry Christmas to you too." But she could see that he didn't look pleased that she and his father had made friends, and finally when his father left the room and went downstairs to make a call, he glared at her.

"What are you looking so pleasant about?" It was good for him to be mad, she didn't mind. It would help bring him back to life.

"You know how I feel about him, Tan. Don't let him do a snow job on you."

"He's not. He wouldn't be here if he didn't care about you. Don't be so goddamn stubborn and give him a chance."

"Oh, for chrissake." He'd have walked out of the room and slammed the door if he could. "What a crock of shit that is. Is that what he's been telling you?" She couldn't tell him all that Harrison had been telling her because she knew he wouldn't want her to, but she also knew by now how he felt about his son, and she was convinced of his sincerity. She was growing fonder of him by the hour, and she wished Harry would try to be more open to him.

"He's a decent man. Give him a chance."

"He's a son of a bitch and I hate his guts." And with that, Harrison Winslow walked into the room, just in time to hear Harry's words, and Tana went pale. The three looked at each other, and Harrison was quick to reassure her.

"That's not the first time I've heard that. And I'm sure it won't be the last."

Harry turned in his bed to snarl at him. "Why the hell didn't you knock?"

"Does it bother you that I heard? So what? You've said it to me before, usually to my face. Are you getting more discreet now? Or less courageous?" There was an edge to the older man's voice and a fire in Harry's eyes.

"You know what I think of you. You were never there when I needed you. You were always somewhere goddamn else, with some girl, in some spa, or on some mountaintop, with your friends . . ." He turned away. "I don't want to talk about it."

"Yes, you do." He pulled up a chair and sat down. "And so do I. You're right, I wasn't there, and neither were you. You were in the boarding schools you chose to be in, and you were a goddamn impossible little snot every time I laid eyes on you."

"Why shouldn't I have been?"

"That was a decision you made. And you never gave me a chance from the time your mother died. I knew by the time you were six that you hated me. I could accept it at the time. But you know, at your age, Harry, I would have thought that you would have gotten a little smarter by now, or at least more compassionate. I'm not really as bad as you like to think, you know." Tana tried to fade into the wall, it was embarrassing being there, but neither of them seemed to mind. And as she listened, she realized that she had forgotten to call her mother again. She made a mental note to do it as soon as she left the hospital, maybe even from one of the phones downstairs, but she couldn't leave the room now, with World War III going on.

Harry stared angrily at his father now. "Why the hell did you come here anyway?"

"Because you're my son. The only one I've got. Do you want me to leave?" Harrison Winslow quietly stood up and his voice was low when he spoke. "I'll leave anytime you like. I will not inflict myself on you, but I will also not allow you to continue to delude yourself that I don't give a damn about you. That's a very nice fairy tale, poor little rich boy and all that, but in the words of your friend here, it's a crock. I happen to love you very much," his voice cracked but he went on anyway, struggling with the emotions and the words and Tana's heart went out to him. "I love you very, very much, Harry. I always have and I always will." He walked over to him then, bent and kissed him gently on the top of his head, and then strode out of the room, as Harry looked away and closed his eyes, and when he opened them, he saw Tana standing there with tears running down her cheeks at what she had just heard.

"Get the hell out of here." She nodded, and quietly left, and as she closed the door softly behind her, she heard the sobs from the direction of Harry's bed. But he needed to be alone now. She respected that, and the tears were good for him.

Harrison was waiting outside for her, he looked more composed now, and relieved as he smiled at her. "Is he all right?"

"He will be now. He needed to hear the things you said to him."

"I needed to say them to him. I feel better now too."

And with that, he took her arm, and they walked downstairs arm in arm. It felt as though they had always been
friends. And he looked at her with a broad smile. "Where
are you going now, young lady?"

"Home, I guess. I still have all that work to do."

"That's a crock." He imitated her, and they both
laughed. "How about playing hooky and going to the
movies with an old man? My son has just thrown me out
of his room, and I don't know a soul in this town, and it's
Christmas, for God's sake. How about it, Tan?" He had
picked the name up from his son and she smiled, wanting
to tell him that she had to go home, but she couldn't do it
somehow; she wanted to be with him.

"I really should go home." But she didn't convince
either of them, and he was in a festive mood as they
climbed into the limousine.

"Good. Now that you've gotten that out of the way,
where shall we go?" She giggled like a little girl, and he
told the limousine driver to drive them around. Eventually, they bought a newspaper, picked out a movie they
both liked, ate as much popcorn as they could stand, and
went to L'Etoile afterwards, for a small supper and
drinks at the bar. She was getting spoiled just being with
him. And she was trying to remind herself of what a cad
Harry said he was, but she didn't believe that anymore,
and she had never been as happy in her life, as when he
drove her home to Berkeley again, and took her in his
arms, and kissed her as naturally as if they had both been
waiting for that all their lives. He looked at her afterwards, touching her lips with his fingertips, wondering if
he should regret what he'd done, but he felt younger and
happier than he had in years. "Tana, I've never met any-

one like you before, my love." He held her tight and she felt a warmth and safety she had never even dreamed of before, and then he kissed her again. He wanted to make her his for the rest of time, but he also wondered if he was half mad. This was Harry's friend . . , his girl . . . but they both insisted that they were just friends, and yet he sensed something different than that, on Harry's part anyway. He looked deep into her eyes. "Tell me the truth about something, Tan. Are you in love with my son?"

Slowly, she shook her head. The driver of the limousine seemed to have disappeared. Actually, he had gone outside for a discreet walk. They were parked outside Tana's house. "No. I've never been in love with anyone . . . until now. . . ." They were brave words for her, and she decided to tell him the truth all at once. He had been honest with her since they'd met. "I was raped four and a half years ago. It kind of stopped everything for me. As though my emotional clock no longer ran, and it hasn't run since. I didn't go out at all for the first couple of years I was in college, and then finally Harry forced me into double dating with him a few times. But it was no big deal, and I don't go out with anyone here. All I do is work." She smiled tenderly at him. She was falling head over heels in love with the father of her best friend.

"Does Harry know?"

"That I was raped?" He nodded. "Yes. I told him eventually. He thought I was weird, and eventually I told him why. Actually, we saw the guy at a party we went to, and he guessed."

"Was it someone you knew?" Harrison looked shocked.

"The son of my mother's boss. Lover and boss, actu-

ally. It was awful . . . no," she shook her head, "it was
much, much worse than that." He pulled her into his
arms again, and he understood things better now. He
wondered if that was why Harry had never allowed himself to be more than friends with her. He instinctively
sensed that the desire was there, even if she was innocent
of what was in his mind. And he also knew what he felt
for the girl. He hadn't been so taken with anyone since he
met his wife twenty-six years before, and then he began to
think of the age difference between them, wondering if it
would bother her. He was exactly thirty years older than
Tana, and there were those who would be shocked. But
more importantly, would she? "So what?" She answered
him when he voiced his fears. "Who cares about them?"
She kissed him this time and she felt something come
alive in herself that she had never felt before, a passion
and desire which only he could fulfill, and she tossed and
turned all night thinking about him, just as he did about
her. She called him at seven o'clock the next day, and he
was already awake, and surprised by her call. But he
would have been even more surprised had he known
what she felt for him.

"What are you doing up at this hour, little one?"

"Thinking about you." He was flattered and touched
and enchanted and infatuated and a thousand other
things. But there was much more to it than that. Tana
trusted this man as she had trusted no other man before,
not even his son, and he represented a great many things
to her, even the father she had never known. He was all
men in one, and had Harrison known, he might have
been frightened that she expected too much of him. They
visited Harry, they met for lunch, they had dinner to-

gether that night, and he had an overwhelming urge to take her to bed, but something told him that he could not, that it was dangerous, that he would form a lasting bond and that was wrong. For the next two weeks, they met and they walked and they kissed and they touched and the feelings and needs they had for each other grew. They visited Harry separately, for fear that he would find out, and finally Harrison sat down beside his son one day. The matter had to be broached, it was getting serious for both of them, and he didn't want to hurt the girl. But more than that, he wanted to offer her something he hadn't offered anyone in years, his heart, and his life. He wanted to marry her, and he had to know how Harry felt, now, before it was too late, before everyone got hurt, especially the one person he cared about most, his son. He would have sacrificed anything for Harry, especially now, even the girl he loved, and he had to know now.

"I want to ask you something. Honestly. And I want you to answer me." There had been a tenuous peace between the two men in the past two weeks, thanks to efforts on Tana's part, and Harrison had been enjoying the fruits of it.

"What's this all about?" Harry looked suspiciously at him.

"What's between you and that enchanting child?" He fought hard to keep his face blank, his eyes calm, and prayed that his son wouldn't see anything there, particularly not how much he loved the girl, though he couldn't imagine how Harry could not see. He felt as though he was wearing a neon sign.

"Tana?" Harry shrugged.

"I told you, I want you to answer me." His whole life depended on it now, as did hers.

"Why? What's it to you?" Harry was restless and his neck had hurt all day. "I told you, she's my friend."

"I know you better than that, whether you like it or not."

"So what? That's all it is. I've never slept with her." But he already knew that, though he didn't tell Harry that.

"That doesn't mean a damn thing. That could have to do with her and not you." There was no joking in his eyes or words. This was no joking matter to him, but Harry laughed and conceded the point.

"That's true, it could." And then suddenly, he lay back against his pillows and looked up at the ceiling, feeling an odd closeness to his father he had never felt before. "I don't know, Dad. . . . I was crazy about her when we first met, but she was as locked up as a stone . . . she still is." He told him about the rape then, and Harrison pretended to hear it for the first time. "I've never known anyone like her before. I guess I've always known that I'm in love with her, but I've been afraid to fuck it up by telling her that. This way, she won't run away. The other way, she might." His eyes filled with sudden tears. "I couldn't stand losing her. I need her too much." Harrison felt his heart sink like a rock, but he had to think for his son now. That was all he really cared about, all he would let himself care about now. He had finally found him and he wasn't willing to lose him again. Not even for Tana, whom he loved so desperately. But Harry's words burned through him like fire. "I need her so much. . . ." The funny thing was the elder Winslow needed her too, but not as Harry did, and he couldn't take her from him, not now. . . .

"One of these days, maybe you should be brave enough to tell her some of this. Maybe she needs you too." Harrison knew now how lonely and isolated Tana had been, but even Harry hadn't fully realized those depths.

"And what if I lose?"

"You can't live like that, son. Afraid to lose, afraid to live, afraid to die. You'll never win like that. She knows that better than anyone. It's the one lesson you can learn from her." And there were so many others he had learned from her too. Lessons he would have to abandon now.

"She's got more guts than anyone I know . . . except about men." Harry shook his head. "She scares me to death as far as that goes."

"Give her time. Lots of time." He fought to keep his voice strong. He couldn't let Harry know. "And lots of love."

Harry was silent for a long time, searching his father's eyes. In the past two and a half weeks they had begun to discover each other as they never had before. "Do you think she could ever be in love with me?"

"Possibly." Harrison felt his heart tear again. "You have plenty of other things to think about right now. But once you're up again," he avoided saying "on your feet," "and out of here, you can think about things like that." They both knew that he wasn't totally impaired sexually, and the doctor had told them both that with a little "creativity" Harry would have a near-normal sex life again one day, he could even impregnate his wife, if he chose, which didn't turn Harry on much, at least not for now, but Harrison knew it could mean a great deal to him one day. He would have loved to have Tana's child. The very thought brought him near to tears.

They chatted on for a little while, and eventually Harrison left. He was supposed to have dinner with Tana that night, and instead he called it off. He explained over the phone that he had a stack of cables that had arrived, and he had to compose answers to all of them. They met for lunch the next day instead, and Harrison was honest with her. It was the worst day in his life since his wife had died. His eyes looked sad and his face was grim, and she knew the moment she met him at the restaurant that he didn't have good news, and she felt her heart stop for an instant as he began to speak once they sat down. She knew instantly that he was going to say something she didn't want to hear.

"I spoke to Harry yesterday." He fought the emotions that were rising up in him. "I had to, for both our sakes."

"About us?" She looked stunned. It was so soon. Nothing had even happened yet. It was an innocent romance . . . but Harrison shook his head.

"About him, and what he feels for you. I had to know, before we went any further with this." He took her hand in his and looked into her eyes, and she felt her heart melt again. "Tana, I want you to know right now, that I'm in love with you. I've only loved one woman in my life as I think I love you, and that was my wife. But I also love my son, and I wouldn't hurt him for anything in this world, no matter what kind of son of a bitch he thinks I am, and I've been one at times. I would have married you . . . but not until I knew where Harry stood." He didn't pull any punches with her. "He's in love with you, Tan."

"What?" She was shocked. "He is not!"

"He is. He's just scared to death to scare you off. He told me about the rape, about how you felt about going out with men. He's been biding his time for years, but I don't have any doubt. He has been in love with you for all those years. He admitted it himself." Harrison's eyes looked sad.

"Oh, my God." She looked shocked. "But I'm not . . . I don't . . . I don't think I ever could. . . ."

"I suspected that too. But that's between you and him. If he ever does get up the guts to declare himself, you'll have to deal with that yourself. What I wanted to know was how he felt. I know how you feel now. I knew it before I talked to him." There were tears spilling in her eyes, and suddenly in his, too, as he held her hand even tighter than before. "Darling, I love you more than life itself, but if I walked off with you now, if you'd even be willing to do that with me, it would kill my son. It would break his heart, and maybe destroy something he needs very much right now. I can't do that to him. Nor can you. I really don't think you could." She was crying openly, and he pulled her into his arms as tears filled his eyes. They had nothing to hide here, or anywhere, only in front of his son. But it was the cruelest trick life had played on her so far, the first man she had loved couldn't love her because of his son . . . who was her best friend, whom she loved, but not like that. She didn't want to do anything that would hurt Harry either, but she was so much in love with Harrison . . . it was a ghastly evening filled with tears and regrets. She wanted to sleep with him anyway, but he wouldn't let her do that to herself. "The first time that happens to you, after that awful experience you had, should be with the right man." He was gentle, and loving, and he held her while she cried, and once he almost cried himself. And the next week was the most painful in her life, and at last he left for London again, and Tana felt as though she had been left on the beach. She was alone, with her studies, with Harry again. She went to the hospital every day, took her books with her, and she looked tired and pale and grim.

"Boy, you're a pleasure to see. What the hell's wrong with you? Are you sick?" She almost was, over Harrison, but she knew he had been right, no matter how painful it was. They had both done the right thing for someone they loved. And now she was merciless with him, forcing Harry to do what the nurses asked, urging him on, insulting him, cajoling him, encouraging him when he needed it. She was tireless, and devoted beyond anything imaginable, and when Harrison called from halfway around the world, sometimes she would talk to him and she would feel her heart leap again, but he hadn't gone back on his resolve. It was a sacrifice he had made for his son, and Tana had to go along with it. He had given her no choice. Or himself, although he knew that he would never recover from what he felt for her. He only hoped she would. She had a lifetime ahead of her, and hopefully, the right man.

Chapter 11

The sun streamed into the room as Harry lay on his bed, trying to read a book. He had already had an hour in the pool and two hours of therapy, and he was sick to death of his schedule. There was a sameness about it all, a tediousness he couldn't stand anymore. He glanced at his watch, knowing Tana would be there soon. He had been at Letterman for more than four months, and she came to see him every day, bringing her stacks of papers and notes, and mountains of books. And almost as soon as he thought of her, the door opened and she walked in. She had lost weight in the past months. She was working too hard at school, and running herself ragged going back and forth between Berkeley and the hospital. His father had offered to buy her a car, but she had absolutely refused to even consider it.

"Hi kid, what's up, or is that rude?" She grinned at him and he laughed.

"You're disgusting, Tan." But at least he wasn't as sensitive about that anymore. Five weeks before, he had actually made love to a student nurse, a little "creatively" as he had said to his therapist, but with a little imagination here and there, things had gone fairly well for both of them, and he didn't give a damn that she was engaged. True love hadn't been on his mind, and he had no intention of trying beginner's luck on Tan. She meant much, much too much to him, as he had told his dad, and she had enough problems of her own. "What'd you do today?"

She sighed and sat down with a rueful smile. "What do I ever do? Study all night, turn in papers, take exams. Christ, I may not live through another two years of this."

"Sure you will." He smiled. She was the light of his life, and he would have been lost without her visits every day.

"What makes you so sure?" Sometimes she doubted it herself, but somehow she always went on. Always. She wouldn't let herself stop. She couldn't let Harry down and she couldn't flunk out of school.

"You've got more guts than anyone I know. You'll make it, Tan." It was something they gave each other now—courage, faith. When he'd get depressed, she'd stand there and shout at him until he wanted to cry, but she made him try all the things he was supposed to do, and when she thought she couldn't make it through another day of Boalt, he quizzed her for exams, woke her up after she got a little sleep, underlined some of the textbooks for her. And now suddenly he grinned at her. "Besides, law school's not that hard. I've been reading some of that stuff you left here."

She smiled. That was what she had had in mind. But she looked nonchalant as she turned to him. "Oh yeah, then why don't you give it a try?"

"Why should I bust my hump?"

"What else have you got to do? Except sit on your

can, and pinch nurses' aides. And how long will that last? They're going to kick you out of here in June."

"That's not sure yet." He looked nervous at the thought. He wasn't sure he was ready to go home. And home where? His father moved around so much, and he couldn't keep up with him now, even if he wanted to. He could go to a hotel, of course, there was the apartment at the Pierre in New York, but that sounded terribly lonely to him.

"You sure don't look excited about going home." Tana was watching him. She had talked to Harrison in Geneva several days before, and they had discussed the same thing. He called her at least once a week to see how Harry was, and she knew that he still felt the same about her as he had before, and she did for him as well, but they had taken their resolve and there was no turning back anymore. Harrison Winslow would not betray his son. And Tana understood.

"I don't have a home to go to, Tan." She had thought of it before, but not with any great seriousness, yet she had an idea. Maybe it was time to broach it to him.

"What about moving in with me?"

"In that dismal room of yours?" He laughed and looked horrified at the same time. "Being confined to a wheelchair is bad enough. But living in that dump, I might kill myself. Besides, where would I sleep? On the floor?"

"No, you ass." She was laughing at him as he made a hideous face. "We could get a place of our own, as long as it's reasonable so I could pay my share too."

"Like where?" The idea hadn't quite sunk in yet, but it had a certain appeal.

"I don't know . . . the Haight-Ashbury maybe?" The hippie boom was just taking hold, and she had driven through the Haight only recently. But she was teasing him. Unless one wore flowing robes and were permanently stoned on LSD, it would have been impossible to tolerate living there. "Seriously, we could find something if we looked."

"It would have to be on the ground floor." He looked pensively at the wheelchair parked at the end of the bed.

"I know that. And I have another idea too." She decided to hit him with it all at once.

"Now what?" He lay back against his pillows and looked happily at her. As difficult as these months had been, it had given them something very special to share, and they were closer than either of them had ever thought two human beings could be. "You know, you never give me a moment's peace. You've always got some damn plot or plan. You exhaust me, Tan." But it wasn't a complaint and they both knew that.

"It's good for you. You know that." He did, but wouldn't give her the satisfaction of admitting it.

"So, what's your thought?"

"How about applying to Boalt?" She held her breath and he looked shocked.

"Me? Are you *nuts?* What the hell would I do there?"

"Probably cheat, but failing that, you could study your ass off like I do every night. It would give you something to do other than pick your nose."

"What a charming image you have of me, my dear."
He swept her a bow from the bed and she laughed. "Why
in God's name would I torture myself with law school? I
don't have to do a dumb thing like that."

"You'd be good at it." She looked at him earnestly
and he wanted to argue with her, but the worst of it was
that he liked the idea.

"You're trying to ruin my life."

"Yes." She grinned. "Will you apply?"

"I probably won't get in. My grades were never as
good as yours."

"I already asked, you can apply as a veteran. They
might even make an exception for you . . ." She was
cautious about the way she said it, but he looked annoyed
anyway.

"Never mind that. If you got in, so can I." And the
damnedest thing was that suddenly he wanted to. He
almost wondered if he had wanted to for a long time.
Maybe he felt left out with all that studying she did,
while he had nothing at all to do except lie around and
watch the nursing shifts change.

She brought him the application forms the next afternoon, and they mulled them over endlessly, and finally
sent them in, and by then Tana was looking at flats for
them. It had to be exactly right, and something that
would work for him.

She had just seen two she liked when her mother
called on an afternoon in late May. It was unusual for her
to be home, but she had some things to take care of at
home, and she knew Harry was all right. One of the girls
from down the hall came and knocked on her door. She
assumed it was Harry, wanting to know how the apart-

ments were. One of them was in Piedmont, and snob that
he was, she knew he would like that one best, but she
wanted to be sure she could afford it too. She didn't have
the income he had, even though she had lined up a good
job for herself that summer. Maybe after that. . . .

"Hello?" There was a long-distance whir and her
heart stopped, wondering if it was Harrison calling her
again. Harry had never realized what had passed between
them, or more importantly what could have and what
sacrifice they had made. "Hello?"

"Tana?" It was Jean.

"Oh. Hi, Mom."

"Is something wrong?" She had sounded strange at
first.

"No. I thought it was someone else. Is something
wrong?" It was an unusual hour for her to call. Maybe
Arthur had had another heart attack. He had stayed in
Palm Beach for three months, and Jean had stayed there
with him. Ann and John and Billy had gone back to New
York, and Jean had stayed to nurse him back to health
even after he left the hospital. They had only been back in
New York for two months, and she must have had her
hands full, because Tana almost never heard from her
now.

"I wasn't sure you'd be home at this hour." She
sounded nervous, as though she wasn't sure what to say.

"Usually I'm at the hospital, but I had something to
do here."

"How's your friend?"

"Better. He's getting out in about a month. I was
just looking at some apartments for him." She hadn't told
her yet that they were thinking of living together. It made

perfect sense to her, but she knew that it wouldn't to Jean.

"Can he live alone?" She sounded surprised.

"Probably if he had to, but I don't think he will."

"That's wise." She had no idea what that meant, but she had other things on her mind. "I wanted to tell you something, sweetheart."

"What's that?"

She wasn't at all sure how Tana would react, but there was no way to beat around the bush any longer. "Arthur and I are getting married." She held her breath and at her end, Tana stared.

"You're *what?*"

"Getting married . . . I . . . he feels that we've gotten older . . . we've been foolish for long enough. . . ." She stumbled over some of the words he had said to her only days before, blushing furiously and at the same time terrified of what Tana would say. She knew that she hadn't liked Arthur for years, but maybe now. . . .

"You weren't the fool in all that, Mom. He was. He should have married you fifteen years ago, at least." She frowned for a moment, mulling over what Jean had said. "Is that what you really want to do, Mom? He's not young anymore, and he's sick . . . he's kind of saved the worst for you." It was blunt, but true, but until his heart attack he hadn't even wanted to marry her. He hadn't thought of it in years, not since his wife had come home from the hospital sixteen years before, in fact. But suddenly, everything had changed, and he realized his own mortality. "Are you sure?"

"Yes, Tana, I am." Her mother sounded strangely

calm suddenly. It was what she had waited almost twenty years for, and she wouldn't have given it up for anything, not even for her only child. Tana had her own life now, and she had nothing at all, without Arthur. She was grateful to him for finally marrying her. They would have a comfortable, easy life, and she could finally relax. All those years of loneliness and worrying; would he show up, would he come by, should she wash her hair, and then just in case . . . and he didn't come for two weeks, until the night when Tana had the flu, or she herself had a bad cold . . . it was all over now, and real life was about to begin. At last. She had earned every minute of it, and she was going to enjoy every minute of it now. "I'm very sure."

"All right, then." But Tana did not sound thrilled. "I guess I should say congratulations or something like that." But somehow she didn't feel like it. It seemed like such a boring bourgeois life, and after all Jean's years of sitting there waiting for him, she would have liked to see her tell him to go to hell. But that was youth thinking, and not Jean. "When are you getting married?"

"In July. You'll come, won't you, sweetheart?" She sounded nervous again, and Tana nodded to herself. She had planned to go home for a month anyway. She had worked it out with her summer job. She was working at a law firm in town, and they understood, or so they said.

"I'll sure try." And then she had an idea. "Can Harry come?"

"In a wheelchair?" Her mother sounded horrified, and something hardened instantly in Tana's eyes.

"Obviously. It's not exactly as though he has a choice."

"Well, I don't know . . . I should think it would be embarrassing for him . . . I mean, all those people, and . . . I'll have to ask Arthur what he thinks. . . ."

"Don't bother." Tana's nostrils flared and she wanted to strangle someone, primarily Jean. "I can't make it anyway."

Tears instantly sprang to Jean's eyes. She knew what she'd done, but why was Tana always so difficult? She was so stubborn about everything. "Tana, don't do that, please . . . it's just . . . why do you have to drag him along?"

"Because he's been lying in a hospital for six months and he hasn't seen anyone except me, and maybe it would be nice for him. Did that occur to you? Not to mention the fact that this did not happen in a car accident, it happened defending a stinking country we have no right to be in anyway, and the least people can do for him now is show him some gratitude and courtesy. . . ." She was in a blind rage and Jean was terrified.

"Of course . . . I understand . . . there's no reason why he can't come. . . ." And then suddenly, out of nowhere, "John and Ann are having another baby, you know."

"What the hell does that have to do with anything?" Tana looked blank. It was hopeless talking to her. They never saw eye to eye about anything anymore. Tana had almost given up.

"Well, you could be thinking of that one of these days. You're not getting any younger, dear. You're almost twenty-three."

"I'm in law school, Mom. Do you have any idea what that's like? How hard I work night and day? Do you have any idea how ridiculous it would be for me to be thinking of marriage and babies right now?"

"It always will be if you spend your time with him, you know." She was picking on Harry again and Tana saw red at the words.

"Not at all." Her eyes were fierce, but her mother couldn't see that. "He can still get it up, you know."

"Tana!" Jean was appalled by Tana's vulgarity. "That's a disgusting thing to say."

"But it's what you wanted to know, isn't it? Well, you can relax, Mother, it still works. I hear he screwed a nurse a few days ago, and she said it was great." She was like a big dog refusing to release its prey, and her mother was hanging there, by the neck, and unable to escape. "Feel better now?"

"Tana Roberts, something has happened to you out there." In the flash of a moment, Tana thought of the grueling hours of studying she had put in, the love she had felt for Harrison, to no avail, the heartbreak of seeing Harry return crippled from Vietnam. . . . Her mother was right. "Something" had happened to her. In fact, a great deal.

"I think I've grown up. That's not always real pretty, is it, Mom?"

"It doesn't have to be ugly or rude, except in California, I suppose. They must be savages out there at that school."

Tana laughed. They were worlds apart. "I guess we are. Anyway, congratulations, Mom." It suddenly dawned on her that she and Billy were going to be step-brother and -sister now, and the thought almost made her sick. He would be at the wedding, and it was almost more than she could stand. "I'll try to be home in time."

"All right." Jean sighed, it was exhausting talking to her. "And bring Harry, if you must."

"I'll see if he's up to it. I want to get him out of the hospital first, and we've got to move. . . ." She cringed at the slip, and there was a deafening silence at the other end. That really was too much.

"You're moving in with him?"

Tana took a breath. "I am. He can't live alone."

"Let his father hire a nurse. Or are they going to pay you a salary?" She could be as cutting as Tana when she tried, but Tana was undaunted by her.

"Not at all. I'm going to split the rent with him."

"You're out of your mind. The least he could do is marry you, but I'd put a stop to that."

"No, you wouldn't." Tana sounded strangely calm. "Not if I wanted to marry him, but I don't. So relax. Mom . . . I know this is hard for you, but I just have to live my life my own way. Do you think you can just try to accept that?" There was a long pause and Tana smiled. "I know, it's not easy." And then suddenly she heard Jean crying at the other end.

"Don't you see that you're ruining your life?"

"How? By helping a friend out? What harm is there in that?"

"Because you'll wake up next week and you'll be forty years old and it'll be all over, Tan. You'll have wasted your youth, just like I did, and at least mine wasn't a total waste, I had you."

"And maybe one day I'll have children of my own. But right now I'm not thinking of that. I'm going to law school so I can have a career and do something useful with my life. And after that, I'll think about all that other stuff. Like Ann." It was a dig, but a friendly one, and it went right over Jean's head.

"You can't have a husband and a career."

"Why not? Who said that?"

"It's just true, that's all."

"That's bullshit."

"No, it's not, and if you hang around with that Winslow boy long enough, you'll marry him. And he's a cripple now, you don't need a heartbreak like that. Find someone else, a normal boy."

"Why?" Tana's heart ached for him. "He's human too. More so than most, in fact."

"You hardly know any boys. You never go out." *Thanks to your darling stepson, Mom.* But actually, lately, it was thanks to law school. Ever since Harrison, she had begun to feel differently about men, in some ways more trusting and open, and yet so far no one measured up to him. He had been so good to her. It would have been wonderful to find someone like him. But she never had time to go out with anyone now. Between going to the hospital every day and preparing for exams . . . everyone complained of it. Law school was enough to destroy an existing relationship, and starting a new one was almost impossible.

"Just wait a couple of years, Mom. And then I'll be a lawyer, and you'll be proud of me. At least I hope you will." But neither of them was too sure just then.

"I just want a normal life for you."

"What's normal? Was your life so normal, Mom?"

"It started out to be. It wasn't my fault that your father was killed and things changed after that."

"Maybe not, but it was your fault you waited almost twenty years for Arthur Durning to marry you." And the truth was that if he hadn't had his heart attack, he might never have married her. "You made that choice. I have a right to my choices too."

"Maybe so, Tan." But she didn't really understand the girl, she didn't even pretend to anymore. Ann Durning seemed so much more normal to her. She wanted what every other girl wanted, a husband, a house, two kids, pretty clothes, and if she'd made a mistake early on, she'd been smart enough to do better the second time. He had just bought her the most beautiful sapphire ring at Cartier's, and that was what Jean wanted for her child, but Tana didn't give a good goddamn.

"I'll call you soon, Mom. And tell Arthur I said congratulations to him too. He's the lucky one in this deal, but I hope you'll be happy too."

"Of course I will." But she didn't sound it when she hung up. Tana had upset her terribly, and she told Arthur about it, as much as she could, but he just told her to relax. Life was too short to let one's children get the best of one. He never did. And they had other things to think about. Jean was going to redecorate the Greenwich house, and he wanted to buy a condo in Palm Beach, as well as a little apartment in town. They were giving up the apartment she had had for years. And Tana was shocked when she discovered that.

"Hell, I don't have a home anymore either." She was shocked when she told Harry that, but he looked unimpressed.

"I haven't had one in years."

"She said there'll always be a room for me wherever they live. Can you imagine my spending the night in the Greenwich house, after what happened there? I get nightmares thinking of it. So much for that." It depressed her more than she wanted to admit to him, and she knew that marrying Arthur was what Jean wanted, but somehow it seemed so depressing to her. It was so ultimately middle class, so boring and bourgeois, she told herself, but what really bothered her was that Jean was still at Arthur's feet after all the crap she had taken from him over the years. But when she told Harry that, he got annoyed with her.

"You know you've been turning into a radical, and it bores the hell out of me, Tan."

"Have you ever considered the fact that you're more than a little right wing?" She started to look uptight.

"Maybe I am, but there's nothing wrong with that. There are certain things I believe in, Tan, and they aren't radical, and they aren't leftist, and they aren't revolutionary, but I think they're good."

"I think you're full of hot air." There was an unusual vehemence about what she said, but they had already disagreed about Vietnam several times. "How the hell can you defend what those assholes are doing over there?" She leapt to her feet and he stared at her, there was an odd silence in the room.

"Because I was one of them. That's why."

"You were not. You were a pawn. Don't you see that, you fucking jerk? They used you to fight a war we shouldn't be fighting in a place we shouldn't be in."

His voice was deathly quiet as he looked at her. "Maybe I think we should."

"How can you say a dumb thing like that? Look what happened to you over there!"

"That's the whole point." He leaned forward in his bed, and he looked as though he wanted to strangle her. "If I don't defend that . . . if I don't believe in why I was there, then what the hell good was it anyway?" Tears suddenly sprang to his eyes and he went on, "what does it all mean, goddamn it, Tan . . . what did I give them my legs for if I don't believe in them? Tell me that!" You could hear him shouting all the way down the hall. "I have to believe in them, don't I? Because if I don't, if I believe what you do, then it was all a farce. I might as well have gotten run over by a train in Des Moines . . ." He turned his face away from her and started to cry openly and she felt terrible. And then he turned to her, still in a rage. "Now get the hell out of my room you insensitive radical bitch!"

She left, and she cried all the way back to school. She knew that he was right—for him. He couldn't afford to feel about it as she did, and yet, ever since he had come back from Vietnam, something had begun to rage in her that had never been there before, a kind of anger that nothing could quench, and possibly never would. She had talked to Harrison about it on the phone one night and he had put it down to youth, but she knew it wasn't just that, it was something more. She was angry at everyone because Harry had been maimed, and if people were willing to take more chances politically, to stick their necks out . . . Hell, the President of the United States had been killed a year and a half before, how could people not

see what was happening, what they had to do . . . but
Tana didn't want to hurt Harry with all of it. She called
him to apologize but he wouldn't talk to her. And for the
first time in six and a half months since he'd gotten to
Letterman, she didn't go to see him for three days. And
when she finally did, she stuck an olive branch through
the door of his room, and followed it in sheepishly.

"What do you want?" He glared at her, and she
smiled tentatively.

"The rent, actually."

He tried to suppress a grin. He wasn't angry at her
anymore. So she was turning into a crazy radical. So
what? That's what Berkeley was all about. She'd grow
out of it. And he was more intrigued by what she had just
said. "You found a place?"

"I sure did." She grinned at him. "It's on Channing
Way, a teeny little two-bedroom house with a living room
and a kitchenette. It's all on one floor, so you'd have to
behave yourself somewhat or at least tell your lady
friends not to scream too loud," they both grinned and
Harry looked ecstatic at the news, "you're going to love
it!" She clapped her hands and described it in detail to
him, and that weekend the doctor let her drive him over
there. The last of the surgeries had been completed six
weeks before; his therapy was going well. They had done
all for him they were going to do. It was time to go home.
Harry and Tana signed the lease as soon as he saw it. The
landlord didn't seem to object to the fact that they had
different last names, and neither of them offered to explain. Tana and Harry shook hands with a look of glee,
and she drove him back to Letterman. Two weeks later,
they moved in. He had to arrange for transportation for

his therapy, but Tana promised to take him. And the week after her exams, he got the letter congratulating him on his acceptance to Boalt. He sat in his wheelchair waiting for her when she got home, with tears streaming down his cheeks.

"They took me, Tan . . . and it's all your fault. . . ." They hugged and kissed, and he had never loved her more. And Tana knew only that he was her very dearest friend as she cooked him dinner that night and he uncorked a bottle of Dom Pérignon champagne.

"Where did you get that?" She looked impressed.

"I've been saving it."

"For what?" He had been saving it for something else, but he decided that enough good things had happened in one day to warrant drinking it.

"For you, you jerk." She was wonderfully obtuse about the way he felt. But he loved that about her too. She was so engrossed in her studies and her exams and her summer job and her political ideas that she had no idea what was going on right beneath her nose, at least not in regard to him, but he wasn't ready yet anyway. He was still biding his time, afraid to lose.

"It's good stuff." She took a big gulp of champagne and grinned at him, slightly drunk, happy and relaxed. They both loved their little house and it was working out perfectly, and then she remembered that she had to ask him something. She had meant to ask him before, but with the rush to move, and buy furniture, she had forgotten to ask. "Listen, by the way, I hate to ask you this . . . I know it's going to be a drag . . . but . . ."

"Oh Jesus, now what? First she forces me to go to law school, and now God knows what other torture she

has in mind . . ." He pretended to look terrified, but
Tana looked sincerely grim.

"Worse than that. My mother's getting married in
two weeks." She had long since told him that, but she
hadn't asked him to go to the wedding with her. "Will
you come with me?"

"To your mother's wedding?" He looked surprised
as he set down his glass. "Is that appropriate?"

"I don't see why not." She hesitated, and then went
on, her eyes huge in her face. "I need you there."

"I take it her charming stepson will be on hand."

"Presumably. And the whole thing is a little much
for me. The happily married daughter with one child and
another on the way, Arthur pretending that he and my
mother fell in love only last week."

"Is that what he's saying?" Harry looked amused
and Tana shrugged.

"Probably. I don't know. The whole thing is just
hard for me. It's not my scene."

Harry thought it over, looking into his lap. He
hadn't been out like that yet, and he had been thinking of
going to Europe to meet his Dad. He could stop on the
way . . . he looked up at her. There was nothing he
would have denied her, after all she had done for him.
"Sure, Tan, no sweat."

"You don't mind too much?" She looked doggedly
grateful to him and he laughed.

"Sure I do, but so do you. At least we can laugh
together."

"I'm happy for her . . . I just . . . I just can't
play those hypocritical games anymore."

"Just behave yourself while we're there. We can fly

in and I'll head on to Europe the day afterwards. I thought I'd meet Dad in the South of France, for a while." It was so good to hear him talking about things like that again. It was amazing to realize that only a year before he had been talking about playing for the rest of his life, and now, thank God, he was playing again, at least for a month or two, before he started law school in the fall. "I don't know how I let you talk me into that." But they were both glad she had. Everything was working out perfectly. They had divided the chores in the house. She did the things he was unable to do, but it was amazing how much he did. Everything from dishes to beds, although he had practically strangled himself vacuuming one week, and now that was her task to do. They were both comfortable. She was about to start her summer job. Both of them thought life pretty damn grand in the summer of '65, and Harry picked up two of the stewardesses on their flight to New York in July. And Tana sat back in her seat, laughing at him, loving every minute of it, and thanking God that Harry Winslow IV was alive.

Chapter 12

The wedding was simple and well done. Jean wore a very pretty gray chiffon dress, and she had bought a pale blue one for Tana to wear, in case she herself didn't have time to shop. It certainly wasn't the kind of thing she would have bought herself, and she was horrified when she saw the price tag on it. Her mother had bought it at Bergdorf's, and it was a gift from Arthur, of course, so Tana couldn't say anything.

Only the family were present at the ceremony, but Tana had insisted on bringing Harry along, much to his chagrin, since they arrived from the city in the same limousine. Tana was staying with him at the Pierre. She insisted to her mother that she couldn't leave him alone. And she was relieved that her mother and Arthur were leaving the next day on a honeymoon so she didn't have to stay in New York for an extended period after all. She would have refused to stay in the Greenwich house, and she was going to fly out of New York when Harry did. He was going to Nice to meet Harrison in Saint-Jean-Cap-Ferrat, and she was flying back to San Francisco to her summer job. And Jean and Arthur were threatening to come out and see her in the fall. Her mother looked pointedly at Harry each time she spoke of it, as though she expected him to disappear by then, and eventually Tana had to laugh at it.

"It's really awful, isn't it?" But the worst of all was Billy, who managed to sidle up to her halfway through the afternoon, drunk as usual, and make some sly comment about her boyfriend not being able to get it up, and he'd be glad to help her out anytime, as he recalled she had been a fairly worthwhile piece of ass, but just as she contemplated putting her fist through his mouth, she saw a larger one come whizzing by, meet Billy's chin, and Billy reeled backwards before collapsing neatly on the lawn. Tana turned to see Harry smiling in his wheelchair just behind where she stood. He had reached up and put Billy out cold with one blow and he was immensely pleased with himself.

"You know, I wanted to do that a year ago." He smiled at her, but her mother was horrified at how they had behaved. And as early as possible Tana and Harry got back into the limousine and went back to New York. There was a tearful goodbye between Tana and Jean before that. Or at least, Jean cried and Tana was tense. Arthur had kissed her on the cheek and announced that she was his daughter now, too, and there wouldn't have to be any more scholarships. But she insisted that she couldn't accept a gift like that, and she couldn't wait to get away from all of them, especially cloying, pregnant Ann, with her whiny voice, her showy gems, and her boring husband, making eyes at someone else's wife halfway through the afternoon.

"Jesus, how can they live like that?" she had fumed to Harry on the way home and he patted her knee.

"Now, now, one day the same thing will happen to you, little one."

"Oh, go fuck yourself." He laughed at her and they went back to the Pierre. They were both leaving the next day, and he took her to "21" that night. Everyone was happy to see him there, although chagrined to see that he was in a wheelchair now. And for old times' sake, they drank too much champagne, and were drunk when they got back to the hotel. Just drunk enough for Harry to do something he had promised himself he wouldn't do for another year or two. They were into their second bottle of Roederer, and actually they had been drinking all day, when he turned to her with a gentle look and touched her chin, and unexpectedly kissed her lips.

"Do you know that I've always been in love with you?" At first Tana looked shocked, and then suddenly she looked as though she might cry.

"You're kidding me."

"I'm not." Was her mother right? Was Harrison?

"But that's ridiculous. You're not in love with me. You never were." She focused on him tipsily.

"Oh yes, I am. I always was." She stared at him, and he took her hand in his. "Will you marry me, Tan?"

"You're crazy." She pulled her hand away and stood up and suddenly there were tears in her eyes. She didn't want him to be in love with her. She wanted them to be friends forever, just friends, no more than that. And he was spoiling everything. "Why are you saying that?"

"Couldn't you love me, Tan?" Now he looked as though he were going to cry and she felt more sober than she had all night.

"I don't want to spoil what we have . . . it's too precious to me. I need you too much."

"I need you too. That's the whole point. If we get married then we'll always be there." But she couldn't marry him . . . she was still in love with Harrison . . . it was insane, the whole thing . . . all of it . . . she lay on her bed and sobbed that night, and Harry never went to bed at all. He was waiting for her when she came out of her room the next morning, looking pale and tired, with circles under her eyes. He wanted to retrieve what they'd had before, and it wasn't too late yet. That meant everything to him. He could live without being married to her, but he couldn't stand losing her. "I'm sorry about what happened last night, Tan."

"So am I." She sat down next to him in the room's spacious living room. "What happens now?"

"We put it down to one drunken night. It was a rough day for both of us . . . your mother getting married . . . my first time out socially in the chair . . . no big deal. We can put it behind us. I'm sure of it." He was praying that she would agree with him and slowly she shook her head, as his heart sank.

"What happened to us? Have you really been . . . in love with me for all that time?"

He looked at her honestly. "Some of it. Sometimes, I hate your guts." They both laughed and she felt some of what they had shared before, and she put her arms around his neck then.

"I'll always love you, Harry. Always."

"That's all I wanted to know." He could have cried if he'd let himself, but instead they ordered room service, laughed, raised hell, teased, trying desperately to regain the ease of what they'd had before, and as she watched his plane take off that afternoon, there were tears in her eyes. It might never be quite the same again, but it would be close. They'd see to that. They both had too much invested in each other by now to let anything spoil it for them.

When Harry finally arrived in Cap Ferrat, brought there by the car and driver Harrison had sent for him, his father came running across the lawn to help his son from the car and into his chair, gripping his arm powerfully and looking at him.

"You all right, Son?" There was something in Harry's eyes that worried him.

"More or less." He looked tired. It had been a long flight, a long couple of days, and this time he hadn't played games with the stewardesses. He had been thinking of Tana as he flew to France. She would always be his first great love, the woman who had brought him back to life again. Feelings like that couldn't be lost, and if she didn't want to marry him . . . he had no choice. He had to accept it. He could see in her eyes that it simply wasn't there for her. And as much as it hurt, he knew that he had to force himself to accept that now. But it wasn't going to be easy for him. He had waited for so long to tell her what he felt. And it was all over now. It was never going to happen between them. The thought of that reality brought tears to his eyes again and Harrison took his son's shoulders in his powerful hands.

"How's Tana?" Harrison was quick to ask, and for just an instant he saw Harry hesitate, and then instinctively he understood. Harry had tried and lost. His father's heart went out to him.

"Tana's fine . . ." he tried to smile ". . . but difficult." He smiled cryptically, and Harrison instantly understood. He knew that one day it would come to that.

"Ah, yes . . ." He smiled, as a pretty girl walked across the lawn to him and caught Harry's eye, just for an instant pushing Tana from his mind. And then the two men's eyes met, and Harry smiled slowly up at him. "You'll get over it, Son."

For an instant he felt the lump in his throat again, and then with a sharp laugh, he whispered, almost to himself, "I'll try."

Chapter 13

When Harry returned from Europe in the fall he was deeply tanned, and happy and rested. He had followed his father everywhere, to Monaco, to Italy, to Madrid for a few days, Paris, New York. It had been the whirlwind life again, the life he had felt so left out of as a boy, but suddenly there was a place reserved in it for him. Pretty women, lovely girls, galas, endless concerts and parties and social events. He was actually tired of it when he finally got on the plane in New York and flew west. Tana met him at the Oakland airport, and she looked reassuringly as she had before. She looked healthy and brown, her blond mane flying in the wind, she had loved her summer job, gone to Malibu for a few days with some friends she'd made at work, and she was talking about going to Mexico over the holidays, and when law school began, they were constantly together, yet apart. She would drop him off at the library, but her classes were different from his. She seemed to be making new friends now. With Harry out of the hospital, she had more free time, and the survivors of the first-year grind seemed to stick together now. It was a healthier arrangement than they'd had before, and by Christmas whenever she saw

Harry at school he was always with the same girl, a pretty, petite blond girl from Australia, named Averil. She seemed to be Harry's shadow. She was studying for a master's degree in art, but she seemed far more interested in following Harry around everywhere, and he didn't seem to object to it. Tana tried to be nonchalant the first time Averil emerged from his room on a Saturday morning and suddenly all three of them laughed nervously.

"Does this mean you guys are kicking me out?" Tana laughed nervously.

"Hell no, you jerk. There's room for all of us." And by the end of Harry's first year, she was living with them. She was actually adorable, shared the chores, was cheerful, pleasant, helpful, she was so sweet she made Tana nervous sometimes, particularly when she had exams, but on the whole the arrangement worked out perfectly. She flew to Europe with Harry that summer to meet Harrison, and Tana worked in the same law firm again. She had promised her mother that she would come East, but she was looking for every possible excuse not to go, and was spared a lie when Arthur had another heart attack, a mild one this time, but her mother took him to Lake George to rest, and promised to come out to see Tana in the fall. But Tana knew what that meant by now. She and Arthur had flown out once the year before, and it was nightmarish. She was "revolted" by the house they shared, "shocked" that she and Harry were still living under one roof, and she would be even more so now when she discovered that they had added another girl. Tana laughed at the thought. She was obviously beyond hope, and the only consolation was that Ann had gotten divorced again, through no fault of hers, of course. John

had actually had the nerve to walk out on her, and was
having a flagrant affair with her best friend. So all was
not entirely wholesome anywhere these days . . . poor
Ann . . . Tana smiled at the thought.

　　Tana actually enjoyed her summer alone that year.
She loved Harry and Averil, too, but there was so much
pressure on her with law school, that it was nice to be
alone now and then. And she and Harry seemed to fight
about politics all the time these days. He continued to
support the war in Vietnam, and she became crazed when
the subject came up at all, as Averil would try desperately
to keep the peace. But Harry and Tana had known each
other for too long. After six years, they no longer felt
they had to be polite and the language they threw at each
other made Averil cringe, although he would never have
spoken that way to her, nor she to him. Averil was a far
gentler soul than Tana was. Tana had been on her own
for a long time. And at twenty-four, she was powerful
and unafraid, and sure of her own ideas. She had a long,
strong stride, and eyes that did not shy from anything or
anyone. She was curious about everything around her,
definite about what she thought, and courageous enough
to say it to anyone. It got her into trouble sometimes, but
she didn't mind. She liked the discussions that arose like
that. And when she registered for school that year—hal-
lelujah her last, she thought to herself with a grin—she
found herself in the midst of a lengthy conversation in
the cafeteria. There were at least eight or nine people
talking heatedly about Vietnam, as usual, and she was
quick to leap into it, as she always did. It was the subject
she felt strongest about, because of Harry of course, no
matter how he chose to feel, she had her own ideas, and

Harry wasn't there anyway. He was off somewhere with Averil, probably, copping a quick feel before class, as Tana teased him often enough. The two of them seemed to spend most of their life in bed, challenging his "creativity," which seemed to pose no problem at all. But Tana was deep in the ideologies of Vietnam and not thinking of Harry specifically as she spoke that day, and was surprised to find herself sitting next to someone even more radical than she. He had a wild mane of tightly curled black hair that sprang from his head almost angrily, sandals, blue jeans, a turquoise T-shirt, strangely electric blue eyes, and a smile that tore at something deep inside of her. When he stood up, every muscle seemed to ripple through his flesh, and everything about him seemed oddly sensual, and she had an almost irresistible urge to reach out and touch his arm, hanging so near to her.

"Do you live nearby?" She shook her head. "I didn't think I'd seen you here before."

"I usually hang out in the library. Third year law."

"Man." He looked impressed. "That's tough."

"You?"

"The master's program in political science, what else?" They both laughed. He had chosen well anyway, and he followed her to the library where she left him regretfully. She liked his ideas and he was strikingly beautiful, and she knew instantly that Harry wouldn't approve of him. He had very square ideas these days, especially with Averil around. It was something Tana knew about them both and it didn't bother her. Harry could have grown ferns on his head and sprouted horns, and she would have loved him anyway. He was her

brother by then, and Averil was a part of him, so she
accepted that. Most of the time, she tried not to discuss
politics with them. It made things easier.

And she was intrigued to see her new friend making
a speech on campus a few days later, about the same
issues they had discussed. It was an impassioned, brilliant
confrontation of the mind and she told him as much
when she saw him afterwards. She knew by then that his
name was Yael McBee. It was a funny name, but he was
not a funny man. He was brilliant and intense and his
anger reached out almost like a lash to touch those he
wished to reach. She admired his skill in addressing
crowds, and she went to see him several more times that
fall, before he finally asked her out to dinner one night.
They each paid their share, and went back to his apartment to talk afterwards. There were at least a dozen people living there, some of them on mattresses, and it didn't
have the neat, well-polished air of the cottage which
Harry and Tana and Averil shared. She would, in fact,
have been embarrassed to bring Yael there. It was too
bourgeois, too sweet, almost too foreign to him. And she
liked visiting him where he lived. She felt uncomfortable
at home anyway these days. Averil and Harry were always making love or hiding out, going in his room and
closing the door. She wondered how he got any studying
done at all, and yet she knew he did from the look of his
grades, which were surprisingly good. But it was more
fun being with Yael and his friends, and when Harry flew
to Switzerland at Christmastime, and Averil flew home,
Tana finally invited Yael to come and see her. And it was
odd to see him in the tidy little house, without his stri-
dent friends around. He had worn a deep green turtle-

neck and his well-worn jeans. He had military combat boots, although he had served a year in jail for refusing to be drafted and go to Vietnam. They sent him to a prison in the Southwest, and paroled him after a year.

"That's incredible." She was awed by him, by his remarkable, almost Rasputin-like eyes, his courage in going against every current imaginable, there was something outstanding about the man, and she wasn't surprised that he had been fascinated by communism as a child. Everything about him was intriguing and unusual, and when he gently took her in his arms and made love to her on Christmas Eve, that seemed intriguing too. Only once did she have to force Harrison Winslow from her mind. And in a peculiar way he had readied her for this. Not that he had anything in common with Yael McBee. Yael managed to unleash her flesh in a way she had never dreamed could happen to her, reaching deep into her, into all she had wanted and denied herself for so long. He reached into her very soul, and pulled out a passion and desire she had never suspected in herself, and gave her something she had never dreamed a man could give, until she felt addicted to everything he gave to her. She was almost his slave by the time Harry and Averil came home, and more often than not, she slept at Yael's apartment now, on a mattress with him, curled up, cold, until he laid a hand on her, and then suddenly life was exotic and tropical, there were brilliant hues everywhere. She couldn't live without him now, and after dinner, they would sit around the living room with the others, talking politics and smoking dope, and Tana suddenly felt like a woman now, a woman in full bloom, living daringly at the feet of her man.

"Where the hell are you all the time, Tan? We never see you anymore." Harry questioned her.

"I have a lot of work to do at the library for exams." She had five months of law school left before finals came up, and then the bar to face, and in some ways it panicked her, but actually most of the time she was with Yael, and she had still said nothing about him to Harry or Averil. She didn't know what to say. They lived in such different worlds that it was impossible to conceive of them in the same place, same house, same school.

"You have a romance going on or something, Tan?" He was suspicious of her now, in addition to her absences. She was looking strange to him, numb almost, glazed, as though she had joined a Hindu cult, or smoked dope all the time, which he suspected too. But it wasn't until Easter that he saw her with Yael, and when he did he was horrified. He waited for her after class, and like an irate parent, he berated her. "What the hell are you doing with that creep? Do you know who he is?"

"Of course I do . . . I've known him all year. . . ." She had known he wouldn't understand and she told him as much.

"Do you know what kind of reputation he has? He is a violent radical, a Communist, a troublemaker of the worst sort. I watched him get arrested last year, and someone told me he's served time in prison before this . . . for chrissake, Tan, wake up!"

"You fucking jerk!" They were screaming at each other outside the main library, and now and then someone turned around but neither of them cared. "He served time for evading the draft, which I'm sure you think is worse than Murder One, but as it so happens, I don't."

"I'm well aware of that. But you better watch your goddamn fucking ass, or you won't have to worry about taking the bar in June. He'll get you arrested and kicked out of school so fast your head will spin."

"You don't know what you're talking about!" But the next week, over Easter holiday, he arranged a major demonstration outside the administration building, and two dozen students were carted off to jail.

"See what I mean?" Harry had been quick to rub it in and she had slammed out of the house again. Harry didn't understand anything. Mostly, he didn't understand what Yael meant to her. Fortunately, he had managed not to get arrested himself, and she stayed with him for the following week. Everything about him excited her. Every sense was aroused when he walked into the room, and things were pretty interesting at his place these days. Everyone seemed to be getting more wound up for demonstrations set up for the end of the school year, but she was so panicked about exams that she had to stay at her own house more than once just to get some studying done. And it was there that Harry tried to reason with her, gently this time, he was terrified that something would happen to her, and he'd do anything to stop it if he could, before it was too late. "Please, Tan, please . . . listen to me . . . you're going to get in trouble with him . . . are you in love with him?" He looked heartbroken at the thought, not because he was still in love with her himself, but because he considered it a hideous fate for her. He hated the guy, he was a rude, boorish, uncivilized, selfish creep, and Harry had heard plenty about him around the school in the last six months. The guy was violent and sooner or later there was going to be

serious trouble involving him. Harry just didn't want him
to pull Tana down with him when he went. And he
thought there was a good chance he might. If she let him.
And she looked as though she would. She had a blind
passion for the man. Even his politics excited her, and the
thought of that made Harry sick.

She insisted that she wasn't in love with him, but he
knew that it wasn't that simple for her, that this was the
first man she had willingly given herself to, and she had
been so chaste for so long that in some ways her judgment was impaired. He knew that if the right man, or the
wrong one as it were, came along and aroused her in a
way she'd never known before, she might fall prey to
him, and in this instance she had. She was mesmerized by
Yael, and his unorthodox life and friends. She was fascinated by something she had never seen before, and at the
same time he played her body like a violin. It was a difficult combination to defeat. And then, just before her final
exams, six months into their relationship, Yael took matters in his own hands, and put her to the test.

"I need you next week, Tan."

"What for?" She looked over her shoulder dis-
tractedly. She had two hundred pages more to read that
night.

"Just a meeting, sort of. . . ." He was vague, smoking his fifth joint of the night. Usually, it didn't affect him
visibly, but lately he was tired.

"What kind of meeting?"

"We want to make a point with the people who
count."

She smiled at him. "Who's that?"

"I think it's time we took things directly to government. We're going to the mayor's house."

"Christ, you'll get busted for sure." But it didn't seem to faze her much. She was used to that by now, not that she'd gotten arrested with him yet, although all the others had.

"So what?" He was unconcerned.

"If I'm with you, and I go, and no one bails me out, I'll miss my exams."

"Oh, for chrissake, Tan, so what? What are you going to be after all? Some two-bit lawyer to defend society as it exists? It sucks, get rid of it first, then go to work. You can wait a year to take your exams, Tan. This is more important." She looked at him, horrified at what she had just heard him say to her. He didn't understand her at all if he could say something like that. Who was this man?

"Do you know how hard I've worked for this, Yael?"

"Don't you realize how meaningless it is?"

It was the first fight they had ever had, and he pressured her for days, but in the end she did not go. She went back to her own house to study for exams, and when she watched the news that night, her eyes almost fell out of her head. The mayor's house had been bombed, and two of his children had almost been killed. As it turned out, they were going to be all right, but an entire side of the house had been destroyed, his wife was badly burned by a bomb that had exploded nearby. "And a radical student group at UC Berkeley had taken credit for it." Seven students had been arrested on charges of attempted murder, assault, assorted weaponry charges,

and sundry other things, and among them Yael McBee
. . . and if she had listened to him, she realized with
trembling knees, her whole life would have been over
. . . not just law school, but her freedom for many,
many years. She was deathly pale as she sat watching
them being loaded into police wagons on TV and Harry
watched her face and said nothing at all. She stood up
after a long moment and looked down at him, grateful
that he hadn't said anything. In one second, everything
she had felt for Yael exploded into nothingness, like one
of his bombs.

"He wanted me to be there tonight, Harry . . ."
She started to cry. "You were right." She felt sick. He
had almost destroyed her life, and she had been completely under his spell. And for what? A piece of ass?
How sick was she? She felt sick thinking of it. She had
never realized how deeply committed they were to their
ideals, and it terrified her now to have known them at all.
She was afraid that she might be taken in for questioning.
And eventually she was, but nothing ever came of it. She
was a student who had slept with Yael McBee. She wasn't
the only one. She took her exams. She passed the bar. She
was offered a job in the district attorney's office, as a
prosecutor, and grown-up life began then and there. The
radical days were past, along with student life, and living
with Harry and Averil in their little house. She rented an
apartment in San Francisco, and slowly packed up her
things. Everything was suddenly painful to her, everything was over, finished, done.

"You look like a picture of cheer." Harry wheeled
slowly into her room, as she threw another stack of law
books into a box. "I guess I should call you Madam Pros-

ecutor now." She smiled and looked at him. She was still
shocked at what had happened to Yael McBee, and almost to her through him. And she was still depressed at
the thought of what she had felt for him. Now it had all
begun to seem unreal. They hadn't come to trial yet, but
she knew that he and his friends would be sent away for a
long, long time.

"I feel like I'm running away from home."

"You can always come back, you know, we'll still be
here." And then he suddenly looked sheepishly at her.
Tana laughed as she looked at him. They had known
each other for too long to be able to get away with anything.

"Now what does that look like? What mischief are
you up to now?"

"Me? Nothing."

"Harry . . ." She advanced on him menacingly and
he wheeled away as he laughed.

"Honest, Tan . . . oh shit!" He ran smack into her
desk and she carefully put her hands around his handsome throat. He looked more like his father every day,
and she still missed him sometimes. It would have been a
lot healthier having an affair with him than Yael McBee.
"All right . . . all right . . . Ave and I are getting
married." For a moment, Tana looked shocked. Ann
Durning had just gotten married for the third time, to a
big movie producer in L.A. He had given her a Rolls
Royce as a wedding present and a twenty-carat diamond
ring, which Tana had heard a lot about from Jean. But
that was something people like Ann Durning did. Somehow she had never thought about Harry getting married.

"You are?"

He smiled. "I thought after all this time . . . she's a terrific girl, Tan . . ."

"I know that, you dummy," Tana grinned, "I've been living with her too. That just seems like such a grown-up thing to do." They were all twenty-five years old, but she didn't feel old enough to get married yet, she wondered why they did. Maybe they had had more sex, she laughed to herself, and then she smiled at him and bent to kiss his cheek. "Congratulations. When?"

"Pretty soon." And then suddenly Tana saw something funny in his eye. It was, at the same time, both embarrassment and pride.

"Harry Winslow . . . do you mean to tell me that . . . you didn't . . ." She was laughing now, and Harry was actually blushing for one of the few times in his life.

"I did. She's knocked up."

"Oh, for chrissake." And then her face sobered suddenly. "You don't have to get married, you know. Is she forcing you to?"

He laughed and Tana thought she'd never seen him look so happy in his life. "No, I forced her. I told her I'd kill her if she got rid of it. It's our kid, and I want it, and so does she."

"My God," Tana sat down hard on the bed, "marriage *and* a family. Jesus, you guys don't mess around."

"Nope." He looked about to burst with pride and his intended walked into the room with a shy smile.

"Is Harry telling you what I think he is?" Tana nodded, watching their eyes. There was something so peaceful and satisfied there. She wondered what it felt like to feel like that, and for a moment she almost envied them. "He has a big mouth." But she bent and kissed his lips

and he patted her behind, and a little while later he
wheeled out of the room. They were getting married in
Australia, where Averil was from, and Tana was invited
to the wedding, of course, and after that they would come
back to the same little house, but Harry was starting to
look for a nice place in Piedmont for them to live until he
finished school, it was time for the Winslow funds to
come into play a little bit. He wanted Averil living decently now. And he turned to Tana later that night.

"You know, if it weren't for you, Tan, I wouldn't be
here at all." He had told that to Averil ten thousand
times at least in the past year, and he believed it with all
his heart.

"That's not true, Harry, you know that. You did it
yourself."

But he grabbed her arm. "I couldn't have made it
without you. Give yourself credit for that, Tan. The hospital, law school, all of it . . . I wouldn't even know
Ave, if it weren't for you . . ."

She was smiling gently at him and she was touched.
"What about the baby, is that my doing too?"

"Oh, you jerk. . . ." He tugged at the long blond
hair and went back to his future wife, sound asleep in the
bed where their baby had been conceived. His "creativity" had paid off, and Tana smiled to herself wistfully
that night as she fell asleep. She was happy for him, for
them both. But she suddenly felt so alone. She had lived
with him for two years, with Averil for half of that, it
would be strange living alone without them, and they
would have their own life . . . it all seemed so strange
. . . why did everyone want to get married . . . Harry
. . . her mother . . . Ann . . . what was the magic

about that? All Tana had wanted was to get through law school, and when she had finally had an affair with someone, he had turned out to be some wild nut, and had wound up in jail for the rest of his life . . . it was mystifying as she fell asleep . . . she didn't have any of the answers, not then or when she moved out.

She moved into a pleasant little flat in Pacific Heights, with a view of the Bay, and it took her fifteen minutes to get to City Hall in the secondhand car she bought. She was trying to save everything she could to go to Harry and Averil's wedding, but Harry insisted on giving her the ticket as a gift. She went just before she started her new job, and she could only stay in Sydney with them for four days. Averil looked like a little doll in a white organza dress, and nothing showed yet at all. Her parents had no idea that there was a baby on the way, and Tana even forgot about it. She forgot everything when she saw Harrison Winslow walk towards her again.

"Hello, Tan." He kissed her gently on the cheek and she thought she would melt. And he was as he had always been, charming, and debonair, sophisticated in every possible way, but the romance that had been stopped so long ago was not destined to be revived again. They talked for hours, and went for a long walk late one night. He found her different and more grown up, but in his mind, she would always be Harry's friend, and he knew that no matter what, in Harry's mind, Tana would always belong to him, and he still respected that.

He took her to the airport when she left. Harry and Averil had already left on their honeymoon, and he kissed her as he had so long ago, and every ounce of her soul reached out to him. There were tears rolling down her cheeks as she boarded the plane, and the stewardesses left her alone, wondering who the handsome man had been. They wondered if she was his girlfriend or his wife, and they watched her curiously. She was a tall, pretty blonde, in a simple beige linen suit, with an assurance about the way she moved, a proud way she held her head, and what they didn't know was that inside she felt frightened and alone. Everything she was going back to was going to be new all over again. New job, new home, and no one to share it with. She suddenly understood why people like Ann Durning and her mother got married. It was safer than being out there on your own, and yet, it was the only way Tana knew by now, as the plane headed for home.

Part III

REAL LIFE

Chapter 14

The apartment Tana had rented had a pretty view of the Bay and a little garden in the back. There was a tiny bedroom, a living room, a kitchen with a brick wall and a little French window that looked out into the garden, where she sat sometimes, soaking up the sun. Unconsciously, she had looked for something on the ground floor, so that when Harry came to see her, he wouldn't have a problem with the chair. And she felt comfortable living there. She was surprised at how quickly she adapted to living alone. Harry and Averil came to see her frequently at first, they missed her, too, and Tana was surprised at how rapidly Averil lost her shape. She blew up into a pretty little balloon, and the whole thing seemed foreign to her. Her own life was involved in such a different world. The world of prosecution, of the D.A., of murders and robberies and rapes. It was all she thought of all day, and the idea of having babies seemed light-years away, although her mother had reported that Ann Durning was pregnant again, not that Tana gave a damn. All of that was too far behind her now. Hearing about the Durnings had no effect at all, even her mother knew that, she had all but given up. And it was the final

295

blow when she heard that Harry had married that other girl. Poor Tana, all those years taking care of him, and he'd gone off with someone else.

"What a rotten thing to do." Tana had been stunned by her words at first and then she had begun to laugh. It seemed too funny to her. Her mother really never had believed that they were just friends.

"Of course it's not. They're perfect for each other."

"But don't you mind?" What was wrong with all of them? How did they think these days? And she was twenty-five years old, when was she ever going to settle down?

"Of course I don't mind. I told you years ago, Mom, Harry and I are just friends. The best of friends. And I'm thrilled for them." She waited a respectable interval to tell her about the child, when she called again.

"And what about you, Tan? When are you going to think about settling down?"

Tana sighed. What a thought. "Don't you ever give up, Mom?"

"Have you, at your age?" What a depressing thought.

"Of course not. I haven't even started to think about that." She was just out of her affair with Yael McBee, who was the last person one would have thought of settling down with, and she didn't even have time to think of romance at her new job. She was too busy learning to be an assistant D.A. It was almost six months into the job before she even had time for her first date. A senior investigator asked her out, and she went because he was an interesting guy, but she had no real interest in him. She went out with two or three lawyers after that, but her

mind was always on her work, and in February she had
her first important case, covered by national press. She
felt as though all eyes were on her, and she was anxious
to do well. It was a fiercely ugly rape and murder. The
rape of a fifteen-year-old girl, who had been lured into an
abandoned house by her mother's lover. She had been
raped nine or ten times, according to the testimony,
badly disfigured, and eventually killed, and Tana wanted
to get the gas chamber for him. It was a case that struck a
chord near her heart, although no one knew that, and she
worked her ass off, preparing the case, and reviewing the
testimony and the evidence every night. The defendant
was an attractive man of about thirty-five, well educated,
decently dressed, and the defense was trying to pull every
trick in the book. She was up until two o'clock every
night. It was almost like trying to pass the bar again.

"How's it going, Tan?" Harry called her late one
night. She glanced at the clock, surprised that he was still
up. It was almost three.

"Okay. Something wrong? Averil all right?"

"She sure is." She could almost see him beam. "We
just had a baby boy, Tan. Eight pounds one ounce, and
she's the bravest girl in the whole world . . . I was
there, and oh Tan, it was so beautiful . . . his little head
just popped out, and there he was, looking at me. They
handed him to me first . . ." He was breathless and excited and he sounded as though he were laughing and
crying at the same time. "Ave just went to sleep so I
thought I'd give you a call. Were you up?"

"Of course I was. Oh Harry, I'm so happy for both
of you!" There were tears in her eyes, too, and she invited
him up for a drink. He was there five minutes later, and

he looked tired, but the happiest she'd ever seen. And it was the strangest feeling, watching him, listening to him tell it all, as though it had been the first baby that had ever been born, and Averil were miraculous. She almost envied them, and yet at the same time, she felt a terrible void deep in her soul, as though that part of her just wasn't there, almost as though it had been left out. It was like listening to someone speak a foreign tongue and admiring them tremendously, but having no understanding of the language at all. She felt completely in the dark, and yet she thought it was wonderful for them.

It was five o'clock in the morning before he left, and she slept for a little less than two hours before getting up to get ready for court, and she went back to her big case. It dragged on for more than three weeks, and the jury stayed out for nine days, after Tana argued before them heroically. And when they finally came in, she had won. The defendant was convicted of every charge and although the judge refused to impose capital punishment on him, he was sentenced to prison for life, and deep within her, Tana was glad. She wanted him to pay for what he had done, although his going to prison would never bring the girl back to life.

The newspapers said that she had argued the case brilliantly, and Harry teased her about it when she came to see the baby in Piedmont after that, calling her Madam Hotshot, and giving her a bad time.

"All right, all right, enough. Let me see this prodigy you've produced, instead of giving me so much flak." She was fully prepared to be acutely bored and was surprised to discover how sweet the baby was. Everything was tiny and perfect and she hesitated when Averil tried to hand him to her. "Oh, God . . . I'm afraid to break him in two. . . ."

"Don't be silly." Harry grabbed the baby easily from his wife and plopped him into Tana's arms, and she sat staring down at him, utterly amazed at how lovely he was, and when she handed him back, she felt as though she had lost something and she looked at them both almost enviously, so much so that when she left, he told Averil victoriously, "I think we got to her, Ave," and indeed she thought about them a great deal that night, but by the following week, she had another big rape case on her hands, and two big murder cases after that. And the next thing she knew, Harry called her victoriously. He had not only passed the bar, but he'd been offered a job, and he could hardly wait to start.

"Who hired you?" She was happy for him. He had worked hard for it. And now he laughed.

"You won't believe this, Tan. I'm going to work for the P.D."

"The public defender's office?" She laughed too. "You mean I have to try my cases against you?" They went out to lunch to celebrate and all they talked about was work. Marriage and babies were the last thing on her mind. And the next thing she knew, the rest of the year had flown by, and another one on its heels, trying murders and rapes and assaults and assorted other crimes. Only once or twice did she actually find herself working on the same case Harry was on, but they had lunch whenever they could, and he had been in the public defender's office for two years when he told her that Averil was pregnant again. "So soon?" Tana looked sur-

prised. It seemed as though Harrison Winslow V had
been born just moments before, but Harry smiled.

"He'll be two next month, Tan."

"Oh, my God. Is that possible?" She didn't see him
often enough, but even at that it seemed impossible. He
was going to be two. It was incredible. And she herself
was twenty-eight years old, which didn't seem so remarkable actually, except that everything had gone so fast. It
seemed like only yesterday when she was going to Green
Hill with Sharon Blake, and taking long walks with her
into Yolan. Only yesterday when Sharon was alive, and
Harry could dance. . . .

Averil had a baby girl this time, with a tiny pink
face, a perfect little mouth, and enormous almond-shaped
eyes. She looked incredibly like her grandfather, and
Tana felt an odd tug at her heart when she looked at her,
but again, it didn't feel like anything she could ever do
herself. She said as much to Harry when they had lunch
the following week.

"Why not, for chrissake? You're only twenty-nine
years old, or you will be in three months." He looked at
her seriously then. "Don't miss out on it, Tan. It's the
only thing I've ever done that really matters to me, the
only thing I really give a damn about . . . my children
and my wife." She was shocked to hear him say that. She
thought his career was more important to him than that,
and then she was even more startled to hear that he was
thinking of giving up his job with the P.D., and going
into practice for himself.

"Are you serious? Why?"

"Because I don't like working for someone else, and
I'm tired of defending those bums. They all did whatever

it is they claim they didn't do, or at least most of them anyway, and I'm just sick of it. It's time for a change. I was thinking of going into partnership with another lawyer I know."

"Wouldn't it be dull for you? Ordinary civil law?" She made it sound like a disease and he laughed as he shook his head.

"No. I don't need as much excitement as you do, Tan. I couldn't run the crusades you do every day. I couldn't survive that day in, day out. I admire you for doing it, but I'll be perfectly happy with a small comfortable practice, and Averil and the kids." He had never set his sights high, and he was happy with things just as they were. She almost envied him that. There was something deeper and hungrier that burned within her. It was the thing that Miriam Blake had seen in her ten years before, and it was still there. It wanted tougher cases, across-the-board convictions, it wanted harder and more, and greater challenges all the time. She was particularly flattered when, the following year, she was assigned to a panel of attorneys that met with the governor over a series of issues that affected the criminal processes all over the state. There were half a dozen lawyers involved, all of them male except for Tana, two of them from Los Angeles, two from San Francisco, one from Sacramento, and one from San Jose, and it was the most interesting week she thought she had ever spent. She was exhilarated day after day. The attorneys and the judges and politicians conferred long into the night, and by the time she got into bed every night, she was so excited about what they'd been talking about that she couldn't sleep for the next two hours. She lay awake running it all through her mind.

"Interesting, isn't it?" The attorney she sat next to on the second day leaned over and spoke to her in an undervoice as they listened to the governor discuss an issue she had been arguing about with someone the night before. He was taking exactly the position she had herself and she wanted to stand up and cheer.

"Yes, it is." She whispered back. He was one of the attorneys from Los Angeles. He was tall and attractive and had gray hair. They were seated next to each other at lunch the next day, and she was surprised to discover how liberal he was. He was an interesting man, from New York originally, he had gone to Harvard Law School, and had then moved to Los Angeles. "And actually, I've been living in Washington for the last few years, working with the government, but I just came back out West again, and I'm glad I did." He smiled. He had an easy way, a warm smile, and she liked his ideas when they talked again that night, and by the end of the week, all of them felt as though they had become friends. It had been a fascinating exchange of ideas for the past week.

He was staying at the Huntington. And he offered her a drink at L'Etoile before he left. Of all the people there, they had had the most thoughts in common, and Tana had found him a pleasant companion on the various panels they'd been on. He was hard working and professional, and pleasant almost all the time.

"How do you like working in the D.A.'s office?" He had been intrigued by that. Generally, the women he knew didn't like it there. They went into family practices, or other aspects of the law, but female prosecutors were rare everywhere, for obvious reasons. It was a damn tough job, and no one made things easy for them.

"I love it." She smiled. "It doesn't leave me much time for myself, but that's all right." She smiled at him, and smoothed back her hair. She still wore it long, but she wore it in a knot when she worked. She was given to wearing suits and blouses when she went to court, but she still lived in jeans at home. And she was wearing a gray flannel suit now, with a pale gray silk shirt.

"Married?" He raised an eyebrow and glanced at her hand, and she smiled.

"No time for that either, I'm afraid." There had been a handful of men in her life in recent years, but they never lasted long. She ignored them for weeks on end, preparing trials, and just never had enough time for them. It wasn't a loss that had bothered her very much, although Harry kept insisting she'd be sorry one day. "I'll do something about it then." "When? When you're ninety-five?"

"What were you doing in government, Drew?" His name was Drew Lands and he had the bluest eyes she'd ever seen. She liked the way he smiled at her, and she found herself wondering how old he was, and correctly guessed that he was around forty-five.

"I had an appointment to the Department of Commerce for a while. Someone died, and I was filling in until they made a permanent change." He smiled at her, and she realized again that she liked the way he looked, more than she had anyone in a long time. "It was an interesting job for a time. There's something incredibly exhilarating about Washington. Everything centers around the government, and the people involved with it. If you're not in

government, you're absolutely no one there. And the
sense of power is overwhelming. It's all that matters
there, to anyone." He smiled at her, and it was easy to see
that he had been part of that.

"That must be hard to give up." She was intrigued
by that, and she herself had wondered more than once if
she would be interested in politics, but she didn't really
think it would suit her as well as the law.

"It was time. I was happy to get back to Los Angeles." He smiled easily and put down his scotch again,
looking at her. "It almost feels like home again. And you,
Tana? What's home to you? Are you a San Francisco
girl?"

She shook her head. "New York originally. But I've
been here since I went to Boalt." It had been eight years
since she arrived, and that in itself was incredible, since
1964. "I can't imagine living anywhere else now . . . or
doing anything else. . . ." She loved the district attorney's office more than anything. There was always excitement for her there, and she had grown up a lot in her five
years on the job. And that was another thing . . . five
years as an assistant D.A. That was as hard to believe as
the rest . . . where did the time run to, while one
worked? Suddenly one woke up and ten years had drifted
past . . . ten years . . . or five . . . or one . . . it all
seemed the same after a while. Ten years felt like one felt
like an eternity.

"You looked awfully serious just then." He was
watching her, and they exchanged a smile.

She shrugged philosophically. "I was just thinking
how quickly time rushes by. It's hard to believe I've been

out here this long . . . and in the D.A.'s office for five
years."

"That was how I felt about Washington. The three
years felt more like three weeks, and suddenly it was time
to go home."

"Think you'll go back one day?"

He smiled, and there was something there she
couldn't quite read. "For a while anyway. My kids are
still there. I didn't want to pull them out of school halfway through the year, and my wife and I haven't resolved
yet where they're going to live. Probably half and half,
eventually. It's the only thing that's fair to us, although it
might be difficult for them at first. But kids adjust." He
smiled at her. He had obviously just gotten divorced.

"How old are they?"

"Thirteen and nine. Both girls. They're terrific kids,
and they're very close to Eileen, but they've stayed close
to me, too, and they're really happier in L.A. than they
are in Washington. That's not really much of a life for
kids back there, and she's awfully busy," he volunteered.

"What does she do?"

"She's assistant to the Ambassador to the OAS, and
actually she has her sights on an ambassadorial post herself. That'll make it pretty impossible to take the kids
with her, so I'd have them then. Everything is still pretty
much up in the air." He smiled again, but a little more
hesitantly this time.

"How long have you two been divorced?"

"Actually, we're working it out right now. We took
our time deciding while we were in Washington, and now
it's definite. I'm going to file as soon as things settle
down. I'm hardly unpacked yet."

She smiled at him, thinking of how difficult it had to be, children, a wife, traveling three thousand miles, Washington, Los Angeles. But it didn't seem to shake up his style. He had made incredible sense at the conference. Of the six attorneys involved, she had been most impressed with him. She had also been impressed with how reasonable he was about being liberal. Ever since her experiences with Yael McBee five years before, her liberalism had been curbed considerably. And five years in the D.A.'s office was making her less liberal by the hour. She was suddenly for tougher laws, tighter controls, and all the liberal ideas she had believed in for so long no longer made as much sense to her, but somehow Drew Lands made them palatable again, and even if the actual positions no longer appealed to her, he didn't alienate anyone expressing his views. "I thought you handled it beautifully." He was touched and pleased, and they had another drink, before he dropped her off at her place in his cab, and went on to the airport to go back to Los Angeles.

"Could I call you sometime?" He asked hesitantly, as though he were afraid there might be someone important to her, but at the moment there was no one at all. There had been a creative director in an ad agency for a few months the year before, and actually no one at all since then. He had been too busy and too harassed and so had she, and the affair had ended as quietly as it had begun. She had taken to telling people that she was married to her work, and she was the D.A.'s "other wife," which made her colleagues laugh. But it was almost true by now. Drew looked at her hopefully, and she nodded with a smile.

"Sure. I'd like that." God only knew when he'd be back in town again anyway. And she was trying a big Murder One case anyway for the next two months.

But he astounded her and called her the next day, as she sat in her office, drinking coffee and making notes, as she outlined her approach for the case. There was going to be a lot of press involved and she didn't want to make a fool of herself. She wasn't thinking of anything but the case when she grabbed the phone and barked into it. "Yes?"

"Miss Roberts please." He was never surprised by the rudeness of the people who worked for the D.A.

"That's me." She sounded playful suddenly. She was so damn tired, she was slaphappy. It was almost five o'clock, and she hadn't left her desk all day. Not even for lunch. She hadn't eaten anything since dining the night before, except for the gallons of coffee she'd consumed.

"It didn't sound like you." His voice was almost a caress, and she was startled at first, wondering if it was a crank call.

"Who's this?"

"Drew Lands."

"Christ . . . I'm sorry . . . I was so totally submerged in my work, I didn't recognize your voice at first. How are you?"

"Fine. I thought I'd give you a call and see how *you* were, more importantly."

"Preparing a big murder case I'm starting next week."

"That sounds like fun." He said it sarcastically and they both laughed. "And what do you do in your spare time?"

"Work."

"I figured as much. Don't you know that's bad for your health?"

"I'll have to worry about that when I take my retirement. Meanwhile, I don't have time."

"What about this weekend? Can you take a break?"

"I don't know . . . I . . ." She usually worked weekends, especially right now. And the panel had cost her a whole week she should have spent preparing her case. "I really should . . ."

"Come on, you can afford a few hours off. I thought I'd borrow a friend's yacht in Belvedere. You can even bring your work along, although it's a sacrilege." But it was late October then, and the weather would have been perfect for an afternoon on the Bay, warm and sunny with bright blue skies. It was the best time of the year, and San Francisco was lyrical. She was almost tempted to accept, but she just didn't want to leave her work undone.

"I really should prepare. . . ."

"Dinner instead . . . ? lunch . . . ?" And then suddenly they both laughed. No one had been that persistent in a long time and it was flattering.

"I'd really like to, Drew."

"Then, do. And I promise, I won't take more time than I should. What's easiest for you?"

"That sail on the Bay sounded awfully good. I might even play hooky for a day." The image of trying to juggle important papers in the breeze did not appeal to her, but an outing on the Bay with Drew Lands did.

"I'll be there, then. How does Sunday sound?"

"Ideal to me."

"I'll pick you up at nine. Dress warmly in case the wind comes up."

"Yes, sir." She smiled to herself, hung up, and went back to work, and promptly at nine o'clock Sunday morning, Drew Lands arrived, in white jeans, sneakers, a bright red shirt, and a yellow parka under his arm. His face already looked tan, his hair shone like silver in the sun, and the blue eyes danced as she followed him out to the car. He was driving a silver Porsche he had driven up from L.A. on Friday night, he said, but true to his word, he hadn't bothered her. He drove her down to the Saint Francis Yacht Club where the boat was moored, and half an hour later they were out on the Bay. He was an excellent sailor, and there was a skipper aboard, and she lay happily on the deck, soaking up the sun, trying not to think of her murder case, and suddenly glad she'd let him talk her into taking the day off.

"The sun feels good, doesn't it?" His voice was deep, and he was sitting on the deck next to her when she opened her eyes.

"It does. Somehow everything else seems so unimportant all of a sudden. All the things one scurries around about, all the details that seem so monumental, and then suddenly *poof* . . . they're gone." She smiled at him, wondering if he missed his kids a lot, and it was as though he read her mind.

"One of these days, I'd like you to meet my girls, Tana. They'd be crazy about you."

"I don't know about that." She sounded hesitant, and her smile was shy. "I don't know much about little girls, I'm afraid."

He looked at her appraisingly, but not accusingly. "Have you ever wanted children of your own?"

He was the kind of man one could be honest with and she shook her head. "No, I haven't. I've never had the desire, or the time," she smiled openly then, "or the right man in my life, not to mention the right circumstances."

He laughed. "That certainly takes care of pretty much everything, doesn't it?"

"Yup. What about you?" She was feeling breezy and carefree with him. "Do you want more?"

He shook his head, and she knew that that was the kind of man she would want one day. She was thirty years old and it was too late for children for her. She had nothing in common with them anyway. "I can't anyway, or not at least without going to an awful lot of trouble. Eileen and I decided when Julie was born that that was it for us. I had a vasectomy." He spoke of it so openly that it shocked her a little bit. But what was wrong with not wanting more kids? She didn't want any, and she didn't have any at all.

"That solves the problem anyway, doesn't it?"

"Yes," he smiled mischievously, "in more ways than one." She told him about Harry then, his two children, Averil . . . and when Harry came back from Vietnam, the incredible year of watching him fight for his life and go through surgery, and the courage he had had.

"It changed my life in a lot of ways. I don't think I was ever the same after that. . . ." She looked out over the water pensively, and he watched the sunlight dancing on her golden hair. ". . . it was as though things mattered so much after that. Everything did. You couldn't afford to take anything for granted after that." She sighed and looked at him. "I felt that way once before too."

"When was that?" His eyes were gentle as he looked at her and she wondered what it would be like to be kissed by him.

"When my college roommate died. We went to Green Hill together, in the South," she explained seriously and he smiled.

"I know where it is."

"Oh." She smiled back. "She was Sharon Blake . . . Freeman Blake's daughter, and she died on a march with Martin Luther King nine years ago. . . . She and Harry changed my life more than anyone else I know."

"You're a serious girl, aren't you?"

"Very, I guess. Maybe 'intense' is the right word. I work too hard, I think too much. I find it hard to turn all that off a lot of the time." He had noticed that, but he didn't mind that. His wife had been like that, too, and it hadn't bothered him. He hadn't been the one who wanted out. She was. She was having an affair with her boss in Washington, and she wanted some "time off," she said, so he gave it to her and came home, but he didn't want to go into details about that.

"Have you ever lived with anyone? I mean, romantically, not your friend, the Vietnam vet." It was funny to hear Harry referred to that way, it was so impersonal.

"No. I've never had that kind of relationship."

"It would probably suit you very well. Closeness without being tied down."

"That sounds about right."

"It does to me too." He looked pensive again, and then he smiled at her almost boyishly. "Too bad we don't

live in the same town." It was a funny thing to say so
soon, but everything happened quickly with him. In the
end, it turned out that he was just as intense as she said
she was. He came back to see her for dinner twice that
week, flying up from Los Angeles, and then flying back
afterwards, and the following weekend he took her sailing again, even though she was totally immersed in her
murder case and she was anxious for it to go well. But if
anything he soothed her, and made things easier for her,
and she was amazed at that. And after their second day
on the Bay in his friend's boat, he brought her home, and
they made love in front of the fire in her living room. It
was tender and romantic and sweet, and he made her
dinner afterwards. He spent the night, and remarkably,
he didn't crowd her at all. He got up at six o'clock,
showered, dressed, brought her breakfast in bed, and left
in a taxi for the airport at seven fifteen. He caught the
eight o'clock plane to Los Angeles, and was in his office
by nine twenty-five, looking neat as a pin. And within
weeks, he had established a regular commuting schedule,
almost without asking her, but it all happened so easily,
and made her life so much happier that she suddenly felt
as though her whole life had improved. He came to see
her in court twice and she won her case. He was there
when the verdict came in and took her out to celebrate.
He gave her a beautiful gold bracelet that day that he had
bought her at Tiffany in Los Angeles, and that weekend
she went down to Los Angeles to visit him. They had
dinner Friday and Saturday nights at the Bistro and Ma
Maison, and spent the days shopping on Rodeo Drive or
lounging around his swimming pool, and on Sunday
night, after a quiet dinner he cooked her himself on his

barbecue, she flew back to San Francisco alone. She
found herself thinking about him all the way home, about
how quickly she had gotten involved with him, and it was
a little frightening to think about, but he seemed so definite, so anxious to establish a relationship with her. She
was also aware of how lonely he was. The house he lived
in was spectacular, modern, open, filled with expensive
modern art, and with two empty rooms for his two girls.
But there was no one else there, and he seemed to want to
be with her all the time. By Thanksgiving she had grown
used to his spending half the week in San Francisco with
her, and after almost two months, it didn't even seem
strange to her anymore. It was the week before the holiday when he suddenly turned to her.

"What are you doing next week, sweetheart?"

"For Thanksgiving?" She looked surprised. She really hadn't thought of it. She had three small cases in her
files that she wanted to close out, if the defendants would
agree to making a deal. It would certainly make life simpler for her, and none of them were really worth taking
to trial. "I don't know. I haven't given it much thought."
She hadn't gone home in years. Thanksgivings with Arthur and Jean were absolutely unbearable. Ann had gotten divorced again several years before, and she lived in
Greenwich now, so she was on hand with her unruly
kids. Billy came and went if he had nothing better to do.
He hadn't gotten married yet. Arthur got more tiresome
with age, her mother more nervous, and she seemed to
whine a lot now, mostly about the fact that Tana had
never married and probably wouldn't now. "A wasted
life" was usually the headline of time spent with her, to
which Tana could only answer, "Thanks, Mom." The

alternative was Thanksgiving with Averil and Harry, but as much as she loved them, their friends in Piedmont were so painfully dull, with their little children and large station wagons. Tana always felt totally out of place with them, and infinitely glad she was. She marveled at how Harry could tolerate it. She and his father had laughed about it together one year. He couldn't stand it any better than Tana could, and he rarely appeared. He knew that Harry was happy, well cared for, and didn't need him, so he kept to the life he enjoyed.

"Want to go to New York with me?" Drew looked at her hopefully.

"Are you serious? Why?" She looked surprised. What was in New York for him? Both of his parents were dead, he had said, and his daughters were in Washington.

"Well," he had already thought it all out ahead of time, "you could see your family, I could stop off in Washington first to see the girls, and then meet you in New York and we could play a little bit. Maybe I could even bring them up with me. How does that sound?"

She thought about it and slowly nodded her head, her hair falling around her like a fan. "Possible." She smiled up at him. "Maybe even very possible, if you leave out the part about my family. Holidays with them are what drive people to suicide."

He laughed. "Don't be so cynical, you witch." He gently tugged a lock of hair and kissed her lips. He was so deliciously affectionate, she had never known a man like him before, and parts of her were opening up to him that had never opened up to anyone. She was surprised at how much she trusted him. "Seriously, could you get away?"

"Actually, right now I could." And that was unusual for her too.

"Well?" Stars danced in his eyes and she threw herself into his arms.

"You win. I'll even offer a visit to my mother up as a
sacrifice."

"You'll go to heaven for that for sure. I'll take care
of everything. We can both fly East next Wednesday
night. You spend Thursday in Connecticut, and I'll meet
you in New York on Thursday night with the girls at
. . . let's see . . ." He looked pensive and she grinned.
"The Hotel Pierre?" She fully intended offering to pay
her share, but he shook his head.

"The Carlyle. I always try to stay there if I can,
especially with the girls, it's nice for them up there." It
was also where he had gone with Eileen for the last nineteen years, but he didn't tell Tana that. He arranged everything, and Wednesday night found them on separate
planes, heading East, she wondering for a moment at
how easily she had let him make her plans for her. It was
sort of a novelty for her, no one had ever done that before, and he seemed to do it so well and so easily. He was
used to it. And when she arrived in New York, she suddenly realized that she was actually there. It was bitter
cold, and traces of the first snow were already on the
ground as she rode in the cab to Connecticut from John
F. Kennedy Airport. She was thinking of Harry as they
rode along, and the time he had punched Billy in the
face. She was sorry he wasn't there now. She was really
not looking forward to Thanksgiving with them. She
would have preferred to go to Washington with Drew,
but she didn't want to intrude on his private Thanksgiv-

ing with his girls after not seeing them for two months. Harry had invited her to join them in Piedmont, as he did every year, but she explained that she was going to New York this year.

"My God, you must be sick," he laughed.

"Not yet. But I will be by the time I leave. I can already hear my mother now . . . 'a wasted life. . . .' "

"Speaking of which, I wanted to introduce you to my associate, finally." He had started his own law firm after all, and Tana had never gotten around to meeting the other half. She just never had time, and they were actually surprisingly busy too. Things were going well for them on a small but pleasant scale. It was exactly what they had both wanted, and Harry was ecstatic about it whenever he talked to her.

"Maybe when I get back."

"That's what you always say. Christ, you're never going to meet him, Tan, and he's such a nice guy."

"Uh oh. I smell a blind date. Am I right? A hungry one even . . . oh, no!" She was laughing now, the way they used to in the old days and Harry laughed too.

"You suspicious bitch. What do you think, everyone wants to get into your pants?"

"Not at all. I just know you. If he's under ninety-five and has no objection to getting married, you want to fix him up with me. Don't you know I'm a hardened case, Winslow? Give up, for chrissake. Never mind, I'll have my mother call you from New York."

"Don't bother, you jerk. But you don't know what you're missing this time. He's *wonderful,* Averil thinks so too."

"I'm sure he is. Fix him up with someone else."

"Why? Are you getting married?"

"Maybe." She was teasing him, but his ears instantly perked up and she regretted saying it.

"Yeah? To who?"

"Frankenstein. For chrissake, get off my back."

"The hell I will. You're seeing someone, aren't you?"

"No . . . yes! . . . I mean no. Shit. Yes, but not seriously. Okay? Will that suffice?"

"Hell, no. Who is he, Tan? Is it serious?"

"No. He's just a guy I'm seeing like all of the others. That's all. Nice guy. Nice date. No big deal."

"Where's he from?"

"L.A."

"What's he do?"

"He's a rapist. I met him in court."

"Not cute. Try again." It was like being a hunted animal and she was getting annoyed at him.

"He's an attorney, now lay off, dammit. It's no big deal."

"Something tells me that it is." He knew her well. Drew was different from the others, but she didn't want to admit that yet, least of all to herself.

"Then you have your head up your ass, as usual. Now, give Averil my love, and I'll see you both when I get back from New York."

"What are you doing for Christmas this year?" He was half inviting and half prying, and she felt like hanging up on him.

"I'm going to Sugar Bowl, is that all right with you?"

"Alone?"

"Harry!" Of course not. She was going with Drew.

They had already decided that. Eileen was taking the girls to Vermont with her, so he would be alone, and the holidays were going to be difficult for him. They both expected it. But Tana wasn't going to tell Harry any of it. "Goodbye. See you soon."

"Wait . . . I wanted to tell you more about . . ."

"No!" She had finally hung up on him, and as she approached Greenwich in the cab, she smiled to herself, wondering what he'd think of Drew. She suspected that they'd like each other, even though Harry would give him the third degree, which was why she wanted to wait awhile. It was rare that she introduced any of her men to him. Only after she decided she didn't give a damn about them. But this time was different. . . .

Her mother and Arthur were waiting for her when she arrived, and it shocked her to see how much he had aged. Her mother was only fifty-two years old, which was still young, but Arthur was sixty-six now and he wasn't aging gracefully. The years of stress with his alcoholic wife had taken their toll, as had running Durning International, and it all showed now. He had had several heart attacks and a small stroke, and he looked terribly old and frail, and Jean was very nervous, watching him. She seemed to cling to Tana like a life raft in a troubled sea, and when Arthur went to bed that night, her mother came to her room and sat at the foot of the bed. It was the first time Tana had actually stayed at the house, and she had the newly decorated bedroom her mother had promised her. It was just too much trouble to stay in town, or at a hotel, and Tana knew her mother would have been terribly hurt. They saw too little of her as it was. Arthur only went to Palm Beach, to their condo-

minium there, and her mother didn't like to leave him to
fly out to San Francisco, so they only saw Tana when she
came East, which was more and more infrequently.

"Is everything all right, sweetheart?"

"Fine." It was better than that, but she didn't want
to say anything about it to Jean.

"I'm glad." She usually waited a day to start complaining about Tana's "wasted life," but this time she
didn't have much time so she would have to move fast,
Tana knew. "Your job's all right?"

"It's wonderful." She smiled and Jean looked sad. It
always depressed her that Tana liked her job as much as
she did. It meant she wouldn't be giving it up soon. She
still secretly thought that one day Tana would drop everything for the right man, it was hard for Jean to imagine that she wouldn't do that. But she didn't know her
daughter very well. She never really had, and she knew
her even less now.

"Any new men?" It was the same conversation they
always had, and Tana usually said no, but this time she
decided to throw her mother a small bone.

"One."

Jean's eyebrows shot up. "Anything serious?"

"Not yet." Tana laughed. It was almost cruel to
tease her that way. "And don't get excited, I don't think
it ever will be. He's a nice man, and it's very comfortable,
but I don't think it's more than that." But the sparkle in
her eyes said that she lied and Jean saw that too.

"How long have you been seeing him?"

"Two months."

"Why didn't you bring him East?"

Tana took a deep breath and hugged her knees on

the single guest bed, her eyes fixed on Jean's. "As a matter of fact, he's visiting his little girls in Washington." She didn't tell her that she was meeting him in New York the following night. She had let Jean think she was flying back out West. It gave her brownie points for coming home just for a day, and gave her the freedom to float around New York at will with Drew. She didn't want to drag him out to meet her family, especially not with Arthur and his offspring around.

"How long has he been divorced, Tana?" Her mother sounded somewhat vague as she glanced away.

"Awhile." She lied, and suddenly her mother's eyes dug into her.

"How long?"

"Relax, Mom. He's actually working on it right now. They just filed."

"How long ago?"

"A few months. For heaven's sake . . . relax!"

"That's exactly what you shouldn't do." She got off the foot of Tana's bed and suddenly paced the room nervously, and then stood glaring at Tana again. "And the other thing you shouldn't do is go out with him."

"What a ridiculous thing to say. You don't even know the man."

"I don't have to, Tana." She spoke almost bitterly. "I know the syndrome. The man doesn't even matter sometimes. Unless he's already divorced, with his papers in his hand, steer clear of him."

"That's the dumbest thing I ever heard. You don't trust anyone, do you, Mom?"

"I'm just a whole lot older than you are, Tan. And as sophisticated as you think you are, I know better than you. Even if he thinks he's going to get divorced, even if he's absolutely sure of it, he may not. He may be so totally wound up in his kids, for all you know, that he just can't divorce his wife. Six months from now, he could go back to her, and you'll be left standing there, in love with him by then, with no way out, and you'll talk yourself into sticking around for two years . . . five years . . . ten . . . and the next thing you know, you'll be forty-five years old, and if you're lucky," her eyes were damp, "he'll have his first heart attack and need you by then . . . but his wife may still be alive, and then you'll never have a chance at him. There are some things you can't fight. And most of the time, that's one of them. It's a bond that no one else can break for him. If he breaks it himself, or already has, then more power to you both, but before you get badly hurt, sweetheart, I'd like to see you stay out of it." Her voice was so compassionate and so sad that Tana felt sorry for her. Her life hadn't been much fun since she and Arthur had gotten married, but she had won him at last, after long, hard, desperately lonely years. "I don't want that for you, sweetheart. You deserve better than that. Why don't you stay out of it for a while, and see what happens to him?"

"Life is too short for that, Mom. I don't have much time to play games with anyone. I have too much else to do. And what difference does it make? I don't want to get married anyway."

Jean sighed and sat down again. "I don't understand why. What do you have against marriage, Tan?"

"Nothing. It makes sense if you want kids, I guess, or have no career of your own. But I do, I have too much else in my life to be dependent on anyone, and I'm too old for children, now. I'm thirty years old, and I'm set in my ways. I could never turn my life upside down for anyone." She thought of Harry and Averil's house which looked as though a demolition squad stopped to visit them every day. "It's just not for me." Jean couldn't help wondering if it was something she had done, but it was a combination of everything, knowing that Arthur had cheated on Marie, seeing how badly her mother had been hurt for so long, and not wanting that for herself, she wanted her career, her independence, her own life. She didn't want a husband and kids, she was sure of it. She had been for years.

"You're missing out on so much." Jean looked sad. What hadn't she given this child to make her feel like that?

"I just can't see that, Mom." She searched her mother's eyes for something she saw but didn't understand.

"You're the only thing that matters to me, Tan." She found that hard to believe and yet for years her mother had sacrificed everything for her, even putting up with Arthur's gifts of charity, just so she would have something more for her child. It tore at Tana's heart to remember that, and it reminded her of how grateful she should be. She hugged her mother tight, remembering the past.

"I love you, Mom. I'm grateful for everything you did for me."

"I don't want gratitude. I want to see you happy, sweetheart. And if this man is good for you, then wonderful, but if he's lying to you or himself, he'll break your heart. I don't want that for you . . . ever. . . ."

"It's not like what happened to you." Tana was sure of it, but Jean was not.

"How can you know? How can you be sure of that?"

"I just can. I know him by now."

"After two months? Don't be a fool. You don't know anything, any more than I did twenty-four years ago. Arthur wasn't lying to me then, he was lying to himself. Is that what you want, seventeen years of lonely nights, Tan? Don't do that to yourself."

"I won't. I've got my work."

"It's no substitute." But in her case it was, she substituted it for everything. "Promise me you'll think about what I said."

"I promise." She smiled and the two women hugged each other goodnight again. Tana was touched by her mother's concern, but she knew for certain that she was wrong about Drew. She went to sleep with a smile on her face, thinking of him and his little girls. She wondered what he was doing with them. She had the name of his hotel in Washington, but she didn't want to intrude on them.

The Thanksgiving dinner at the Durning home the next day was predictably dull for everyone, but Jean was grateful that Tana was there. Arthur was somewhat vague, and fell asleep twice in his chair, the maid gave him a gentle nudge, and eventually Jean helped him upstairs. Ann arrived with her three brats, who were even worse than they had been several years before. She was talking about marrying a Greek shipping magnate and Tana tried not to listen to her, but it was impossible. The only blessing of the day was that Billy had gone to Florida with friends instead of being there.

And by five o'clock Tana was checking her watch regularly. She had promised Drew she would be at the Carlyle by nine, and they hadn't called each other all day. She was suddenly dying to see him again, to look into his eyes, touch his face, feel his hands, peel away his clothes as she dropped her own. She wore a veiled smile as she went upstairs to pack her bags, and her mother came into the room as she did. Their eyes met in the large mirror over the chest of drawers, and Jean spoke to her first.

"You're going to meet him, aren't you?"

She could have lied to her, but she was thirty years old, what was the point? "Yes." She turned to face her mother across the room. "I am."

"You frighten me."

"You worry about things too much. This isn't a replay of your life, Mother, it's mine. There is a difference."

"Not always as much as we'd like to think, I'm afraid."

"You're wrong this time."

"I hope for your sake that I am." But she looked grief stricken when Tana finally called a cab, and rode into New York at eight o'clock. She couldn't get her mother's words out of her mind, and by the time she arrived at the hotel, she was angry with her. Why did she burden her with her own bad experiences, her disappointments, her pain? What right did she have to do that? It was like a blanket of cement one had to wear everywhere to prove that one had been loved, well, she didn't want to be loved that much. She didn't need it anymore. She wanted to be left alone to lead her own life now.

The Carlyle was a beautiful hotel, with thickly carpeted steps down to the lobby's marble floor, Persian rugs, antique clocks, handsome paintings on the walls, and gentlemen at the desk in morning coats. It was all from another world, and Tana smiled to herself. This was not her mother's life, it was her own. She was sure of that now. She gave Drew's name, and went upstairs to the room. He had not yet arrived, but they obviously knew him well. The room was as sumptuous as the lobby had promised it would be, with a sweeping view of Central Park, the skyline shimmering like jewels, more antiques, this time upholstered in a deep rose silk, heavy satin drapes, and a magnum of champagne waiting in a bucket of ice, a gift from the management. "Enjoy your stay" were the bellboy's final words, and Tana sat down on the handsome couch, wondering if she should run a bath for herself, or wait. She still wasn't sure if he was bringing the girls, but she thought he was. She didn't want to shock them by being undressed when they came. But an hour later, they had not yet arrived, and it was after ten o'clock when he finally called.

"Tana?"

"No, Sophia Loren."

He laughed. "I'm disappointed. I like Tana Roberts better than her."

"Now I know you're crazy, Drew."

"I am. About you."

"Where are you?"

There was the briefest pause. "In Washington. Julie has an awful cold, and we thought that Elizabeth might be coming down with the flu. I thought maybe I ought to wait here, and I might not bring them up at all. I'll come up tomorrow, Tan. Is that all right?"

"Sure." She understood, but she had also noticed the "we" that had snuck in. "*We* thought that Elizabeth. . . ." And she wasn't too crazy about that. "The room is fabulous."

"Aren't they wonderful? Were they nice to you?"

"They sure were." She looked around the room, "but it's no fun without you, Mr. Lands. Keep that in mind."

"I'll be there tomorrow. I swear."

"What time?"

He thought for a minute. "I'll have breakfast with the girls . . . see how they feel . . . that should make it ten o'clock. I could catch a noon plane . . . I'll be at the hotel by two without fail." That meant half the day was shot, and she wanted to say something about that, but thought wiser of it.

"All right." But she didn't sound pleased, and when she hung up the phone she had to push her mother's words out of her head again. She took a hot bath, watched television, ordered a cup of hot chocolate from room service, and wondered what he was doing in Washington, and then suddenly she felt guilty for what she hadn't said to him. It wasn't his fault the kids were sick. It was certainly a nuisance for them, but it was no one's fault. She picked up the phone and asked for the hotel where he was staying in Washington, but he wasn't there. She left a message that she had called, watched the late show, and fell asleep with the television still on. She woke up at nine o'clock the next day, and went out to discover that it was an absolutely gorgeous day. She went for a

long walk down Fifth Avenue, and over to Bloom-
ingdale's where she puttered for a while and bought a few
things for herself, a handsome blue cashmere sweater for
him, and gifts for the girls, a doll for Julie and a pretty
blouse for Elizabeth, and then she went back to the Carlyle to wait for him, but there was a message this time.
Both the girls were deathly ill, "will arrive Friday night,"
which he did not. Julie had a fever of one hundred and
five, and Tana spent another night at the Carlyle alone.
On Saturday she went to the Metropolitan, and on Saturday afternoon at five o'clock, he arrived finally, in time to
make love to her, order room service, apologize to her all
night, and take the plane back to San Francisco with her
the next day. It had been a great weekend for them in
New York.

"Remind me to do that again with you sometime,"
she said half sarcastically as they finished dinner on the
plane.

"Are you furious with me, Tan?" He had looked
miserable ever since he'd arrived in New York, consumed
with guilt toward her, worried about the girls, he talked
too much, too fast, and he wasn't himself for days.

"No, I'm disappointed more than furious. How was
your ex-wife by the way?"

"Fine." He didn't seem anxious to talk about her
and was surprised Tana had asked. It didn't seem an
appropriate subject for them, but she was haunted by her
mother's words. "What made you ask that?"

"Just curious." She took a mouthful of the dessert
on the tray, looking strangely cool as she glanced at him.
"Are you still in love with her?"

"Of course not. That's ridiculous. I haven't been in

love with her for years." He looked downright annoyed
and Tana was pleased. Her mother was wrong. As usual.
"You may not be aware of it, Tan," he hesitated, looking
pale, "but I happen to be in love with you." He looked at
her for a long time, and she watched his face searchingly.
And then at least she smiled, but she said nothing at all.
She kissed his lips, put down her fork, and eventually
closed her eyes for a nap. There was nothing she wanted
to say to him, and he was so oddly uncomfortable. It had
been a difficult weekend for both of them.

Chapter 15

December flew by, with a series of small cases on Tana's desk, and a number of parties she went to with Drew. He seemed to think nothing of flying up for the night, and sometimes he came just to have dinner with her. They shared delicious tender moments, quiet nights at home, and a kind of intimacy that Tana had never known before. She realized now how lonely she had been for so long. There had been her mad affair with Yael years before, and since then only casual relationships that came and went, without meaning much to her. But everything about Drew Lands was different. He was so sensitive, so intense, so thoughtful in small ways that meant a great deal to her. She felt surrounded and protected and alive, and they laughed most of the time. By the time the holidays came, he was excited about seeing his two little girls again. They were coming out from Washington to spend Christmas with him. He had cancelled his skiing trip to Sugar Bowl with her.

"Will you come down and spend some time with us, Tan?"

She smiled at him; she knew how crazy he was about his kids. "I'll try." She had a big case coming up, but she

was pretty sure it wouldn't actually go to trial for a while.
"I think I can."

"Do your best. You could come down on the twenty-
sixth, and we could spend a few days in Malibu." He was
renting a little weekend place there, but she was not surprised by that so much as by the date he had said . . .
the twenty-sixth . . . she realized then that he wanted
to be alone with the girls for the holidays. "Will you,
Tan?" He sounded like a little kid and she hugged him
tight and laughed at him.

"Okay, okay, I'll come down. What do you think
the girls would like?"

"You." They exchanged a smile and he kissed her
again.

He spent the week before getting everything ready
for them in L.A. Tana was trying to clean up the work on
her desk so she could take a few days off from the District Attorney's office, and she had lots of shopping to do.
She bought Drew a suede shirt, and a very expensive
briefcase that he'd seen and loved, the eau de cologne
that he wore, and a wild tie she knew he'd love. And she
bought each of the girls a beautiful doll at F.A.O.
Schwarz, some stationery, some barrettes, an adorable
sweat suit for Elizabeth that looked just like one Tana
had, and a rabbit made of real fur for the little one. She
wrapped all the gifts, and put them in a suitcase to take
to L.A. with her. She hadn't bothered with a tree this
year; she didn't really have time and there was no one to
see it anyway. She spent Christmas Eve with Harry and
Averil and their kids, and it was relaxing just being with
them. Harry had never looked better, and Averil looked
contented as little Harrison ran around waiting for Santa

Claus. They sliced carrots for the reindeer, put chocolate chip cookies out, a big glass of milk, and finally got him into bed. His sister was already asleep, and when he finally fell asleep too, Averil tiptoed into their rooms to look at them with a quiet smile, as Harry watched her go, and Tana watched him. It made her feel good just to see him like that, contented and alive. His life had turned out well, although it certainly wasn't what he had expected to do with his life. He glanced at Tana with a smile, and it was as though they both understood.

"Funny, isn't it, Tan, how life works out . . ."

"Yeah, it is." She smiled at him. They had known each other for twelve years, almost half their lives. It was incredible.

"I figured you'd be married in two years when I met you that first time."

"And I thought you'd die a hopeless degenerate . . . no . . . ," she looked pensive and amused, ". . . a playboy drunk . . ."

He laughed at the idea. "You've got me mixed up with my old man."

"Hardly." She still had a soft spot for Harrison, but Harry had never been quite sure of that. He had suspected it once, but he had never been sure, and his father had never let on to anything. Nor had Tan.

Harry looked at her oddly then. He hadn't expected to be spending Christmas with her this year, not after the hints she had dropped about Drew once or twice. He had the strangest feeling that it was serious for her, more so even than she would let on to him. "Where's your friend, Tan? I thought you were going to Sugar Bowl." She looked blank at first, but she knew instantly who he meant and he grinned. "Come on, don't pull that 'who do you mean' shit on me. I know you better than that."

She laughed at him. "All right, all right. He's in L.A. with his kids. We cancelled Sugar Bowl because his kids were coming out. I'm going down on the twenty-sixth." Harry thought that strange but he didn't say anything to her.

"He means a lot to you, doesn't he?"

She nodded cautiously, but she didn't meet his eyes. "He does . . . for whatever that's worth."

"What is it worth, Tan?"

She sighed and leaned back in her chair. "God only knows."

Harry kept wondering something and he finally had to ask. "How come you're not down there today?"

"I didn't want to intrude." But that wasn't true. He hadn't invited her.

"I'm sure you're not an intrusion to him. Have you met his kids yet?" She shook her head.

"Day after tomorrow will be the first time."

Harry smiled at her. "Scared?"

She laughed nervously. "Hell, yes. Wouldn't you be? They're the most important thing in his life."

"I hope you are too."

"I think I am."

And then Harry frowned. "He's not married, is he, Tan?"

"I told you before, he's in the process of getting a divorce."

"Then why didn't he spend Christmas with you?"

"How the hell do I know?" She was annoyed at the

persistent questions and she was beginning to wonder where Averil was.

"Didn't you ask?"

"No. I was perfectly comfortable like this," she glowered at him, "until now."

"That's the trouble with you, Tan, you're so used to being alone that it doesn't even occur to you to do things differently. You should be spending Christmas with him. Unless . . ."

"Unless what?" She was angry at him now. It was none of his business whether or not she spent Christmas with Drew, and she respected his need to be alone with his kids.

But Harry wasn't content to leave it alone. "Unless he's spending Christmas with his wife."

"Oh, for chrissake . . . what an asinine thing to say. You are the most cynical, suspicious son of a bitch I know . . . and I thought I was bad. . . ." She looked furious, but there was something else lurking in her eyes, as though he had hit a nerve. But that was ridiculous.

"Maybe you're not bad enough."

She stood up and didn't answer him. She looked for her bag, and when Averil finally came back, she found them both tense, but she didn't think anything of it. They were like that sometimes. She was used to them by now, they had their own special relationship and sometimes they fought like cats and dogs but they didn't mean any harm.

"What have you two been up to out here? Beating each other up again?" she smiled.

"I'm considering it." Tana glared irritatedly at her.

"It might do him good." All three of them laughed then.

"Harry's been making an ass of himself, as usual."

He suddenly grinned at her. "You make it sound as though I've been exposing myself."

Averil laughed. "Did you do that again, sweetheart?" And then finally Tana warmed up again.

"You know, you're the biggest pain in the neck in the world. World cup goes to you."

He bowed politely from his chair, and Tana went to get her coat. "You don't have to leave, Tan." He was always sorry to see her go, even when they disagreed. They still had a special bond between them. It was almost like being twins.

"I should go home and get organized. I brought home a ton of work."

"To do on Christmas Day?" He looked horrified, and she smiled.

"I have to do it sometime."

"Why don't you come here instead?" They were having friends over, his partner and another dozen or so, but she shook her head. She didn't mind being home alone, or at least so she said.

"You're weird, Tan." But he kissed her cheek and his eyes were filled with the love he felt for her.

"Have a good time in L.A." He wheeled beside her to the door and looked at her pensively. "And Tan . . . take care of yourself . . . Maybe I was wrong . . . but it doesn't hurt to be careful about things. . . ."

"I know." Her voice was soft again, and she kissed them both as she left. But driving home in the car, she found herself thinking about what he had said. She knew

he couldn't be right. Drew was *not* spending Christmas
with his wife . . . but nonetheless she *should* have been
spending it with him. She had tried to tell herself that it
didn't matter, but it did. And suddenly it reminded her of
all the lonely years she had felt so sorry for Jean
waiting for Arthur, sitting by the phone, hoping he would
call . . . they were never able to spend major holidays
together when Marie was alive, and even afterwards there
was always an excuse . . . his in-laws, his children, his
club, his friends . . . and there was poor Jean, with
tears in her eyes, holding her breath . . . waiting for
him. . . . Tana fought back the thoughts. It was *not* like
that with Drew. It was *not.* She wouldn't let it be. But the
next afternoon, as she worked, the questions kept coming
to her. Drew called her once, but it had been a very brief
call, and he sounded rushed. "I have to go back to the
girls," he had said hastily and then hung up on her.

And when she landed in Los Angeles the next day,
he was waiting for her at the airport, and he swept her
into his arms, and held her so tight she could barely
breathe.

"My God . . . wait . . . ! stop . . . !" But he
crushed her to him, and they were laughing and kissing
all the way to the parking lot as he juggled her bags and
packages, and she was ecstatic to see him. It had been a
lonely holiday without him after all. And she had secretly
wanted it to be different and exciting this year. She hadn't
even admitted that to herself, but suddenly she knew it
was true. And it was, it was wonderful driving into town
with him. He had left the girls at the house with a babysitter he knew, just so he could pick her up alone, and
spend a few quiet minutes with her.

". . . before they drive us both nuts." He looked at
her and beamed.

"How are the girls?"

"Wonderful. I swear they've doubled in size in the
last four weeks. Wait till you meet them, Tan." And she
was enchanted with them when she did. Elizabeth was
lovely and grown up and looked strikingly like Drew,
and Julie was a cuddly little ball who almost instantly
climbed onto Tana's lap. They loved the presents she had
brought, and they seemed to have no resistance to her,
although Tana saw Elizabeth looking her over more than
once. But Drew handled it remarkably well. He cut out
all the necking and the cuddly stuff. It was as though
they were just friends, spending a cozy afternoon. It was
obvious that he knew Tana well, but it would have been
impossible to guess the relationship they shared from the
way he behaved to her. And Tana wondered if he always
acted that way around the girls.

"What do you do?" Elizabeth was looking her over
again, and Julie was watching them both, as Tana smiled,
shaking back her mane of pale blond hair. Elizabeth had
envied her that since they first met.

"I'm an attorney like your dad. In fact, that's how
we met."

"So's my mom," Elizabeth was quick to add. "She's
assistant to the ambassador of the OAS in Washington,
and they might give her her own ambassadorship next
year."

"Ambassadorial post." Drew corrected her and
glanced at the three "girls."

"I don't want her to do that." Julie pouted. "I want
her to come back here to live. With Daddy." She stuck

her lower lip out defiantly, and Elizabeth was quick to add, "He could come with us wherever Mom's sent. It depends on where it is." Tana felt an odd feeling in her gut, and she looked at him, but he was doing something else, and Elizabeth went on. "Mom may even want to come back here herself, if they don't offer her the right job. That's what she said, anyway."

"That's very interesting." Tana noticed that her mouth felt dry, and she wished that Drew would regain control of the conversation again, but he didn't say anything. "Do you like living in Washington?"

"Very much." Elizabeth was painfully polite and Julie hopped into Tana's lap again, and smiled up into Tana's eyes.

"You're pretty. Almost as pretty as our mom."

"Thank you!" It was definitely not easy talking to them, and other than with Harry's children, it was rare for Tana to be in a spot like this, but she had to make the effort for Drew. "What'll we do this afternoon?" Tana felt almost breathless as she asked, desperate to divert them from the topic of his almost ex-wife.

"Mommy's going shopping on Rodeo Drive." Julie smiled up at her, and Tana almost gasped.

"Oh?" Her eyes turned towards Drew in astonishment and then back to them. "That's nice. Let's see, how about a movie? Have you seen *Sounder?*" She felt as though she were running up a mountain as fast as she could and she wasn't getting anywhere . . . Rodeo Drive . . . that meant she had come to Los Angeles with the girls . . . and why hadn't he wanted Tana to come down yesterday? Had he spent Christmas with her after all? The next hour seemed to trickle by as Tana chatted with the girls, and finally they ran outside to play, and Tana finally turned to him. Her eyes spoke volumes before her mouth said a word. "I take it your wife is in Los Angeles." She looked rigid and inside something had gone numb.

"Don't look at me like that." His voice was soft while his eyes avoided her.

"Why not?" She stood up and walked towards him. "Did you spend the holiday with her, Drew?" He couldn't avoid her now, she was standing directly in front of him. And she already assumed he had. And when he lifted his eyes to face her, she knew instantly that she was right and the girls had given him away. "Why did you lie to me?"

"I didn't lie to you. I didn't think . . . oh, for chrissake . . ." He looked at her almost viciously. She had cornered him. "I didn't plan it that way, but the girls have never had a Christmas with us separated before, Tan . . . it's just too damn hard on them . . ."

"Is it, now?" Her eyes and voice were hard, concealing the pain she felt inside . . . the pain he had inflicted on her by lying to her . . . "And just exactly when do you plan to let them get used to it?"

"*Goddammit,* do you think I like seeing my children hurt by this?"

"They look fine to me."

"Of course they do. That's because Eileen and I are civilized. That's the least we can give them now. It's not their fault things didn't work out for us." He looked at Tana sorrowfully and she had to fight the urge to sit down and cry, not for him or the girls, but for herself.

"Are you sure it's not too late to salvage it with Eileen?"

"Don't be ridiculous."

"Where did she sleep?" He looked as though he had received an electric shock.

"That's an inappropriate thing to ask, and you know it damn well."

"Oh, my God . . ." She sat down again, unable to believe how transparent he was. "You slept with her."

"I did *not* sleep with her."

"You did, didn't you?" She was shouting now and he strode around the room like a nervous cat as he turned to face her again.

"I slept on the couch."

"You're lying to me. Aren't you?"

"Goddammit, Tana! Don't accuse me of that! It isn't as easy as you think. We've been married for almost twenty years, Goddammit. . . . I can't just walk out on everything from one day to the next, and not when the girls are involved," he looked at her mournfully and then walked slowly to where she sat. "Please . . ." There were tears in his eyes. "I love you, Tan . . . I just need a little time to work this out. . . ." She turned away from him and walked across the room, keeping her back to him.

"I've heard that before." She wheeled to face him then, and there were tears in her eyes too. "My mother spent seventeen years listening to bullshit like that, Drew."

"I'm not giving you bullshit, Tan. I just need time. This is very difficult for all of us."

"Fine." She picked up her bag and coat from a

chair. "Then call me when you've recovered from it. I
think I'd enjoy you more then." But before she reached
the door, he grabbed her arm.

"Don't do this to me. Please . . ."

"Why not? Eileen is in town. Just give her a call.
She'll keep you company tonight." Tana smiled at him
sardonically to hide the hurt. "You can sleep on the
couch . . . together, if you like." She yanked open the
door and he looked as though he were going to cry.

"I love you, Tan." But as she heard the words, she
wanted to sit down and cry. And suddenly she turned to
him and her energy seemed to drain as she looked at him.

"Don't do this to me, Drew. It's not fair. You're not
free . . . you have no right to . . ." But she had opened
the door to her heart just wide enough for him to slip into
it again. Wordlessly, he pulled her into his arms, and
kissed her hard, and she felt everything inside her melt.
And when he pulled away from her, she looked at him.
"That doesn't solve anything."

"No." He sounded calmer now. "But time will. Just
give me a chance. I swear to you, you won't regret it."
And then he said the words that frightened her most. "I
want to marry you one day, Tan." She wanted to tell him
to stop, to move the film back to before he had said those
words, but it didn't matter anyway, the girls came running in, laughing and shouting and ready to play with
him and he looked over their heads at her and whispered
two words to her, "please stay." She hesitated. She knew
she should go back, and she wanted to. She didn't belong
here with them. He had just spent the night with the
woman he was married to, and they had had Christmas
with their two girls. Where did Tana belong in all this?

And yet when she looked at him, she didn't want to
leave. She wanted to be part of it, to be his, to belong to
him and the girls, even if he never married her. She didn't
really want that anyway. She just wanted to be with him,
the way they had been since they first met, and slowly she
put down her bag and coat and looked at him, and he
smiled at her, and her insides turned to mush, and Julie
hugged her around the waist while Elizabeth grinned at
her.

"Where were you going, Tan?" Elizabeth was curious, she seemed fascinated by everything that Tana did
and said.

"Nowhere." She smiled at the pretty adolescent
child. "Now, what would you girls like to do?" The two
girls laughed and teased and Drew chased them around
the room. She had never seen him as happy as this, and
later that afternoon they went to the movies, and ate
buckets of popcorn, then he took them to the La Brea
Tar Pits, and to Perino's for dinner that night, and when
they finally came home all four of them were ready to fall
into bed. Julie fell asleep in Drew's arms, and Elizabeth
made it into bed before falling asleep, too, and Tana and
Drew sat in front of a fire in the living room, whispering,
as he gently touched the golden hair he loved

"I'm glad you stayed, sweetheart . . . I didn't want
you to go. . . ."

"I'm glad I stayed too." She smiled at him, feeling
vulnerable and young, which didn't make sense for a
woman her age, at least not to her. She imagined that she
should be more mature than that by now, less sensitive.

But she was more sensitive to him than she had ever been to any man. "Promise it won't happen again. . . ." Her voice drifted off and he looked at her with a tender smile.

"Baby, I promise you."

Chapter 16

The spring Tana and Drew shared was so idyl-
ic it was almost like a fairy tale. Drew flew up roughly
three times a week, she went to L.A. every weekend.
They went to parties, sailed on the Bay, met each other's
friends. She even introduced him to Harry and Ave, and
the two men had gotten along splendidly. And Harry
gave her the okay when he took her out to celebrate the
following week.

"You know, kid, I think you finally did good for
yourself." She made a face and he laughed. "I mean it. I
mean, look at the guys you used to drag around. Remem-
er Yael McBee?"

"Harry!" She threw her napkin at him in the restaurant and they both laughed. "How can you compare
Drew to him? Besides, I was twenty-five years old. I'm
almost thirty-one now."

"That's no excuse. You're no smarter than you used
to be."

"The hell I'm not. You just said yourself . . ."

"Never mind what I said, you jerk. Now, are you
going to give me some peace of mind and marry the
guy?"

"No." She laughed, and she said it too fast, and Harry, looking at her, saw something he had never seen before. He had been looking for it for years, and suddenly there it was. He saw it as clearly as he saw the big green eyes, a kind of vulnerable, sheepish look she had never worn before for anyone.

"Holy shit, it's serious, isn't it, Tan? You're going to marry him, aren't you?"

"He hasn't asked." She sounded so demure that he roared.

"My God, you will! Wait till I tell Ave!"

"Harry, calm down." She patted his arm. "He isn't even divorced yet." But it didn't worry her. She knew how hard he was working on it. He told her every week about his meetings with his lawyer, his conversations with Eileen to speed things up, and he was going East to see the girls for Easter week, and hopefully she'd sign the settlement papers then, if they were drawn up in time.

"He's working on it, isn't he?" Harry looked momentarily concerned, but he had to admit, he liked the guy. It was almost impossible not to like Drew Lands. He was easygoing, intelligent, and it was easy to see he was crazy about Tan.

"Of course he is."

"Then relax, you'll be married six months from now, and nine months after that, you'll have a baby in your arms. Count on it." He looked thrilled and Tana sat back and laughed at him.

"Boy, do you have a wild imagination, Winslow. In the first place, he hasn't asked me to marry him yet, at least not seriously. And in the second place, he's had a vasectomy."

"So he'll have it reversed. Big deal. I know plenty of guys who've done that." But it made him a little nervous thinking about it.

"Is that all you think about? Getting people pregnant?"

"No," he smiled innocently, "just my wife."

She laughed and they finished the meal, and they both went back to their offices. She had an enormous case coming up, probably the biggest of her career. There were three murder defendants involved in the most gruesome series of murders committed in the state in recent years, and there were three defense attorneys and two prosecutors and she was in charge of the case for the D.A. There was going to be a lot of press involved and she had to really know her stuff, which was why she wasn't going East with Drew when he went to see the girls over the Easter holiday. It was probably just as well she didn't anyway. Drew would be a nervous wreck getting the papers signed, and she had the case on her mind. It made more sense to stay home and do her work than to sit around in hotel rooms waiting for him.

He came up to San Francisco to spend the weekend with her before he left, and they lay on the rug in front of the fire for hours on his last night, talking, thinking aloud, saying almost anything that came to mind, and she realized again how deeply she was falling in love with him.

"Would you ever consider marriage, Ian?" He looked pensively at her and she smiled in the firelight. She looked exquisite in the soft glow, her delicate features seeming to be carved in a pale peach marble, her eyes dancing like emeralds.

"I never have before." She touched his lips with her fingertips and he kissed her hands and then her mouth.

"Do you think you could be happy with me, Tan?"

"Is that a proposal, sir?" He seemed to be beating around the bush and she smiled at him. "You don't have to marry me, you know, I'm happy like this."

"You are, aren't you?" He looked at her strangely and she nodded her head.

"Aren't you?"

"Not entirely." His hair looked even more silvery, his eyes a bright topaz blue, and she never again wanted to love any man but him. "I want more than this, Tan . . . I want you all the time. . . ."

"So do I. . . ." She whispered the words to him, and he took her in his arms and made love to her ever so gently in front of the fire, and afterwards he lay for a long, long time and looked at her, and then finally he spoke, his mouth nestled in her hair, his hands still stroking the body he loved so much.

"Will you marry me when I'm free?"

"Yes." She said the word almost breathlessly. She had never said it to anyone, but she meant it now, and suddenly she understood what people felt when they promised . . . for better or worse . . . until death do us part. She never wanted to be without him again, and when she took him to the airport the next day, she was still a little overwhelmed by what she felt, and she looked at him searchingly. "Did you mean what you said last night, Drew?"

"How can you ask me something like that?" He looked horrified, and instantly crushed her against his chest as they stood in the terminal. "Of course I did."

She grinned at him, looking more like his thirteen-year-old child than the Assistant D.A. "I guess that means we're engaged then, huh?" And suddenly he laughed, and he felt as happy as a boy as he looked at her.

"It sure does. I'll have to see what kind of ring I can find in Washington."

"Never mind that. Just come back safe and sound." It was going to be an endless ten days of waiting for him. And the only thing that would help was her enormous case.

He called her two and three times a day for the first few days, and told her everything he did from morning till night, but when things began to get rough with Eileen, he called once a day and she could hear how uptight he was, but they had started jury selection by then, and she was totally engrossed in that, and by the time he got back to Los Angeles, she realized that they hadn't spoken to each other in more than two days. He had stayed longer than he had expected to, but it was for a "worthy cause," he said, and she agreed with him, and she could barely think straight anymore by then. She was too worried about the jury that was being picked, and the tack the defense was going to take, the evidence that had just turned up, the judge to whom they had been assigned. She had plenty on her mind, and one of Drew's rare litigation situations had occurred. Almost everything he did settled before it went to court, and this was a rare exception for him, and it kept him away from her for almost another week, and when they both finally met, they almost felt like strangers again. He teased her about it, asked if she had fallen in love with anyone else, and made passionate love to her all night long.

"I want you to be so bleary eyed all day in court that everyone wonders what the hell went on last night." And he got his wish. She was half asleep and she couldn't get him out of her mind she was so hungry for him. She never seemed to get enough of him anymore, and all through the trial, she was lonely for him, but it was too important to screw up and she kept her nose to the grindstone constantly. It went on till late May, and finally, in the first week in June, the verdict came in. It went just the way she had wanted it to, and the press gave her high praise as usual. Over the years, she had earned a reputation for being rigid, tough, conservative, merciless in court, and brilliant at the cases she tried. They were nice reviews to have, and it often made Harry smile when he read about her.

"I'd never recognize the liberal I knew and loved in this, Tan." He grinned broadly at her.

"We all have to grow up sometime, don't we? I'm thirty-one this year."

"That's no excuse to be as tough as you are."

"I'm not tough, Harry, I'm good." And she was right, but he knew it too. "Those people killed nine women and a child. You can't let people get away with something like that. Our whole society will fall apart. Someone has to do what I do."

"I'm glad it's you and not me, Tan." He patted her hand. "I'd lie awake at night, worrying that they'd get me eventually." He hated even saying it, and he worried about it sometimes for her, but it didn't seem to bother her at all. "By the way, how's Drew?"

"Fine. He's going to New York on business next week, and he's bringing the girls back with him."

"When are you getting married?"

"Relax." She smiled. "We haven't even talked about it since I started this case. In fact, I've hardly talked to him." And when she told him about her success before it hit the press, he sounded strange.

"That's nice."

"Well, don't get too excited. It might be bad for your heart."

He laughed at her. "All right, all right, I'm sorry. I had something else on my mind."

"What?"

"Nothing important." But he was that way until he left, and he sounded worse from the East, and when he got back to Los Angeles, he didn't call her at all. She almost wondered if something was wrong, or if she should fly down to surprise him and get everything on the right track again. All they needed was a little time alone to sort things out, they'd both been working too hard, and she knew all the signs. She looked at her watch late one night, trying to decide if she should catch the last plane down, and decided to call him instead. She could always go down the next day, and they had a lot of catching up to do after her two months of grueling work. She dialed the phone number she knew by heart, heard it ring three times, and smiled when it was picked up, but not for long. A woman's voice answered it.

"Hello?" Tana felt her heart stop, and she sat there endlessly staring into the night, and then hurriedly she put down the phone.

Her heart was pounding hideously, she felt dizzy,

awkward, disoriented, strange. She couldn't believe what
she had heard. She had to have dialed the wrong number,
she told herself, but before she could compose herself to
try again, the phone rang, and she heard Drew's voice,
and suddenly she knew. He must have known she'd
called and now he was panicking. She felt as though her
whole life had just come to an end.

"Who was that?" She sounded half hysterical, and
he sounded nervous too.

"What?"

"The woman who answered your phone." She
fought for composure but her voice was totally out of
control.

"I don't know what you mean."

"Drew! . . . answer me . . . ! Please . . ." She
was half crying, half shouting at him.

"We have to talk."

"Oh, my God . . . goddammit, what have you
done to me?"

"Don't be so melodramatic for chrissake . . ." She
cut him off with a shriek.

"Melodramatic? I call you at eleven o'clock at night
and a woman answers your phone, and you tell me I'm
being melodramatic? How would you like to have a man
answer you when you call me here?"

"Stop it, Tan. It was Eileen."

"Obviously." Instinctively, she had known.

"And where are the girls?" She didn't even know
why she had asked.

"In Malibu."

"In Malibu? You mean you're alone with her?"

"We had to talk." His voice sounded dead suddenly.

"Alone? At this hour? What the hell does that mean? Did she sign?"

"Yes, no . . . look, I have to talk to you. . . ."

"Oh, now you have to talk to me . . ." She was being cruel to him and now they were both beginning to sound hysterical. "What the fuck is going on down there?" There was an endless silence which he couldn't fill. Tana hung up and cried all night, and he arrived in San Francisco the next day. It was Saturday and he found her at home, as he knew he would. He used his key and let himself in, and he found her sitting mournfully on her deck looking out over the Bay. She didn't even turn when she heard him come in, but spoke to him with her back turned. "Why did you bother to come up?"

He knelt beside her and touched her neck with his fingertips. "Because I love you, Tan."

"No, you don't." She shook her head. "You love her. You always did."

"That's not true. . . ." But they both knew it was, in fact, all three of them did. "The truth is that I love both of you. That's an awful thing to say, but it's the truth. I don't know how to stop loving her, and at the same time I'm in love with you."

"That's sick." She continued to stare out at the Bay, passing judgment on him, and he tugged at her hair to make her look at him, and when she did, he saw tears on her face and it broke his heart.

"I can't help what I feel. And I don't know what to do about what's happening. Elizabeth almost flunked out of school, she's so upset about us, Eileen and me. Julie is having nightmares. Eileen quit her job at the OAS, she

turned down the ambassadorial post they tried to tempt
her with, and she came home, with the girls. . . ."

"They're living with you?" Tana looked as though
he had just driven a stake into her heart, and he nodded.
He didn't want to lie to her anymore. "When did all this
happen?"

"We talked about it a lot in Washington on Easter
week . . . but I didn't want to upset you when you were
working so hard, Tan . . ." She wanted to kick him for
what he'd said. How could he not tell her something like
that? "And nothing was sure. She did it all without consulting me, and just showed up last week. And now what
do you expect me to do? Throw them out?"

"Yes. You should never have let them in again."

"She's my wife, and they're my kids." He looked as
though he were on the verge of tears but Tana stood up
then.

"I guess that solves it then, doesn't it?" She walked
slowly to the door and looked at him. "Goodbye, Drew."

"I'm not leaving here like this. I'm in love with
you."

"Then get rid of your wife. It's as simple as that."

"No it's *not,* goddammit!" He was shouting now.
She refused to understand what he was going through.
"You don't know what it's like . . . what I feel . . .
the guilt . . . the agony . . ." He started to cry and she
felt sick as she looked at him. She turned away and had
to fight to speak above the tears in her own voice.

"Please go. . . ."

"I won't." He pulled her into his arms, and she tried
to push him away, but he wouldn't let her do that, and
suddenly, without wanting to, she succumbed, and they

made love again, crying, begging, shouting, railing at each other and the Fates, and when it was all over, they lay spent in each others' arms and she looked at him.

"What are we going to do?"

"I don't know. Just give me time."

She sighed painfully. "I swore I'd never do something like this . . ." But she couldn't bear the thought of losing him, nor he the pain of giving her up. They cried and lay in each other's arms for the next two days, and when he flew back to Los Angeles, nothing was solved, except they both knew it wasn't over yet. She had agreed to give him more time, and he had promised her he'd work it out, and for the next six months they drove each other mad with promises and threats, ultimatums and hysteria. Tana called and hung up on Eileen a thousand times. Drew begged her not to do anything rash. The children were even aware of what terrible shape he was in. And Tana began avoiding everyone, especially Harry and Averil. She couldn't bear the questions she saw in his eyes, the sweetness of his wife, the children which only reminded her of Drew's. It was an intolerable situation for all of them, and Eileen was even aware of it, but she said that she wasn't moving out again. She would wait for him to work it out, she wasn't going anywhere, and Tana felt as though she were going mad. She spent her birthday and the Fourth of July and Labor Day and Thanksgiving alone, predictably. . . .

"What do you expect of me, Tana? You want me to just walk out on them?"

"Maybe I do. Maybe that's exactly what I expect of you. Why should I be the one who's always alone? It matters to me too. . . ."

"But I've got the kids. . . ."

"Go fuck yourself." But she didn't say that for real until she had spent Christmas alone. He had promised to come up, both then and on New Year's Eve, and she sa and waited for him all night and he never came. She sa in an evening dress until nine A.M. on New Year's Day and then slowly, irrevocably, she took it off and threw i in the trash. She had bought the dress just for him. She had the locks changed the next day, and packed up al the things he'd left with her over the past year and a hal and had them sent to him in an unmarked box. And afte that she sent him a telegram which said it all. "Goodbye Don't come back again." And she lay drowning in he tears. For all the bravery, the final straw had almost bro ken her back, and he came flying up as soon as he bega to get the messages, the telegram, the package, he wa terrified that she might mean it this time, and when h tried his key in her lock, he knew she did. He drov frantically to her office and insisted on seeing her, and when he did her eyes were cold and the greenest he ha ever seen.

"I have nothing left to say to you, Drew." A part o her had died. He had killed it with the hopes that ha never been fulfilled, the lies he'd told to both of them, an most of all himself. She wondered now how her mothe had stood it for all those years without killing herself. I was the worst torture Tana had ever been through an she never wanted to go through it again, for anyone. An least of all for him.

"Tana, please. . . ."

"Goodbye." She walked out of her office and dow the hall, disappearing into a conference room, and sh

left the building shortly after that, but she didn't go home
for hours. And when she did, he was still waiting there,
outside, in the driving rain. She slowed her car, and she
saw him and drove off again. She spent the night in a
motel on Lombard Street, and the next morning when
she went back, he was sleeping in his car. When instinctively he heard her step, he woke and leapt out to talk to
her. "If you don't leave me alone, I'll call the police." She
sounded tough and threatening, looked furious to his
eyes, but what he didn't see was how broken she felt
inside, how long she sobbed once he was gone, how desperate she felt at the thought of never seeing him again.
She actually thought of jumping off the Bridge, but something stopped her when she thought of it and she didn't
even know what. And then, as though by miracle, Harry
sensed something wrong when he called repeatedly and
no one answered the phone. She thought it was Drew,
and she lay on the living room floor and sobbed, thinking
of the time when they had made love there and he had
proposed to her. And then suddenly there was a pounding on the door and she heard Harry's voice. She looked
like a derelict when she opened it, standing there in her
tear-stained face and bare feet, her skirt covered with lint
from the rug, her sweater all askew.

"My God, what happened to you?" She looked as
though she'd been drinking for a week, or had been
beaten up, or as though something terrible had happened
to her. Only the last was true. "Tana?" She dissolved in
tears as he looked at her, and he held her close to him as
she hovered awkwardly over his chair, and then he sat
her down on the couch and she told him her tale.

"It's all over now . . . I'll never see him again.
. . ."

"You're better off." Harry looked grim. "You can't
live like this. You've looked like shit for the past six
months. It's just not fair to you."

"I know . . . but maybe if I'd waited . . . I think
eventually . . ." She felt weak and hysterical, and suddenly she had lost her resolve and Harry shouted at her.

"No! Stop that! He's never going to leave his wife if
he hasn't by now. She came back to him seven months
ago, damn it, Tan, and she's still there. If he wanted out,
he'd have found the door by now. Don't kid yourself."

"I have been for a year and a half."

"That's how things go sometimes." He tried to
sound philosophical, but he wanted to kill the son of a
bitch who had done this to her. "You just have to pick
yourself up and go on."

"Oh yeah, sure . . ." She started to cry again, forgetting who she was talking to, "That's easy for you to
say."

He looked long and hard at her. "Do you remember
when you dragged me back to life by the teeth, and then
into law school the same way? Remember me? Well,
don't give me that shit, Tan. If I made it, so can you.
You'll live through it."

"I've never loved anyone like I loved him." She
whimpered horribly and it broke his heart as she looked
at him, with those huge green eyes. She didn't look more
than twelve years old and he wanted to make everything
all right for her, but he couldn't make Drew's wife disappear, although he would have liked to do that for her.
Anything for Tan, his best and dearest friend.

"Someone else will come along. Better than him."

"I don't want someone else. I don't want anyone." And Harry feared that more than anything.

And in the next year she set out to prove just that. She refused to see anyone except her colleagues at work. She went nowhere, saw no one, and when Christmas came, she even refused to see Averil and Harry. She had turned thirty two alone, had spent her nights alone, would have eaten Thanksgiving turkey alone, if she'd bothered to eat any at all, which she didn't. She worked overtime and double time and golden time and all the time, sitting at her desk until ten and eleven o'clock at night, taking on more cases than she ever had before, and for literally a year, she had no fun at all. She rarely laughed, called no one, had no dates with anyone, and took weeks to answer Harry's calls.

"Congratulations." He finally reached her in February. She had mourned Drew Lands for more than a year, and she had inadvertently learned through mutual friends that he and Eileen were still together and had just bought a beautiful new home in Beverly Hills. "Okay, asshole." Harry was tired of chasing her. "How come you don't return my calls anymore?"

"I've been busy for the last few weeks. Don't you read the papers? I'm waiting for a verdict to come in."

"I don't give a fuck about that, in case you're interested, and that doesn't account for the last thirteen months. You never call me anymore. I always call you. Is it my breath, my feet, or my IQ?" She laughed. Harry never changed.

"All of the above."

"Asshole. Are you going to go on feeling sorry for

yourself for the rest of your life? The guy wasn't worth it,
Tan. And a whole year is ridiculous."

"It had nothing to do with that." But they both
knew that wasn't true. It had everything to do with Drew
Lands, and his not leaving his wife.

"That's new too. You never used to lie to me."

"All right, all right. It's been easier not to see anybody."

"Why? You ought to celebrate! You could have done
what your mother did and sat there for fifteen years. Instead, you were smart enough to get the hell out. So what
did you lose, Tan? Your virginity? Eighteen months? So
what? Other women lose ten years over married men
. . . they lose their hearts, their sanity, their time, their
lives. You got off lucky if you ask me."

"Yeah." Somewhere in her heart, she knew he was
right, but it still didn't feel good yet. Maybe it never
would. She still alternated between missing him and being angry at him. It wasn't the indifference she would
have liked to feel, and she finally admitted that to Harry
when she let him take her to lunch.

"That takes time, Tan. And a little water over the
dam. You have to go out with some other people. Fill
your head with other stuff, not just him. You can't just
work all the time." He smiled gently at her, he loved her
so much, and he knew he always would. It wasn't like
what he felt for his wife. She was more like a sister to him
now. He remembered the tremendous crush he had had
on her for years and he reminded her of that now. "And I
survived."

"That wasn't the same thing. Shit, Drew had proposed marriage to me. He was the only man I'd ever even wanted to marry. Do you know that?"

"Yes, I do." He knew her better than anyone. "So, he's a jerk. We already know that. And you're a little slow. But you'll want to get married again. Someone else will come along."

"That's all I need." She looked revolted at the thought. "I'm too old. Teen romance is not my style anymore, thanks."

"Fine, then find some old fart who thinks you're cute, but don't sit around like this and waste your life."

"It isn't exactly wasted, Harry." She looked somberly at him. "I have my work."

"That's *not* enough. Christ, you're a pain." He looked at her and shook his head, and invited her to a party they were giving the following week, but she never showed up in the end. And he had to go on a campaign to drag her out of her shell again. It was as though she had been raped again. And then, to make matters worse, she lost a major case and got depressed about that. "Okay, okay, so you're not infallible. Give yourself a break for chrissake. Get off the cross. I know it's Easter week, but one's enough. Can't you find something else to do except torment yourself? Why don't you come spend a weekend in Tahoe with us?" They had just rented a house, and Harry loved going up there with the kids. "We can't go up for much longer anyway."

"Why not?" She glanced at him as he paid the check, and he smiled at her. She had given him a hard time for the past few months, but she was starting to come out of it.

"I can't take Averil up much longer. She's pregnant

again, you know." For a minute, Tana actually looked shocked and he laughed at her, and then blushed. "It's happened before, after all . . . I mean, it's not that remarkable. . . ." But they both knew it was. And suddenly Tana grinned at him. It was as if life had come back into focus again, and suddenly Drew Lands was gone and she wanted to shout and sing. It was like having had a toothache for over a year, and discovering miraculously that the tooth was gone.

"Well, I'll be damned. Don't you two ever stop?"

"Nope. And after this, we'll go for four. I want another girl this time, but Ave wants a boy." Tana was beaming at him, and she gave him a big hug as they left the restaurant.

"I'm going to be an aunt again."

"That's the easy way, if you ask me. Not fair, Tan."

"It suits me just fine." One thing she knew she didn't want was children, no matter what man wandered into her life. She didn't have time for that, and she was too old now anyway. She had made that decision long ago; her baby was the law. And she had Harry's children to spoil when she wanted someone little to sit on her lap. They were both adorable, and she was happy for them that a third one was coming along. Averil always had a pretty easy time, and Harry was always so proud of himself, and he could certainly afford as many as they chose to have. Only her mother disapproved when she talked to her.

"That seems awfully unreasonable to me." She was always opposed to everything these days; babies, trips, new jobs, new homes. It was as though she wanted to play out the rest of her life cautiously and thought everyone else should too. It was a sign of age which Tana recognized but her mother seemed too young for that. She had aged rapidly since she and Arthur had gotten married. Nothing had turned out quite right for her, and when she had gotten what she had wanted for so long, it was not the same as it had once been. Arthur was sick and getting old.

But Tana was happy for Harry and Ave, and when the baby came on November twenty-fifth, Averil got her wish. It was a bouncing, squalling boy. They named him after his great grandfather, Andrew Harrison, and Tana smiled down at him in his mother's arms and felt tears come to her eyes. She hadn't had that reaction to the others before, but there was something so sweet and touching about the baby's innocence, his perfect pink flesh, the big round eyes, the tiny fingers so gently curled. Tana had never seen such perfection, and all of it so small. She and Harry looked at each other and exchanged a smile, thinking of how far they had come, and he looked so proud, one hand tightly holding his wife's, and the other gently touching his son.

Averil went home the day after Andrew was born, and made the Thanksgiving dinner herself, as she always did, practically refusing any help at all, as Tana stared at her, amazed at all she did, and did so well.

"It kind of makes you feel dumb, doesn't it?" She was nursing in the window seat looking out at the Bay, and Tana looked at her as Harry grinned.

"You could do it too, Tan, if you wanted to."

"Don't count on it. I can barely boil myself an egg, let alone give birth, and cook a turkey two days later for my family, making it seem as though I had nothing to do all week. You'd better hang on to her, Harry, and don't get her knocked up again." She grinned at him, and she knew that they had never been happier. Averil just radiated happiness and so did he.

"I'll do my best. Will you come to the christening, by the way? Ave wants to do it on Christmas Day, if you're going to be here."

"Where else would I be?" She laughed at him.

"What do I know? You might go home to New York. I was thinking of taking the kids to Gstaad to see Dad, but now he says he's going to Tangiers with some friends, so that blows that."

"You're breaking my heart." She laughed at him. She hadn't seen Harrison in years, but Harry said he was all right. He seemed the kind of man who would be handsome and healthy for all his life. It was a little startling to realize that he was in his early sixties now, sixty-three, to be exact, Harry reminded her, though he didn't look more than half of it, Harry had told her. It was odd to remember how much Harry had once hated him, but he didn't anymore. It was Tana who had changed all that, and Harry never forgot any of it. He wanted her to be godmother again, and she was touched by it.

"Don't you have any other friends? Your kids are going to be sick to death of me by the time they grow up."

"Too bad for them. Jack Hawthorne is Andrew's godfather. At least you two will finally meet. He thinks you've been avoiding him." In all the years of Harry's partnership with him, the two had never met. But Tana had no reason to meet him, although she was curious to now. And when they met at St. Mary the Virgin Church on Union Street on Christmas Day, he was almost as she had expected him to be. Tall, blond, handsome, he looked like an all-American football player in a college game, and yet he looked intelligent as well. He was tall and broad and had enormous hands, and he held the baby with a gentleness that startled her. He was talking to Harry outside afterwards and she smiled at him.

"You do that awfully well, Jack."

"Thanks. I'm a little rusty, but I can still manage in a pinch."

"Do you have children?" It was casual conversation outside the church. The only other thing they could have talked about was law, or their mutual friend, but it was easier and more pleasant to talk about the new godchild that they shared.

"I have one. She's ten."

"That seems incredible." Ten seemed so old somehow . . . of course Elizabeth had been thirteen, but Drew had been a lot older than this man. Or at least he looked that way. Tana knew Jack was in his late thirties, but he had a boyish air. And at the party at Averil and Harry's house later that day, he told funny stories and jokes, and had everyone laughing, including Tana, for most of the day. She smiled at Harry when she found him in the kitchen pouring someone another drink. "No wonder you like him so much. He's a nice guy."

"Jack?" Harry didn't look surprised. Other than Tana and Averil, Jack Hawthorne was his best friend, and they had worked well together for the past few years. They had established a comfortable practice, and they worked in the same way, not with Tana's burning drive, but with something a little more reasonable. And the two men were well matched. "He's smart as hell, but he's very relaxed about it."

"I noticed that." At first he seemed very casual, almost indifferent to what was going on, but Tana had noticed rapidly that he was a lot sharper than he looked.

Eventually, at the end of the day, he offered her a ride home, and she accepted gratefully. She had left her own car outside the church in town. "Well, I finally meet the famous Assistant D.A. They certainly like to write about you, don't they?" She was embarrassed by what he said but he seemed unconcerned.

"Only when they have nothing else to do."

He smiled at her. He liked her modesty. He also liked the long, shapely legs peeking out beneath the black velvet skirt she wore. It was a suit she had bought at I. Magnin just for her godchild's christening day. "Harry is very proud of you, you know. I feel as though I know you myself. He talks about you all the time."

"I'm just as bad. I don't have kids, so everyone has to listen to stories about Harry and when we went to school."

"You two must have been hell on wheels back then." He grinned at her and she laughed.

"More or less. We had a hell of a good time, most of the time, anyway. And some nasty run-ins now and then." She smiled at the memories and then smiled at Jack. "I must be getting old, all this nostalgia. . . ."

"It's that time of year."

"It is, isn't it? Christmas always does that to me."

"Me too." She wondered where his daughter was, if that was part of the nostalgia for him. "You're from New

York, aren't you?" She nodded her head. That seemed light-years away too.

"And you?"

"I'm from the Midwest. Detroit, to be exact. A lovely place." He smiled and they both laughed again. He was easy to be with, and it seemed harmless to her when he offered to take her out for drinks. But everything seemed so empty when they looked around and it was depressing to go to a bar on Christmas night, she wound up inviting him back to her place instead, and he was perfectly agreeable to her. So much so he was almost innocuous, and she didn't even recognize him at first when she ran into him at City Hall the next week. He was one of those tall, blond, handsome men who could have been almost anyone, from a college pal, to someone's husband or brother or boyfriend and then suddenly she realized who he was and blushed with embarrassment.

"I'm sorry, Jack . . . I was distracted. . . ."

"You have a right to be." He smiled at her, and she was amused at how impressed he was by her job. Harry must have been lying to him again. She knew he exaggerated a lot about her, about the rapists she fought off in holding cells, the judo holds she knew, the cases she cracked herself without investigators' help. None of it true, of course. But Harry loved to tell tales, and especially war stories about her.

". . . Why do you lie like that?" She had challenged Harry more than once but he felt no remorse.

"Some of it's true anyway."

"The hell it is. I ran into one of your friends last

week who thought I had been knifed by a coke dealer in the holding cell. For chrissake, Harry, knock it off."

She thought of it now and assumed he had been at it again as she smiled at Jack. "Actually, things are pretty quiet right now. How 'bout you?"

"Not bad. We have a few good cases. Harry and Ave went up to Tahoe for a few weeks, so I'm holding the fort on my own."

"He's such a hardworking type." They both laughed and he looked at her hesitantly. He had been dying to call her for a week and he hadn't dared.

"You wouldn't have time for lunch, would you?" Oddly enough, for once she did. He was ecstatic when she said yes, and they went to the Bijou, a small French restaurant on Polk, which was more pretentious than good, but it was pleasant chatting with Harry's friend for an hour or so. She had heard about him for so many years, and between her heavy caseload and her turmoil over Drew Lands they'd never met.

"It's ridiculous, you know. Harry should have gotten us together years ago."

Jack smiled. "I think he tried." He didn't say anything that indicated he knew about Drew, but Tana could talk about it now.

"I was being difficult for a while." She smiled.

"And now?" He looked at her with the same gentle look he had used on their godchild.

"I'm back to my old rotten self again."

"That's good."

"Actually, Harry saved my life this time."

"I know he was worried about you for a while."

She sighed. "I made an ass of myself . . . I guess we all have to sometime."

"I sure did." He smiled at her. "I got my kid sister's best friend pregnant in Detroit ten years ago when I went home over the holidays. I don't know what happened to me, except I must have gone nuts or something. She was this pretty little redhead . . . twenty-one years old . . . and bang, the next thing I knew I was getting married. She hated it out here, she cried all the time. Poor little Barb had colic for the first six months of her life, and a year later, Kate went back again and it was all over. I now have an ex-wife and a daughter in Detroit, and I don't know anything more about them than I did then. It was the craziest thing I ever did, and I'm not about to do it again!" He looked extremely determined as he said the words, and it was easy to see that he meant every bit of it. "I've never drunk straight rum either since then." He grinned ruefully and Tana laughed.

"At least you have something to show for it." It was more than she could say, not that she would have wanted Drew's child, even if he hadn't had the vasectomy. "Do you see your daughter sometimes?"

"She comes out once a year for a month," he sighed with a careful smile. "It's a little difficult to build a relationship based on that!" He had always thought it was unfair to her, but what else could he do? He couldn't ignore her now. "We're really strangers to each other. I'm the oddball who sends her birthday cards every year and takes her to baseball games when she's here. I don't know what else to do with her. Ave was pretty good about keeping an eye on her in the daytime last year. And they lent me the house in Tahoe for a week. She loved

that," he smiled at Tana, "and so did I. It's awkward
making friends with a ten-year-old child."

"I'll bet it is. The relationship . . . the man I was
involved with had two of them, and it was odd for me. I
don't have children of my own, and it wasn't like Harry's
kids, suddenly here were these two big people staring at
me. It felt awfully strange."

"Did you get attached to them?" He seemed intrigued by her and she was surprised at how easy it was
to talk to him.

"Not really. There wasn't time. They lived in the
East," she remembered the rest of it, "for a while."

He nodded, smiling at her. "You've certainly managed to keep your life simpler than the rest of us." He
laughed softly then. "I guess you don't drink rum."

She laughed too. "Usually not, but I've managed to
do a fair amount of damage to myself in other ways. I
just don't have any children to show for it."

"Are you sorry about that?"

"Nope." It had taken thirty-three and a half years to
say it honestly. "There are some things in this life that
aren't for me, and children are one of them. Godmother
is more my style."

"I probably should have stuck to that myself, for
Barb's sake, if no one else's. At least her mother is remarried now, so she has a real father figure to relate to for the
eleven months I'm not around."

"Doesn't that bother you?" She wondered if he felt
possessive about the child. Drew had been very much so
about his, especially Elizabeth.

But Jack shook his head. "I hardly know the kid.
That's an awful thing to say, but it's true. Every year I

get to know her again, and she leaves and when she comes back she's grown up by a year and changed all over again. It's kind of a fruitless venture, but maybe it does something for her. I don't know. I owe her that much. And I suspect that in a few years she'll tell me to go to hell, she has a boyfriend in Detroit and she's not coming out this year."

"Maybe she'll bring him." They both laughed.

"God help me. That's all I need. I feel the way you do, there are some things in this life I never want inflicted on me . . . malaria . . . typhoid . . . marriage . . . kids. . . ." She laughed at his honesty, it was certainly not a popular view or one that one could admit to most of the time, but he felt he could with her, and she with him.

"I agree with you. I really think it's impossible to do what you do well and give enough to relationships like that."

"That sounds noble, my friend, but we both know that that has nothing to do with it. Honestly? I'm scared stiff, all I need is another Kate out from Detroit and crying all night because she has no friends out here . . . or some totally dependent woman with nothing to do all day except nag me at night, or decide after two years of marriage that half of the business Harry and I built is hers. He and I see too much of that as it is, and I just don't want any part of it." He smiled at her. "And what are you scared of, my dear? Chilblains, childbirth? Giving up your career? Competition from a man?" He was surprisingly astute and she smiled appreciatively at him.

"Touché. All of the above. Maybe I'm afraid of jeopardizing what I've built, of getting hurt . . . I don't know. I think I had doubts about marriage years ago,

although I didn't know it then. It's all my mother ever
wanted for me, and I always wanted to say 'but wait . .
not yet . . . I've got all these other things to do first.
It's like volunteering to have your head cut off, there's
never really a good time." He laughed, and she remembered Drew proposing to her in front of the fire one
night, and then she forced it from her with a flash of pain
Most of the time the memories of him didn't hurt much
now, but a few still did. And that one most of all, maybe
because she felt he had made a fool of her. She had been
willing to make an exception for him, she had accepted
the proposal and then he had gone back to Eileen. . .
Jack was watching her as she frowned.

"No one is worth looking that sad for, Tana."

She smiled at him. "Old, old memories."

"Forget them, then. They won't hurt you anymore.'

There was something wonderfully easy and wise
about the man, and she began going out with him almost
without thinking about it. A movie, an early dinner, a
walk on Union Street, a football game. He came and
went, and became her friend, and it wasn't even remarkable when they finally went to bed with each other late
that spring. They had known each other for five months
by then, and it wasn't earth shattering, but it was comfortable. He was easy to be around, intelligent, and he
had a wonderful understanding of what she did, a powerful respect for her job, they even shared a common best
friend, and by summertime when his daughter came out,
even that was comfortable. She was a sweet eleven-year-
old child with big eyes and hands and feet and bright red
hair, like an Irish setter puppy. They took her to Stinson
Beach a few times, went on picnics with her. Tana didn'

have much time—she was trying a big case just then—but it was all very pleasant, and they went up to Harry's place where Harry eyed them carefully, curious as to whether it was serious with them. But Averil didn't think it was and she was usually right. There was no fire, no passion, no intensity, but also no pain. It was comfortable, intelligent, amusing at times, and extremely satisfying in bed. And at the end of a year of going out with him, Tana could well imagine herself going out with Jack for the rest of her life. It was one of those relationships one saw between two people who had never married, and never wanted to, much to the chagrin of all their friends who had been in and out of divorce courts for years, one saw people like that eating in restaurants on Saturday nights, going on holidays, attending Christmas parties and gala events, and enjoying each other's company, and sooner or later they'd wind up in bed, and the next day the other one would go home to his or her own place, to find the towels exactly the way they wanted them, the bed undisturbed, the coffee pot in perfect readiness for their needs. It was so perfect for both of them that way, but they drove Harry nuts and that amused them too.

"I mean, look at you both, you're so goddamn complacent I could cry." The three of them were having lunch, and neither Tana nor Jack looked concerned.

She looked up at Jack with a smile. "Hand him a handkerchief, sweetheart."

"Nah, let him use his sleeve. He always does."

"Don't you have any decency? What's wrong with you?"

They exchanged a bovine glance. "Just decadent, I guess."

"Don't you want kids?"

"Haven't you ever heard of birth control?" Jack looked at him and Harry looked as though he wanted to scream as Tana laughed.

"Give it up, kid. You aren't gonna win this one with us. We're happy like this."

"You've been dating for a year. What the hell does that mean to you both?"

"That we have a lot of stamina. I now know that he gets homicidal if anyone touches the sports section on Sundays and he hates classical music."

"And that's it? How can you be so insensitive?"

"It comes naturally." She smiled sweetly at her friend and Jack grinned at her.

"Face it, Harry, you're outnumbered, outclassed, outdone." But when Tana turned thirty-five six months later, they surprised Harry after all.

"You're getting *married?*" Harry barely dared to breathe the words to Jack when he told him they were looking for a house, but Jack laughed at him.

"Hell no, you don't know your friend Tan if you think there's even a chance of that. We're thinking about living together."

Harry spun his wheelchair around, glaring at Jack. "That's the most disgusting thing I've ever heard. I won't let you do that to her."

Jack roared. "It was her idea, and besides—you and Ave did it." His daughter had just gone home, and it had gotten very complicated going back and forth from his house to hers for a month. "Her place is too small for both of us, and so is mine. And I'd really like to live in Marin. Tana says she would too."

Harry looked miserable. He wanted a happy ending, ice, rose petals, babies, and neither of them was cooperating with him. "Do you realize how complicated it is to invest in real estate if you're not married?"

"Of course I do, and so does she. That's why we'll probably rent." And it was exactly what they did. They found the house they wanted with an overwhelming view, a Tiburon. It had four bedrooms, and was dirt cheap compared to what it might have cost, and it gave them each an office, a bedroom for them, and a bedroom for Barb when she came to town from Detroit, or if they had guests. It had a lovely sun deck, a porch, a hot tub, which looked out at the view, and neither of them had ever been happier. Harry and Averil came to check it out with the kids, and they had to admit that the setting was beautiful but it still wasn't what Harry had hoped for her, but she only laughed at him. And worst of all, Jack shared all of her views. He had no intention of getting hooked into marriage again, by anyone. He was thirty-eight years old, and his little escapade in Detroit twelve years before had cost him dearly.

Jack and Tana did Christmas dinner that year, and it was beautiful, with the Bay below, and the city shimmering in the distance. "It's like a dream, isn't it, sweetheart?" Jack whispered to her after everyone went home. They had exactly the life that suited them, and she had even finally given up her own apartment in town. She had hung onto it for a while to play it safe, but in the end, she had let it go. She was safe with him, and he took good care of her. When she had appendicitis that year, he took two weeks off from work to take care of her. When she turned thirty-six, he gave her a party in the Trafalgar

Room at Trader Vic's for eighty-seven of her closest
friends, and the following year, he surprised her with a
cruise in Greece. She came home rested and brown, and
happier than ever with their life. There was never any
talk of marriage between the two, although once in a
while they talked about buying the house in which they
lived, but Tana wasn't even sure about that, and secretly
Jack was leary of it too. Neither of them wanted to rock
the boat that had sailed along so comfortably for so long.
They had lived together for almost two years and it was
perfect for them both. Until October after the cruise to
Greece. Tana had a big case coming up, and she had
stayed up almost all night going over her notes and the
files, and she'd fallen asleep at her desk, looking out over
the Bay in Tiburon. The phone woke her before Jack did
with her cup of tea, and she stared at him as she picked it
up.

"Huh?" She looked blank and Jack grinned at her.
She was a mess when she stayed up all night like that,
and as though hearing his thoughts, she turned her eyes
toward him, and then suddenly he saw them open wide
and stare at him. "What? Are you crazy? I'm *not* . .
oh, God. I'll be there in an hour." She put down the
phone and stared at him as he set down the cup of tea
with a worried frown.

"Something wrong?" It couldn't be anything back
home if she'd promised to be there in an hour, it had to
be work . . . and it wasn't for him. "What happened,
Tan?" She was still staring at him.

"I don't know. . . . I have to talk to Frye."

"The district attorney?"

"No. God. Who the hell do you think?"

"Well, what are you getting so excited about?" He till didn't understand. But neither did she. She had done a fantastic job. It just didn't make sense. She'd been there or years . . . there were tears in her eyes when she looked at Jack and stood up at her desk, spilling the tea across her files, but she didn't even care now.

"He said I'm being fired." She started to cry and sat down again as he stared at her.

"That can't be, Tan."

"That's what I said . . . the D.A.'s office is my whole life. . . ." And the saddest thing of all was that they both knew it was true.

Chapter 17

Tana showered, dressed, and drove into the city within the hour, her face set, eyes grim. It was obvious that it was an emergency. She looked as though someone had died. Jack offered to go with her, but she knew he had his own problems that day, and Harry had been out of the office a lot recently, so everything rested on him.

"Are you sure you don't want me to drive you in, Tan? I don't want you to have an accident." She kissed him vaguely on the lips and shook her head. It was so odd. They had lived together for so long, but they were almost more friends than anything else. He was someone to talk to at night, share her problems with, talk about her cases with, as she worked on her strategy. He understood her life, her quirks, he was content with the life they shared and he wanted relatively little from her, it seemed. Harry claimed it was unnatural, and it was certainly different from what he and Averil shared. But she felt Jack's concern now as she started her car and he watched her leave. He still couldn't understand what had happened to her, and neither could she. She walked into her office, feeling numb, half an hour later, and without even knocking walked into the office of the D.A. She couldn't hold the tears back anymore, and they rolled down her face as she looked at him.

"What the hell did I do to deserve this?" She looked stricken and he felt instant remorse at what he'd done. He had just thought it would be fun to give her the news in a roundabout way, but he never realized she'd be so heartbroken. It made him all the sorrier to lose her now. But he had been sorry anyway.

"You're too good at your job, Tan. Stop crying and sit down." He smiled at her and she felt even more confused.

"So you're firing me?" She was still on her feet, staring at him.

"I didn't say that. I said you were out of a job." She sat down with a thump.

"Well, what the hell does that mean?" She reached into her handbag and pulled out a handkerchief and blew her nose. She was unashamed of how she felt. She loved her job, and she had from the first day. She'd been in the D.A.'s office for twelve years. That was a lifetime to give up now, and she would have preferred to give up anything but that. Anything. The district attorney felt sorry for her then, and he came around his desk to put an arm around her.

"Come on, Tan, don't take it so hard. We're going to miss you, too, you know." A fresh burst of tears escaped from her and he smiled. It brought tears to his eyes too. She would be leaving soon, if she accepted it. And she had suffered long enough. He forced her to sit down, looked her square in the eye. "You're being offered a seat

on the bench, sweetheart. Judge Roberts of the Municipal
Court. How does that sound to you?"

"I am?" She stared at him, unable to absorb it all. "*I
am?* I'm not being fired?" She started to cry all over
again, and she blew her nose again, suddenly laughing at
the same time. "I'm not . . . you're kidding me. . . ."

"I wish I were." But he looked delighted for her and
she suddenly gave a small scream, realizing what he'd
done to her.

"Oh, you son of a bitch . . . I thought you were
firing me!" He laughed.

"I apologize. I just thought I'd create a little excitement in your life."

"Shit." She looked at him in disbelief and blew her
nose again but she was too stunned at what he was telling
her to even be angry at him. "My God . . . how did
that happen?"

"I've seen it coming for a long time, Tan. I knew it
would happen eventually. I just didn't know when. And
I'll lay you odds you're in superior court by this time
next year. You're perfect for it after your track record
here."

"Oh, Larry . . . my God . . . an appointment to
the bench . . ." The words were almost beyond her ken.
"I just can't believe it." She looked up at him. "I'm
thirty-seven years old, and I never even thought of that."

"Well, thank God someone did." He held out a hand
and shook hers as she beamed. "Congratulations, Tan,
you deserve every bit of it. They want to induct you in
three weeks."

"So soon? What about my work . . . Christ, I have
a case that goes to trial on the twenty-third . . ." She

knit her brows and he laughed at her and waved a hand magnanimously.

"Forget it, Tan. Why don't you take some time off, and get ready for the new job? Just dump it all on someone else's desk for a change. Use this week to wrap up and then get yourself sorted out at home."

"What do I have to do?" She still looked stunned and he smiled at her. "Shop for robes?"

"No." He laughed. "But I think you may have some house hunting to do. Do you still live in Marin?" He knew she'd lived with someone for the past couple of years, but he wasn't sure if she'd kept her own place in town or not. She nodded at him. "You've got to have a place in town, Tan."

"How come?"

"It's a condition of being a San Francisco judge. You can keep the other place, but your main residence has to be here."

"Do I really have to stick to that?" She looked upset.

"Pretty much. During the week anyway."

"Christ." She stared into space for a minute, thinking of Jack. Suddenly her whole life had turned upside down. "I'll have to do something about that."

"You've got plenty to do in the next few weeks, and first of all you have to respond." He put on an official voice. "Tana Roberts, do you accept the seat on the bench that has been offered you, to serve as a municipal court judge in the city and county of San Francisco?"

She looked at him in awe. "I do."

He stood up and smiled at her, happy at the good fortune that had befallen her so deservedly. "Good luck,

Tan. We'll miss you here." Tears sprang to her eyes again and she was still in shock when she went back to her own desk and sat down. There were a thousand things she had to do. Empty her desk, look over her caseload, brief someone else about the cases she was passing on, call Harry, tell Jack . . . Jack . . . ! she suddenly looked at her watch and grabbed the phone. The secretary said he was in a meeting but Tana told her to get him anyway.

"Hi, babe, you okay?"

"Yes." She sounded breathless on the phone. She didn't know where to start. "You won't believe what happened, Jack."

"I wondered what the hell was going on when they called you at home. What is it, Tan?"

She took a deep breath. "They just offered me a seat on the bench." There was total silence at the other end.

"At your age?"

"Isn't that incredible?" She was beaming now. "I mean, would you believe . . . I never thought. . . ."

"I'm happy for you, Tan." He sounded quiet, but pleased, and then she remembered what the D.A. had said. She had to find a place in town, but she didn't want to tell him that on the phone.

"Thank you, sweetheart. I'm still in shock. Is Harry there?"

"No, he's not in today."

"He's sure out a lot lately, isn't he? What's up?"

"I think he's in Tahoe with Ave and the kids for a long weekend. You can call him there."

"I'll wait till he gets back. I want to see his face." But the face she didn't want to see was Jack's when she told him she had to move out of Marin.

"I wondered about that after you called." He looked sad when she told him that night. He was obviously upset and so was she, but she was terribly excited too. She had even called her mother, and Jean had been stunned. "My daughter, a judge?" She had been thrilled for Tana. Maybe things did work out in the end, and she had met Jack once and he seemed nice to her. She hoped they would get married eventually, even if Tana was too old for children now. But as a judge, maybe that didn't matter as much. Even Arthur had been thrilled for her. Jean had explained it to him several times.

Tana looked at Jack now. "How do you feel about living in town during the week?"

"Not great." He was honest with her. "It's so damn comfortable for us here."

"I thought I'd look for something small that we don't have to worry about. An apartment, a condo, a studio, even. . . ." As though she could pretend it wasn't happening but he shook his head.

"We'd go nuts after all the room we're used to here." For two years they had lived like kings, with a huge master bedroom, offices for each of them, a living room, dining room, guest room for Barb, sweeping view of the Bay. A studio would feel like a jail cell after that.

"Well, I've got to do something, Jack, and I only have three weeks." She looked faintly annoyed at him, he wasn't making it easier for her, and she wondered if the appointment bothered him. It would be natural that it would, at least at first, but she hardly had time to think of that in the next few weeks. She divided her case load up, emptied her desk, and ran around looking at every condo available until the real estate agent called halfway into the second week. She had something "very special" she wanted Tana to see, in Pacific Heights.

"It's not exactly what you had in mind, but it's worth a look." And when she went, it was more than that. It was a dollhouse that took her breath away, a tiny gingerbread jewel, painted beige with dollops of cinnamon and cream. It was absolutely impeccable, with inlaid floors, marble fireplaces in just about every room, huge closets, perfect lighting, double French doors, and a view of the Bay. Tana would never have thought of looking for something like it, but now that she was here, there was no way she could resist.

"How much is the rent?" She knew it would be ferocious. The place looked like something out of a magazine.

"It's not for rent." The agent smiled at her. "It's for sale." She told her the price, and Tana was amazed at how reasonable it was. It wasn't cheap, but it wouldn't have destroyed her savings at one blow, and at the price that was being asked, it was actually a good investment for her. It was irresistible in every possible way, and it was perfect for her. One large bedroom on the second floor, a dressing room with mirrored walls, a tiny den with a brick fireplace, and downstairs, one large, beautiful living room and a tiny country kitchen that gave out onto a patio framed with trees. She signed away her life, put the deposit down, and turned up in Jack's office, looking nervous about what she'd done. She knew it wasn't a mistake, but still . . . it was such an independent thing to do, so solitary, so grown up . . . and she hadn't asked him.

"Good Lord, who died?" He stepped into the anteroom and saw her face, as she laughed nervously. "That's better." He kissed her neck. "You practicing to be a judge? You're going to scare people half to death running around with a face like that."

"I just did a crazy thing." The words tumbled out and he smiled. He had had a rough day, and it wasn't even two o'clock yet.

"So what else is new? Come on in and tell me about it." Tana saw that Harry's door was closed, and she didn't knock. She passed right into Jack's large, pleasant room in the Victorian they'd bought five years before. That had been a good investment for them, maybe it would help make him understand what she'd done. He smiled at her from across his desk. "So what'd you do?"

"I think I just bought a house." She looked like a frightened kid and he laughed at her.

"You *think* you did. I see. And what makes you think that?" He sounded as he always did, but his eyes were different now and she wondered why.

"Actually, I signed the papers . . . oh Jack . . . I hope I did the right thing."

"Do you like it?"

"I'm in love with it." He looked surprised, neither of them had wanted to own a house before. They had talked about it several times. They had no need of permanence, and he hadn't changed his mind. But apparently she had and he wondered why. A lot seemed to have changed in the last ten days, mostly for her. Nothing had changed for him.

"Won't that be a lot of trouble for you, Tan? Keeping it up, worrying about a leaky roof, and all that stuff we talked about before and didn't want."

"I don't know . . . I guess . . ." She looked ner-

vously at him. It was time to ask. "You'll be there too,
won't you?" Her voice was frightened and soft and he
smiled at her. She was at once so vulnerable and soft, and
yet so incredibly powerful as well. He loved that about
her and knew he always would. It was what Harry loved
in her, too, that and her loyalty, her fierce heart, bright
mind. She was such a lovely girl, judge or not. She looked
like a teenager sitting there, watching him.

"Is there room in it for me?" His voice sounded
tentative and she nodded vehemently, as her hair swung
wild. She had cut it straight to her shoulders only weeks
before she got the news, and it looked very elegant and
sleek, hanging in a smooth blond sheet from crown to
nape.

"Of course there is." But he wasn't sure he agreed
when he saw the place that night. He agreed that the
place was beautiful, but it was awfully feminine to his
eyes. "How can you say a thing like that? There's nothing
here but walls and floors."

"I don't know. It just feels that way, maybe because
I know it's your house." He turned to her and he looked
sad all at once. "I'm sorry, Tan, it's beautiful . . . I
don't mean to rain on your parade."

"It's all right. I'll make it comfortable for both of us.
I promise you." He took her to dinner that night and
they talked for hours, about her new job, the "judges'
school" she would have to attend in Oakland for three
weeks, holed up in a hotel with other recent appointees.
Everything seemed suddenly exciting and new, and she
hadn't felt that way in years.

"It's like starting life all over again, isn't it?" Her
eyes danced as she looked at him and he smiled at her.

"I guess." They went home after that and made love, and nothing seemed to have changed in important ways. She spent the next week shopping for furniture for her new house, closing the deal, and buying a new dress for her induction ceremony. She had even asked her mother to come out, but Arthur wasn't well enough and Jean didn't want to leave him alone. But Harry would be there, and Averil, and Jack, and all the friends and acquaintances she had collected over the years. In the end, there were two hundred people at the ceremony, and Harry gave her a reception afterwards at Trader Vic's. It was the most festive occasion she had ever been to, and she laughed as she kissed Jack halfway through the afternoon.

"It's kind of like getting married, isn't it?" He laughed back at her and they exchanged a look which said they both understood.

"Better than that, thank God." They laughed again and he danced with her, and they were both a little drunk when they went home that night, and the following week, she started "judges' school."

She stayed at the hotel, in the room they had given her, and she had planned to spend weekends in Tiburon with Jack, but there was always something to do at her new house, a painting she wanted to hang, lights she had to fix, a couch that had arrived, a gardener she wanted to interview, and for the first two weeks she slept in town when she wasn't at "judges' school."

"Why don't you come sleep here with me?" There was a plaintive note in her voice and she sounded irritable. He hadn't seen her in days but that was par for the course these days. She had too much else to do.

"I've got too much work to do." He sounded curt.

"You can bring it here, sweetheart. I'll make some soup and a salad, you can use my den." He noticed the possessive term, and like everything else these days, it rankled him, but he had a lot on his mind just then.

"Do you know what it's like to drag all your work over to someone else's house?"

"I'm not someone else. I'm me. And you live here too."

"Since when?" She was hurt by his tone and she backed off, and even Thanksgiving was strained, spent with Harry and Averil and the kids.

"How's the new house, Tan?" Harry was happy about everything that had happened to her, but she noticed that he looked tired and drawn, and Averil looked strained too. It was a difficult day for everyone and even the children whined more than usual, and Jack and Tana's godchild cried most of the day. She sighed as they drove back to town at last, and Jack visibly unwound in the silence in the car.

"Doesn't it make you glad you don't have kids?" He looked at her as he spoke and she smiled at him.

"Days like this do, but when they're all dressed up and cute, or sound asleep, and you watch Harry look at Ave . . . sometimes I think it would be sweet to be like that. . . ." She sighed then and glanced at him. "I don't think I could stand it, though."

"You'd look cute on the bench, with a string of kids." He said it sarcastically and she laughed. He had been sharp with her a lot recently and she noticed that he was driving her into town and not to Tiburon, and she looked at him, surprised.

"Aren't we going home, sweetheart?"

"Sure . . . I thought you wanted to go back to your place. . . ."

"I don't mind . . . I . . ." She took a deep breath. It had to be said eventually. "You're mad at me for buying the house, aren't you?"

He shrugged and drove on, keeping his eyes on the other cars. "I guess it was something you had to do. I just didn't think you'd do something like that."

"All I did was buy a little house because I had to have a place in town."

"I just didn't think you wanted to *own* something, Tan."

"What difference does it make if I own or rent? It's a good investment this way. We've talked about doing something like that."

"Yeah, and we decided not to. Why do you have to get yourself locked into something permanent?" The thought of that almost gave him hives. He was happy renting where they were in Tiburon. "You never thought like that before."

"Things change sometimes. This just made sense at the time, and I fell in love with it."

"I know you did. Maybe that's what bothers me. It's so 'yours,' not ours."

"Would you rather have bought something with me?" But she knew him better than that and he shook his head.

"That would just complicate our lives. You know that."

"You can't keep things simple all the time. And as those things go, I think we've done damn well. We're the

most unencumbered people I know." And they had done
it purposely. Nothing was permanent, written in stone.
Their whole life could be unwound in a matter of hours,
or so they thought, at least it was what they had told
themselves for two years.

Tana went on, "Hell, I used to have an apartment in
town. What's the big deal?" But it wasn't the house, it
was her job, she had begun to suspect it weeks before. It
bothered him, the fuss, the press, he had tolerated it before because she was only an assistant D.A., but suddenly
she was a judge . . . Your Honor . . . Judge Roberts,
she had noticed the look on his face everytime someone
said the words to her. "You know, it really isn't fair of
you to take it out on me, Jack. I can't help it. Something
wonderful happened and now we have to learn to live
with it. It could have happened to you too. The shoe
could be on the other foot, you know."

"I think I'd have handled it differently."

"How?" She was instantly hurt by his words.

"Actually," he looked at her accusingly, the anger
between them finally had words put to it, like a sym-
phony with a chorale, but it was a relief to get it out. "I
think I'd have turned it down. It's a goddamn pompous
thing to do."

"Pompous? What an awful thing to say. Do you
think I'm pompous for accepting the seat they offered
me?"

"Depends on how you handle it." He answered
cryptically.

"Well?"

They stopped at a light and he turned to look at her,
and then suddenly looked away. "Look . . . never mind

. . . I just don't like the changes it's made for us. I don't like you living in town, I don't like your goddamn house, I don't like any of it."

"So you're going to punish me, is that it? Christ, I'm doing my best to handle it gracefully, give me a chance. Let me figure it out. It's a big change for me, too, you know."

"You'd never know it to look at you. You look happy as can be."

"Well, I am happy." She was honest with him. "It's wonderful and flattering and interesting, and I'm having fun with my career. It's very exciting for me, but it's also scary and new, and I don't quite know how to handle it and I don't want it to hurt you. . . ."

"Never mind that. . . ."

"What do you mean, never mind? I love you, Jack. I don't want this to destroy us."

"Then it won't." He shrugged and drove on, but neither of them was convinced, and he remained impossible for the next few weeks. She made a point of spending the night in Tiburon whenever she could, and she cajoled him constantly, but he was angry at her, and the Christmas they spent at her house was grim. He made it clear that he hated everything about her house, and he left at eight o'clock the next day, claiming he had things to do. He made life difficult for her for the next few months, and in spite of it, she enjoyed her job. The only thing she didn't like were the long hours she kept. She stayed in her chambers until midnight sometimes, but she had so much to learn, so many points of law to read and refer to for each case. So much depended on her that she became blind to almost all else, so much so that she didn't see how unwell Harry looked, never realized how seldom he went to work anymore, and it was late April before Jack turned to her and screamed.

"What are you, blind? He's dying, for God's sake. He has been for the last six months, Tan. Don't you give a shit about anyone else anymore?" His words cut her to the quick and she gaped at him in horror.

"That's not true . . . he can't be. . . ." But suddenly the pale face, the ghostly eyes, all of it suddenly made sense. But why hadn't he told her? Why? She looked up at Jack accusingly. "Why didn't you say something?"

"You wouldn't have heard. You're so fucking wrapped up in how important you are these days, you don't see anything that goes on." They were bitter accusations, angry words, and without saying a word she left Tiburon that night and drove home to her own house, called Harry on the phone, and before she could say anything, she began to cry.

"What's the matter, Tan?" He sounded tired, and she felt as though her heart were going to break.

"I can't . . . I . . . oh God, Harry. . . ." All the pressures of the past months suddenly began to pile up on her, Jack's anger, and what he had told her that night about Harry being ill. She couldn't believe he was dying, but when she saw him the next day for lunch, he looked at her quietly and told her it was true. She felt her breath catch as though on a sharp nail and she stared at him. "But that can't be true . . . that's not fair. . . ." She sat there and sobbed like a little child, unable to comfort him, desolate, in too much pain herself to help anyone and he wheeled to where she sat and put his arms around

her. There were tears in his eyes, too, but he was
strangely calm. He had known for almost a year, and
they had told him that a long time ago: his wounds could
cut his life short, and they were. He was suffering from
hydronephrosis, which was devouring him by degrees as
he headed towards kidney failure. They had tried everything they could, but his body was just quietly giving up.
She looked at him with terror in her eyes. "I can't live
without you."

"Yes, you can." He was more worried about Averil
and the kids. He knew Tana would survive. She had
saved him. She would never give up. "I want you to do
something for me. I want you to make sure Ave is all
right. The kids are all set, and she has everything she'll
need, but she's not like you, Tan . . . she's always been
so dependent on me."

She stared at him. "Does your father know?"

He shook his head. "No one does, except Jack and
Ave, and now you." He was angry that Jack had said
something to her and especially in anger, but he wanted a
promise from her now. "You promise you'll keep an eye
on her?"

"Of course I will." It was hideous, he was talking as
though he were planning to leave on a trip. She looked at
him and twenty years of love raced before her eyes . . .
the dance where they had met . . . the years at Harvard
and BU . . . coming West . . . Vietnam . . . the hospital . . . law school . . . the apartment they had
shared . . . the night his first child was born . . . it
was incredible, impossible. His life wasn't over yet, it
couldn't be. She needed him too much. But then she remembered the spate of bladder infections and she knew

suddenly where all this would lead—he was dying. She
began to cry again and he held on to her, and then she
looked at him and sobbed. "Why? . . . It's not fair."

"Damn little in life is." He smiled at her, a small,
gray, wintry smile. He didn't care so much for himself as
he did for his wife and kids. He had been worried sick
about them for months, and he was trying to teach Averil
to handle everything herself, to no avail. She was totally
hysterical, and she refused to learn anything, as though
that way she could keep it from happening, but nothing
would. He was getting weaker by the day, and he knew it
himself. He only came in to the office now once or twice a
week; it was why he was never there when she went in to
see Jack from time to time, and she talked to him about
that now.

"He's beginning to hate me now." She looked so
bleak that it frightened him. He had never seen her like
that. These were difficult times for all of them. He still
couldn't believe he was going to die, but he knew he
would. It was like stuffing running out of a rag doll, he
felt as though he were slowly disappearing until he would
be no more one day. Only that. They would wake up and
he would be gone. Quietly. Not with the squall and the
pushes and the screams with which one comes into the
world, but with a tear and sigh and a breath of air as one
passes on into the next life, if there even was such a thing.
He didn't even know that anymore, and he wasn't sure he
cared. He was too worried about the people he was leaving behind, his partner, his wife, his children, his friends.
They all seemed to be resting on him and it was exhausting for him. But in some ways it also kept him alive, like
right now with Tana. He felt he had something to share

with her, before he went. Something important for her. He wanted her to change her life before it was too late. And he had said the same thing to Jack, but he didn't want to hear.

"He doesn't hate you, Tan. Look, the job is threatening to him. Besides, he's been upset about me for the past few months."

"He could have said something at least."

"I made him swear he wouldn't, you can't blame that on him. And as for the rest, you're an important woman now, Tan. Your job is more important than his. That's just the way things are. It's difficult for both of you, and he'll have to adjust to it."

"Tell him that."

"I have."

"He punishes me for what's happened. He hates my house, he's not the same man."

"Yes he is." Too much so for Harry's taste. He was still devoted to the same ridiculous things; staying unattached, a total lack of commitment or permanence. It was an empty life, and Harry had told him so often enough, but Jack only shrugged. He liked the way he lived, or at least he had until Tana's new job came along. That was giving him a major pain in the ass, and he made no bones about it to Harry. "Maybe he's jealous of you. That's not attractive, but it's possible, and he's human, after all."

"So when will he grow up? Or do I have to resign?" It was a relief talking about normal things, as though the nightmare weren't happening, as though she could make it stop by talking about something else with him. Like the

old days . . . they had been so sweet . . . tears filled
her eyes as she thought of them. . . .

"Of course you don't have to resign. Just give him
time." And then he looked at Tana, with something else
on his mind. "I want to say something to you, Tan. Two
things." He looked at her so intensely it was as though
his whole body turned to flame, she could feel the
strength of his words boring right into her soul. "I don't
know from one day to the next what tomorrow will
bring, if I'll be here . . . if . . . I have two things to
say to you, and it's all I have to leave you, my friend.
Listen well. The first is thank you for what you did for
me. The last sixteen years of my life have been a gift from
you, not from my doctor, or anyone else, but from you.
You forced me to live again, to go on . . . if it weren't
for you I'd never have met Averil, or had the kids. . . ."
There were tears in his eyes now, too, and they rolled
slowly down his cheeks. Tana was grateful that they had
met in her chambers for lunch. They had needed to be
alone. "And that brings me to the second thing. You're
cheating yourself, Tan. You don't know what you're
missing, and you won't know till you're there. You're
depriving yourself of marriage, commitment, real love
. . . not borrowed, or rented, or temporary, or kind of. I
know that fool's in love with you and you love him but
he's devoted to 'hanging loose,' to not making a mistake
again and that's the biggest mistake of all. Get married,
Tan . . . have kids . . . it's the only thing that makes
sense in life . . . the only thing I care about . . . the
only important thing I'm leaving behind . . . no matter
who you are or what you do, until you have that and are
that and give that, you are nothing and no one . . .

you're only half alive. . . . Tana, don't cheat yourself
. . . please. . . ." He was crying openly now. He had
loved her so much for so long and he didn't want her to
miss what he and Averil had shared. And as he spoke to
her, her mind went instantly to the countless looks she
had watched them share, the quiet joy, the laughter that
never seemed to end . . . and would end so soon now,
and deep in her heart she had always known that what he
said was true, in some ways she had wanted it for herself,
and in other ways she was scared . . . and the men in
her life had always been wrong for that . . . Yael McBee
. . . Drew Lands . . . and now Jack . . . and the people who didn't matter in between. There had never been
anyone who might have come close. Maybe Harry's father would have, but that was so long ago now . . . "If
the opportunity ever comes, grab it, Tan. Give up everything, if you have to. But if it's the right thing, you
won't."

"What do you propose I do? Go out on the street
and wear a sign? 'Marry me. Let's have kids.' " They
laughed together, for a moment, just like old times.

"Yeah, asshole, why not?"

"I love you, Harry." The words sprang from her and
she was crying again and he held her tight.

"I'll never really be gone, Tan. You know that. You
and I had too much to ever lose that . . . just like Ave
and I do in a different way. I'll be here, keeping an eye on
things." They were crying openly and she didn't think
she could live without him. And she could only imagine
how Averil felt. It was the most painful time of their
lives, and for the next three months, they watched him
roll slowly downhill, and on a warm summer day, with

the sun high in the sky, she got the call. It was from Jack. There were tears in his voice, and she felt her heart stop. She had seen Harry only the night before. She went to see him every day now, no matter what, at lunchtime or at night, or sometimes before her day began. She never knew how hectic things would get, but she wouldn't give that up. And he had held her hand and smiled just the night before. He could barely talk, but she had kissed his cheek, and suddenly thought of the hospital so long ago. She wanted to shake him back to life, to make him fight for what he had been, but he couldn't anymore, and it was easier to go.

"He just died." Jack's voice broke, and Tana began to cry. She wanted to see him just once more . . . to hear him laugh . . . see those eyes . . . She couldn't speak for a minute, and then she nodded her head and took a breath to fight back the sobs.

"How's Ave?"

"She seems all right." Harrison had arrived the week before and he was staying with them. Tana looked at her watch.

"I'll go over there right now. I just called a recess for the afternoon anyway." She could feel him tense at her words, as though he felt she were showing off for him. But that was what she did. She was a municipal court judge, and she had called a recess. "Where are you?"

"I'm at work. His father just called."

"I'm glad he was there. Are you going over now?"

"I can't for a little while." She nodded, realizing that if she had said that, he would have said something unpleasant to her about how important she thought she was. There was no winning with him now and Harry hadn't been able to soften him before he died, no matter how hard he tried. There had been so much he wanted to say, so much to share with those he loved. And it was over so soon. Tana drove over the Bay Bridge with tears streaming down her face, and then suddenly, it was as though she felt him next to her and she smiled. He was gone, but he was everywhere now. With her, with Ave, with his father, his kids . . .

"Hi, kid." She smiled into the air as she drove, and the tears continued to flow and when she arrived at the house, he was already gone. They had taken him to prepare him for the services, and Harrison was sitting in the living room, looking stunned. He looked suddenly very old, and Tana realized he was almost seventy now. And with grief etched on his still handsome face, he looked even older than that. She said nothing at all, she just went to him, and they held each other tight, and Averil came out of the bedroom after that, wearing a simple black dress, her blond hair pulled back and her wedding ring on her left hand. Harry had given her some beautiful things from time to time, but she wore nothing now— only her grief and her pride and their love, as she stood surrounded by the life and the home and the children they had shared. She looked oddly beautiful as she stood there, and in a strange way Tana envied her. She and Harry had shared something that few people ever had, for however long, and it had been worth everything to them. And suddenly, for the first time in her life, she felt a void. She was sorry that she hadn't married him a long time before, or someone else . . . gotten married . . . had kids . . . it left an aching hole in her that refused to be filled. All through the services, at the cemetery as they left him there, and afterwards, when she was alone again, she felt something she couldn't have explained to anyone, and when she tried to tell Jack, he shook his head and stared at her.

"Don't go crazy now, Tan, just because Harry died." She had told him that she suddenly felt her life was a waste because she had never married and had kids. "I've done both, and believe me it doesn't change a damn thing. Don't kid yourself, not everyone has what they did. In fact, I've never known anyone who did, except them. And if you got married looking for that, you'd be disappointed, because it wouldn't be there."

"How do you know that? It might." She was disappointed by what he said.

"Take my word for it."

"You can't make a judgment on that. You knocked up some twenty-one-year-old girl and got married lickety split because you had to. That's different from making an intelligent choice at our age."

"Are you trying to put pressure on me, Tan?" He suddenly looked angrily at her, and all the handsome blond good looks seemed suddenly drawn and tired. Losing Harry had been rough on him too. "Don't do that to me now. This isn't the time."

"I'm just telling you what I feel."

"You feel like shit because your best friend just died. But don't go getting all romantic about it, and the secret of life being marriage and kids. Believe me, it's not."

"How the hell do you know that? You can't decide for anyone but yourself. Don't try to evaluate things for me, goddammit, Jack," all her feelings suddenly came rushing out, "you're so fucking scared to give a damn about anyone, you squeak anytime someone comes too close. And you know what? I'm fucking sick of you punishing me all the time because I got made a judge last year!"

"Is that what you think I do?" It was a relief for both of them to scream a little bit, but there was truth in her words, and they hit home so hard he slammed out of her house, and she didn't see him for three weeks. It was the longest they'd been apart voluntarily since they'd met, but he didn't call her and she didn't call him. She heard nothing at all from him until his daughter arrived in town for her annual visit, and Tana invited her to stay with her in town. Barb was excited at the idea, and when she arrived at the little house on her own the following afternoon, Tana was stunned by how much she had changed. She had just turned fifteen, and she suddenly looked like a woman now, with long lean lines, and pretty little hips and big blue eyes with her flash of red hair.

"You look great, Barb."

"Thanks, so do you." Tana kept her for five days, and even took her to court with her, and it was only toward the end of the week that they finally talked about Jack, and how things had changed with them.

"He yells at me all the time now." Barbara had noticed it too, and she wasn't having a very good time with him. "My mom says he was always like that, but he never was when you were around, Tan."

"I think he's probably pretty nervous these days." She was making excuses for him for Barb's sake, so she didn't think it was her fault, but in truth it was a conglomerate of things. Tana, Harry, pressures in his work. Nothing seemed to be going right for him, and when

Tana attempted to have dinner with him after Barbara
went back to Detroit, it ended in more bickering again.
They were arguing about what Averil should do with the
house. He thought she should sell and move into town,
and Tana disagreed. "That house means a lot to her;
they've been there for years."

"She needs a change, Tan. You can't hang on to the
past."

"Why the hell are you so desperately afraid to hang
on to anything? It's almost as if you're afraid to give a
damn." She had noticed that a lot about him of late. He
always wanted to be free and unattached, never tied
down. It was a wonder the relationship had lasted as long
as it had, but it certainly wasn't in good shape now, and
at the end of the summer, fate dealt them another blow.
Just as she had been told, when she was offered her seat
on the municipal court bench a year before, an opening
had come up, and she was being kicked up into superior
court. She almost didn't have the heart to tell Jack, but
she didn't want him to hear it from someone else first.
Gritting her teeth, she dialed him at home one night. She
was in her cozy little house, reading some law books she
had brought home, to check some remote statutes of the
penal code, and she held her breath as he answered the
phone.

"Hi, Tan, what's up?" He sounded more relaxed
than he had in months, and she hated to spoil his good
mood, which she knew her news would. And she was
right. He sounded as though someone had punched him
in the gut when she told him she was being made a superior court judge.

"That's nice. When?" He sounded as though she had just planted a cobra at his feet.

"In two weeks. Would you come to my induction, or would you rather not be there?"

"That's a hell of a thing to say. I gather you'd just as soon I not come." He was so sensitive, there was no talking to him.

"I didn't say that. But I know how uptight you get about my work."

"What makes you think that?"

"Oh, please, Jack . . . let's not get into that now. . . ." She was too tired after a long day, and everything seemed harder and sadder and more difficult now that Harry was gone. And with the relationship with Jack on the rocks, it wasn't the happiest time of her life, to say the least. "I hope you'll come."

"Does that mean I won't see you till then?"

"Of course not. You can see me whenever you want."

"How about tomorrow night?" It was almost as if he were testing her.

"Great. Your place or mine?" She laughed but he did not.

"Yours gives me claustrophobia. I'll pick you up outside City Hall at six."

"Yes, sir." She put a mock salute in her voice, but he didn't laugh, and when they met the next day, their mood was gray. They both missed Harry terribly and the only difference was that Tana talked about it, and Jack would not. He had taken another attorney into the partnership, and he seemed to like the man. He talked about that a lot, and about how successful the man had been, how

much money they were going to make. It was obvious
that he still had a chip on his shoulder over Tana's work,
and by the next morning, it was a relief when he dropped
her off at City Hall again. He was going to Pebble Beach
that weekend to play golf with a bunch of guys and he
hadn't invited her, and she was relieved as she walked up
the steps of City Hall with a sigh. He certainly didn't
make her life easy these days, and now and then she
thought of what Harry had said to her before he died.
But it was hopeless thinking of anything permanent with
Jack. He just wasn't that kind of man. And Tana didn't
kid herself anymore. She wasn't that kind of girl anyway.
It was probably why they had gotten along for as long as
they had. Not that that seemed to apply anymore. The
friction between them was almost more than she could
bear, and she was actually grateful when she discovered
that he was going to be in Chicago on a business trip
when she was inducted into superior court.

It was a small, simple ceremony this time, presided
over by the presiding judge of the superior court. There
were half a dozen other judges there, her old friend the
D.A., who happily said "I told you so" over her swift
move up, and a handful of other people she cared about,
and Averil was in Europe with Harrison and the kids.
She had decided to winter in London that year, just to get
away for a while, and she had put the children in school
there. Harrison had talked her into it, and he looked
happy when he left with his grandchildren in tow. There
had been a heartbreaking moment alone with Tana just
before that, when he actually put his face in his hands
and cried, wondering if Harry had known how much he
had loved him, and she insisted that he had. It helped

assuage his sorrow and his guilt over the early years to
ake care of his daughter-in-law and his grandchildren
now. But it wasn't the same without them at Tana's
swearing-in and it was odd to look around and not see
Jack.

The actual swearing-in was done by a judge of the
court of appeals, a man Tana had met once or twice over
the years. He had thick black hair, ferocious dark eyes,
and a look which would have frightened anyone, as he
towered over them all in his dark robes, but he also had
quick laughter, a keen mind, and a surprising gentleness.
He was particularly well known for some very controversial decisions he had made, which had been played up in
the national press, and in particular the New York Times,
and the Washington Post, as well as the Chronicle. Tana
had read about him a lot, and wondered just how ferocious he was, but she was intrigued to see now that he
was less lion and more lamb, or at least he was at her
wearing-in. They chatted for a while about his superior
court days, and she knew that he had also run the biggest
law firm in town, before being made a judge. He had an
interesting career behind him, though she suspected that
he wasn't more than forty-eight or forty-nine. For a long
time, he had been kind of a "wunderkind," and she liked
him very much as he shook her hand, and congratulated
her warmly again, before he left.

"I'm impressed." Her old friend the D.A. smiled at
her. "That's the first time I've ever seen Russell Carver at
a swearing-in. You're getting to be awfully important, my
friend."

"He probably had to pay his parking tickets downstairs, and someone recruited him." They both laughed.

Actually, he was a close friend of the presiding judge, and had volunteered his services for the swearing-in. He looked the part anyway, with his dark hair and serious face.

"You should have seen him when he was the presiding judge here, Tan. Shit, he threw one of our D.A.'s into the can on contempt of court for three weeks and couldn't get the poor bastard out."

Tana laughed, just imagining it. "I'm lucky that never happened to me, I guess."

"Didn't you ever have him as a judge?"

"Only twice. He's been on the court of appeals for a hell of a long time."

"I guess he has. He's not very old though, as I recall. Forty-nine, fifty, fifty-one . . . something like that . . ."

"Who's that?" The presiding judge wandered over to them and shook Tana's hand again. It was a nice day for her, and she was suddenly glad that Jack wasn't there. It was so much easier like this, and not having to hold her breath or apologize to him.

"We were talking about Justice Carver."

"Russ? He's forty-nine. He went to Stanford with me." The presiding judge smiled, "although I'll admit he was a few years behind." In fact, he had been a freshman when the presiding judge graduated from law school, but their families had been friends. "He's a hell of a nice guy, smart as hell."

"He has to be." Tana spoke admiringly. There was another leap to contemplate. The court of appeals. What a thought. Maybe in another decade or two. And in the meantime, she was going to enjoy this. Superior court was going to be just her cup of tea. They were going to have her trying criminal cases in no time at all, since that was her area of expertise. "It was nice of him to do my swearing-in today." She smiled at everyone.

"He's a nice guy." Everyone said that about the man, and she sent him a little note, thanking him for taking the time to make her induction an even more special event, and the next day, he called and there was laughter in his voice.

"You're awfully polite. I haven't had a bread-and-butter letter like that in twenty years at least."

She laughed in embarrassment and thanked him for the call. "It was just a very nice thing to do. Like having the Pope around when you take religious vows."

"Oh, my God . . . what a thought. Is that what you were doing last week? I take it all back . . ." They both laughed and they chatted for a while. She invited him to stop into her court whenever he was around, and she felt a comfortable warmth at the confrerie she was a part of now, judges and justices, all working together. It was like having arrived at Mount Olympus at last, and it was a hell of a lot easier in some ways than prosecuting cases against rapists and murderers, building a case and arguing, although she had enjoyed that too. Here, she had to keep a clearer head, an objective outlook, and she had never studied so much law in her life. She was buried in a stack of books in her chambers two weeks later, when Justice Carver took her at her word and came by. 'Is this what I condemned you to?" He stood in her doorway and smiled. Her clerk had long since gone home, and she was frowning in concentration as she pored over six open books at once, comparing statutes

and precedents as he wandered in and she looked up wit
a smile.

"What a nice surprise." She stood up quickly an
waved him toward a large, comfortable leather chai
"Please sit down." He did and she looked at him. He wa
good-looking, in a quiet, virile, rather intellectual way
They weren't the same football team good looks a
Jack's. They were much quieter, and much more powe
ful, just as he was in myriad ways. "Would you like
drink?" She kept a small bar well hidden for occasion
such as this.

"No, thanks. I have too much homework to do to
night."

"You too? How do you ever get through it all?"

"I don't. Sometimes it makes you want to just s
there and cry, but you get through it eventually. Wha
are you working on?" She described the case to him a
briefly as she could and he nodded thoughtfully. "Tha
should be an interesting one. It may even wind up in m
lap eventually."

She laughed. "That's not much of a vote of conf
dence if you think they'll appeal my decision."

"No, no," he was quick to explain, "it's just tha
you're on new turf there and whatever you decide, if the
don't like it, they'll appeal. They may even try to ove
turn it. Be careful you don't give them grounds." It wa
good advice and they chatted on for quite a while. H
had dark, thoughtful eyes that gave him an almost se
sual air, which didn't seem in keeping with his seriou
ness. There were a lot of contrasts about the man, an
she was intrigued by him. He walked her out eventuall
and helped her carry a stack of books to her car, and the

e seemed to hesitate. "I couldn't talk you into a ham-
urger somewhere, could I?"

She smiled at him. She liked this man. She had never
nown anyone quite like him before. "You might, if you
romise to get me home early enough to do some work."
hcy chose Bill's Place on Clement. It was a simple,
holesome environment amidst the hamburgers and
ench fries and milkshakes and kids, and no one would
ave suspected who they were, how important their jobs,
s they chatted on about cases they had suffered with
ears before, and the comparison of Stanford to Boalt,
nd eventually Tana laughed at him.

"All right, all right I concede. Your school is better
an mine."

"I didn't say that." He laughed. "I said we had a
etter football team."

"Well, that's not my fault at least. I had nothing to
o with that."

"I somehow didn't think you did." It was very re-
xing being with him. They had common interests, com-
on friends, and the time flew by. He took her home,
nd was about to drop her off when she invited him in-
de for a drink, and he was surprised by how pretty the
ttle bijou house was, how well she'd decorated it. It was
real haven, that made one want to stretch out in front
f the fire and stay for a while.

"I'm happy here." And she was, whenever she was
one. It was only when Jack was there, that it got so
ncomfortable. But especially now, with Russ there, it
ited her perfectly. Russ lit the fire for her, and she
oured him a glass of red wine, and they chatted for a
hile, about their families, their lives. She discovered

that he had lost his wife ten years before, and he had tw
daughters who were both married now.

"At least I'm not a grandfather yet." Russell Carv
smiled at her. "Beth is going to architectural school
Yale, while her husband studies law, and Lee is a fashi
designer in New York. She's actually pretty good, ar
I'm proud of them . . . but grandchildren," he almo
groaned, and she smiled at him, "I'm not ready for th
yet."

"Did you ever want to marry again?" She was cu
ous about him. He was an interesting man.

"No. No one that important has come along,
guess." He looked around her house and then back
her. "You know how it is, you get comfortable with yo
own way of life. It's difficult to change all that for som
one else."

She smiled. "I suppose. I've never really tried. N
very courageous of me, I suppose." Sometimes she regr
ted it now, and if Jack had twisted her arm before thin
began to fall apart. . . . She looked up at Russ ar
smiled. "Marriage used to scare the hell out of me."

"As well it should. It's a mighty delicate operati
at best. But when it works, it's wonderful." His ey
glowed and it was easy to guess that he'd been happ
with his wife. "I have nothing but good memories abo
that." And they both knew that that made it harder
marry again too. "And my girls are great. You'll have
meet them sometime."

"I'd like that very much." They chatted on for a fe
minutes, he finished his wine, and then he left. She we
up to her den with the books he'd helped her bring hon
and she worked late into the night and the next day s

laughed when a court messenger appeared with an envelope in his hand. He had written her a bread-and-butter letter much like the one she'd written him for her swearing-in and she called to laugh with him. It was a far easier conversation than the one she shared with Jack later that day. He was on the warpath again, and they were fighting about their weekend plans, so much so that eventually she got out of them, and sat peacefully in her house alone on Saturday, going through some old photographs when the doorbell rang. Russell Carver was standing there, looking at her apologetically, with a bunch of roses in his hand.

"This is a terribly rude thing to do, and I apologize in advance." He looked handsome in a tweed jacket and a turtleneck sweater and she smiled at him delightedly.

"I never heard that bringing someone roses was rude before."

"That's to compensate for dropping by unannounced, which *is* rude, but I was thinking of you and I didn't have your number at home. I gather it's unlisted, so I took a chance. . . ." He smiled sheepishly and she waved him in.

"I had absolutely nothing to do, and I'm delighted you came by."

"I'm surprised I found you here. I was sure you'd be out." She poured him a glass of wine, and they sat down on the couch.

"Actually, I had plans but I cancelled them." Things were impossible with Jack, and she wondered how to handle it. Sooner or later, they'd either have to work things out or give up, but she didn't want to face that now, and he was away anyway.

"I'm glad you did." Russ Carver smiled at her. "Would you like to go to Butterfield's with me?"

"The auction house?" She looked intrigued, and half an hour later they were wandering amidst antiques and Oriental works of art, chatting about sundry things. He had an easy way about him that was relaxing to her, and they shared similar views about almost everything. She even tried to explain her mother to him. "I think that's a big part of the reason why I never wanted to get married. I kept thinking of her sitting there waiting for him to call. . . ." She hated the memory, even now.

"Then all the more reason to marry someone and have security."

"But I knew he was cheating on his wife by then. I never wanted to be either one of those women . . . my mother . . . or the wife he cheated on."

"That must have been difficult for you, Tana." He was sympathetic about so many things. And she told him about Harry that afternoon when they walked on Union Street. She told him about the friendship they had shared, the years at school, the time at the hospital, and how lonely it was without him now. Tears came to her eyes as she talked about him, but there was something gentle on her face, too, as she looked up at him. "He must have been a fine man." His voice touched her like a caress and she smiled at him.

"He was more than that. He was the best friend I'll ever have. He was remarkable . . . even as he died, he gave something to everyone, a piece of himself . . . some part of himself. . . ." She looked up at Russ again. "I wish you'd known him."

"So do I." He looked at her gently then. "Were you in love with him?"

She shook her head, and then she smiled, remembering. "He had a crush on me when we were kids. But Averil was perfect for him."

"And you, Tana?" Russell Carver looked searchingly at her. "Who was perfect for you? Who has there been? Who was the love of your life?" It was an odd question to ask, but he had the feeling that there had been someone. It was impossible that a girl like this should be unattached. There was a mystery there, and he couldn't find the answer to it.

"No one." She smiled at him. "Some hits, some misses . . . the wrong people mostly. I haven't had much time."

He nodded. He understood that too. "You pay a price for getting where you are. It can be a very lonely place sometimes." He wondered if it was for her, but she looked content to him. He wondered who there was in her life now, and he asked her as much, in so many words.

"I've been seeing someone for the last few years, more than that actually, I guess. We lived together for a while. And we still see each other," she smiled wistfully and looked into Russ's dark eyes, "but things aren't what they used to be. 'The price you pay,' as you put it. Things haven't been the same since I got appointed to the bench last year . . . and then Harry died . . . it's made a lot of dents in us."

"Is it a serious affair?" He looked both concerned and intrigued.

"It was for a long time, but it's limping badly now.
think we're still together out of loyalty."

"You're still together, then?" He watched her fac
carefully, and she nodded. She and Jack had never reall
called it quits. At least not yet, although neither of then
knew what the future would bring.

"We are for now. It suited us both for a long time
We had the same philosophy. No marriage and no kids
And as long as we both agreed on that, it worked prett
well. . . ."

"And now?" The big dark eyes were probing her
and she looked at him, suddenly hungry for his touch, hi
hands, his lips. He was the most attractive man she'
ever seen, but she had to reproach herself. She still be
longed to Jack . . . didn't she? She was no longer quit
so sure.

"I don't know. Things have changed for me sinc
Harry died. Some of what he said makes me wonde
about my own life." She looked hard at Russ. "I mean i
this it? Is this all there is? I go on from here, with m
work . . . with or without Jack," Russ gathered wh
she meant, "and that's all? Maybe I want more of a fu
ture than that. I've never felt that way before, and sud
denly I do. Or at least I wonder about it sometimes."

"I think you're on the right track." He sounde
worldly and wise, and in some ways he reminded her c
Harrison.

She smiled at him. "That's what Harry would say.
And then she sighed. "Who knows, maybe it doesn't ma
ter anyway. Suddenly it's all over, and then so what, wh
cares, you're gone . . ."

"It matters all the more then, Tana. But I felt tha

way too after my wife died ten years ago. It's difficult to adjust to something like that, it forces the realization on us that we have to face our own mortality one day. It all counts, every year, every day, every relationship, if you're wasting it, or unhappy where you are, one day you wake up, and it's time to pay the check. So in the meantime, you might as well be happy where you are." He waited a moment and then looked at her. "Are you?"

"Happy?" She hesitated for a long time and then looked at him. "In my work, I am."

"And the rest?"

"Not very, right now. It's a difficult time for us."

"Am I intruding, then?" He wanted to know everything, and sometimes it was difficult to answer him.

She shook her head and looked into the brown eyes she was coming to know so well. "No, you're not."

"You're still seeing your friend . . . the one you lived with for a while?" He smiled at her and he looked terribly sophisticated and grown up. She felt almost like a child with him.

"Yes, I still see him off and on."

"I wanted to know how things stand with you." She wanted to ask him why, but she didn't dare. Instead, he took her to his house, and showed her around. It took her breath away, from the moment they walked into the front hall. Nothing about him bespoke that kind of wealth. He was simple, easy, quietly well dressed, but when you saw where he lived, you understood who he was. It was a house on Broadway, in the last block before the Presidio, with small, carefully kept grounds, a marble entrance hall in inky green and sparkling white, tall marble columns, a Louis XV chest with a white marble top and a

silver tray for calling cards, gilt mirrors, parquet floors
satin curtains sweeping the floor. The main floor was a
series of exquisite reception rooms. The second floor was
more comfortable, with a large master suite, a pretty
wood-panelled library, a cozy little den with a marble
fireplace, and upstairs were the children's rooms he no
longer used.

"It doesn't make much sense for me anymore, but
I've been here for so long, I hate to move. . . ."

There was nothing she could do but laugh as she sat
down and looked at him. "I think I'll burn my house
down after this." But she was happy there too. This was
just another life, another world. He had need of this and
she did not. She remembered hearing now that he had
considerable personal wealth, knew he had owned a profitable law firm a number of years ago. The man had done
well in his life, and he had nothing to fear from her. She
wanted nothing from him materially. He showed her
proudly from room to room, the billiard room and the
gym downstairs, the racks of guns he kept for duck hunting. He was a whole man, of many interests and pursuits.
And as they went back upstairs, he turned to her and
took her hand with a small, careful smile.

"I'm very taken with you, Tana. . . . I'd like to see
more of you, but I don't want to complicate your life just
now. Will you tell me when you're free?" She nodded,
totally amazed by all that she had seen and heard. A little
while later, he took her home, and she sat staring into the
fire in her living room. He was like the kind of men one
read about in books, or saw in magazines. And suddenly
there he was, on the threshold of her life, telling her that
he was "taken with her," bringing her roses, walking her

through Butterfield's. She didn't know what to make of him, but one thing she knew, and that was that she was "very taken" with him too.

It made things difficult with Jack for the next few weeks. She attempted to spend several nights in Tiburon, almost out of guilt, and all she could think about was Russ, especially when they made love. It was beginning to make her as testy as Jack was with her, and by Thanksgiving she was a nervous wreck. Russ had gone East to see his daughter Lee, and he had invited her to go with him, but that would have been dishonest of her. She had to resolve the situation with Jack, but by the time the holidays came, she felt hysterical every time she thought of him. All she wanted to do was be with Russ, for their quiet talks, their long walks in the Presidio, their ventures into antique shops, art galleries, their long hours over lunch in tiny coffee shops and restaurants. He brought something into her life that had never been there before and which she longed for now, and whenever a problem arose, it was Russ she called, not Jack. Jack would only bark at her. He still had a need to punish her, and it was tiresome now. She wasn't feeling guilty enough to put up with it anymore.

"Why are you hanging on to him?" Russ asked her one day.

"I don't know." Tana stared miserably at Russ over lunch before court was recessed for the holidays.

"Maybe because in your mind he's attached to your friend." It was a new idea to her, but she thought it might be a possibility. "Do you love him, Tan?"

"It isn't that . . . it's that we've been together for so long."

"That's no excuse. From what you say, you're no happy with him."

"I know. That's the crazy part. Maybe it's just tha it's been so safe."

"Why?" He pushed her hard sometimes, but it wa good for her.

"Jack and I have always wanted the same thing . . . no commitment, no marriage, no kids . . ."

"Is that what you're afraid of now?"

She took a breath and stared at him. "Yes . . . think I am. . . ."

"Tana," he reached out and took her hand. "A you afraid of me?" Slowly, she shook her head, and the he said what she had both feared and wanted most. Sh had wanted it since they'd met, since she'd first looke into his eyes. "I want to marry you. Do you know that? She shook her head, and then stopped and nodded it, an they both laughed, she with tears in her eyes.

"I don't know what to say."

"You don't have to say anything. I just wanted t make things clear for you. And now you have to clear u the other situation, for your own peace of mind, whateve you decide about us."

"Wouldn't your daughters object?"

"It's my life, not theirs, isn't it? Besides, they' lovely girls, there's no reason for them to object to m happiness." Tana nodded her head. She felt as though sh were living a dream.

"Are you serious?"

"Never more so in my life." His eyes met hers an held. "I love you very much." He hadn't even kissed he yet, and she felt herself melting toward him where the

t. And as they left the restaurant, he gently pulled her
wards him and kissed her lips, and she felt as though
er heart would melt as he held her in his arms.

"I love you, Russ." The words were suddenly so
asy for her. "I love you so much." She looked up at him
ad there were tears in her eyes and he smiled down at
er.

"I love you too. Now go straighten out your life, like
good girl."

"It may take a little time." They walked slowly back
wards City Hall. She had to go back to work.

"That's all right. How about two days?" They both
ughed. "We could go to Mexico over the holidays."

She cringed. She had already promised Jack she
ould go skiing with him. But she had to do something
ow. "Give me till the first of the year and I promise I'll
raighten everything out."

"Then maybe I'll go to Mexico alone." He frowned
ensively and she glanced worriedly at him. "What are
ou worried about, little one?"

"That you'll fall in love with someone else."

"Then hurry up." He laughed at her, and kissed her
gain before she went back to court. And all afternoon
he sat on the bench with a strange expression in her
es, a small smile on her lips. She couldn't concentrate
n anything, and when she saw Jack that night, she felt
reathless every time she looked at him. He wanted to
now if she had all her skiing gear. The condo was rented
ad they were going with friends, and then suddenly half-
ay through the evening, she stood up and looked at
m.

"What's wrong, Tan?"

"Nothing . . . everything. . . ." She closed h
eyes. "I have to go."

"Now?" He looked furious. "Back to town?"

"No." She sat down and started to cry. Where cou
she begin? What could she say? He had finally driven h
away, with his resentment of her work and her succe
his bitterness, his unwillingness to commit. She want
something now that he didn't have to give, and she kn
she was doing the right thing, but it was so difficult. S
stared unhappily up at him, sure of what she was doi
now. She could almost feel Russ sitting next to her, a
Harry on the other side, cheering her on. "I can't." S
looked at Jack and he stared at her.

"Can't what?" He was mystified. She wasn't maki
any sense and that was unusual for her.

"Can't go on like this."

"Why not?"

"Because it's no good for either of us. You've be
pissed at me for the past year, and I've been miser
ble. . . ." She stood up and walked across the roo
glancing at familiar things. This house had been part h
for two years, and now it looked like a stranger's house
her. "I want more than this, Jack."

"Oh, Christ." He sat down, looking furious. "Li
what?"

"Like something permanent, like what Harry a
Averil had."

"I told you, you'll never find something like th
That was them. And you're not like Averil, Tan."

"That's no excuse to give up. I still want someo
for the rest of my life who's *mine,* who's willing to sta

up in front of God and man and take me on for the rest of
my life. . . ."

He looked at her, horrified. "You want me to marry
you? I thought we agreed. . . ." He looked terrified but
she shook her head and sat down again.

"Relax, we did, and that isn't what I want from you.
I want out, Jack, I think it's time." He was silent for a
long, long time, he knew it too, but it hurt anyway. And
it spoiled all his plans for the holidays.

He looked up at her. "This is why I believe what I
do. Because sooner or later it comes to an end. And it's
easier like this. I pack my bag, you pack yours, we say
goodbye, and we hurt for a while, but at least we never
lied to each other, and we're not dragging along a flock of
kids."

"I'm not even sure that would be so terrible. At least
we'd know how much we'd cared." She looked sad, as
though she had lost someone dear to her, and she had.
She had cared about him for a long time.

"We cared a lot, Tan. And it was good." There were
tears in his eyes and he came to her and sat down. "If I
thought it was right, I'd marry you."

"It wouldn't be right for you." She looked at him.

"You'd never be happy married anyway, Tan."

"Why not?" She didn't want him to say that. Not
now. Not with Russ standing in the wings, wanting to
marry her. It was like putting a curse on her. "Why
would you say a thing like that?"

"Because you're not the type. You're too strong."
She was stronger than he was, she knew. But she had
only come to understand that recently, mostly since she
had known Russ. He was so different from Jack. So much

stronger than anyone she had known before. An
stronger than she was. Finally. "You don't need marriag
anyway," he smiled bitterly, "you're married to the law
That's a full-time love affair for you."

"Can't one have both?"

"Some can. You can't."

"Did I hurt you that much, Jack?" She looked wo
fully at him and he smiled and stood up, opened a bottl
of wine, and handed her a glass, and somehow she felt a
though she had never known this man. Everything was s
bitter, so shallow. Nothing in him ran deep, and she wor
dered how she could have stayed with him for so long
but it had suited her. She hadn't wanted depth durin
those years. She had wanted to be as free as he did. Onl
now she had grown up, and as much as the challeng
Russ offered terrified her, she wanted it, wanted it mor
than anything she'd ever done before. She looked int
Jack's eyes and smiled at him as he toasted her.

"To you, Tan. Good luck." She drank, and a mc
ment later she set down her glass and looked at him.

"I'm going now."

"Yeah. Call me sometime." He turned his back t
her, and she felt a knife of pain slice through her. Sh
wanted to reach out to him, but it was too late. For bot
of them. She touched his back and whispered one word

"Goodbye."

And then she drove home as fast as she could, took
bath and washed her hair, as though she were washin
away the disappointments and the tears. She was thirty
eight years old and she was starting all over again, but i
a way she never had before, with a man like no man sh
had ever known. She thought of calling him that nigh

ut her mind was still filled with Jack, and she was sud-
enly afraid to tell Russ that she was free. She didn't say
nything to him until their lunch the day he left for Mex-
o, and then suddenly she looked at him and smiled
mysteriously.

"What are you grinning at, Funny Face?"

"Just life, I guess."

"And that amuses you?"

"Sometimes. I . . . uh . . . er. . . ." He was
aughing at her and she was blushing furiously. "Oh, shit.
Don't make things so hard for me."

He took her hand in his and smiled at her. "What
re you trying to say?" He had never seen her so tongue
ed before.

She took a deep breath. "I straightened things out
nis week."

"With Jack?" He looked amazed as she nodded her
ead with a shy smile. "So soon?"

"I couldn't go on like that."

"Was he very upset?" Russ looked concerned.

She nodded, looking sad for a moment, "Yes, but he
ouldn't admit it. He likes to keep everything easy and
ree." She sighed jaggedly, then, "he says I'd never be
appy married to anyone."

"That's nice." Russ smiled and showed absolutely
o concern. "When you move out, be sure to burn the
ouse down. It's an old custom with some men. Believe
ie, it doesn't mean a thing. I'll take my own chances,
nanks." Russ smiled ecstatically at her.

"Do you still want to marry me?" She couldn't be-
eve what was happening to her, and for just a minute
. . just a minute . . . there was the temptation to run

back to her old life, but that wasn't what she want
anymore. She wanted this . . . and him . . . s
wanted both marriage and a career, no matter h
frightening it was to her. It was a chance she had to ta
She was ready now. It had taken her a long, long tin
but she had gotten there and she was proud of hersel

"What do you think? Of course I do." He reassur
her at once and his eyes smiled at her.

"Are you sure?"

"Are you? That's more to the point."

"Maybe we should talk about this for a little while
She was suddenly very nervous at the thought and
laughed at her.

"How long? Six months? A year? Ten years?"

"Maybe more like five. . . ." She was laughing, t
and then suddenly she looked at him. "You don't w
children, do you?" She hadn't gone that far. She was t
old for that, but he only shook his head and grinned
her.

"You worry about everything, don't you? No,
don't want children. I'll be fifty years old next month a
I already have two. And no, I will not have a vasecton
thanks, but I'll do anything else you want to guaran
that I won't knock you up. Okay? Want me to sign it
blood?"

"Yes." They were both laughing and he paid t
check and they walked outside and he held her as no m
had ever held her before, pulling her heart right throu
her soul, and she had never been happier. And then su
denly he looked at his watch, and hurried her to his c
"What are you doing?"

"We have a plane to catch."

"We do? But I can't . . . I'm not . . ."

"Is your court recessed over the holidays?"

"Yes, but . . ."

"Is your passport in order?"

"I . . . yes . . . I think it is. . . ."

"We'll check when I get you home . . . you're coming with me . . . we can plan the wedding there . . . I'll call the girls . . . what do you think about February . . . say in about six weeks? . . . Valentine's Day? . . . corny enough for you, Tan?" He was crazy and she was crazy about him. They caught the plane to Mexico that night, and spent a blissful week soaking up the sun, and making love at last. He had waited until she had broken things off with Jack for good. And when they returned he bought her an engagement ring, and they told all their friends. Jack called her when he read it in the papers, and what he said cut her to the quick.

"So that was what that was all about? Why didn't you tell me you were shacked up with someone else? A justice too. That must be a step up for you."

"That's a rotten thing to say . . . and I wasn't shacked up with him."

"Tell that to someone else. Come to think of it," he laughed bitterly, "tell it to the judge."

"You know, you've been so damn busy trying not to get involved with anyone all your life that you don't know your ass from a hole in the ground anymore."

"At least I know when I'm cheating on someone, Tan."

"I wasn't cheating on you."

"What were you doing then, fucking him at lunchtime, it doesn't count before six o'clock?" She had hung

up on him, sorry that it had to end that way. And sh
had written to Barbara, too, explaining that her marria
to Russ was precipitous, but he was a lovely man, an
when she came out to see her father the following yea
the door to Tana's home would be open to her as it ha
been before. She didn't want the girl to feel that she wa
pushing her away. And there were so many other thing
to do too. She wrote to Averil in London, and her moth
almost had a heart attack when she called her.

"Are you sitting down?"

"Oh Tana, something's happened to you." He
mother sounded on the verge of tears. She was only six
years old, but mentally she was twice that, and Arth
was getting senile now at seventy-four, which was ha
on her.

"It's something nice, Mother. Something you'v
waited for, for a long, long time."

Jean stared blankly at the far wall, holding t
phone. "I can't imagine what it is."

"I'm getting married in three weeks."

"You're *what?* To whom? That man you've been li
ing with for all these years?" She never thought much
him, but it was about time they took a decent position
the world, especially with Tana being a judge. But sh
was in for a shock.

"No. To someone else. A justice on the court of a
peals. His name is Russell Carver, Mom." She went on
tell her the rest and Jean cried, and smiled and laughe
and cried some more.

"Oh, sweetheart . . . I've waited so long for this

"So have I." Tana was laughing and crying to
"And it was worth waiting for, Mom. Wait till you se

him. Will you come out for the wedding? We're getting married on February fourteenth."

"Valentine's Day . . . oh, how sweet. . . ." It still embarrassed Tan but it seemed funny to both her and Russ. "I wouldn't miss it for the world. I don't think Arthur will be well enough to come, so I can't stay long." She had a thousand arrangements to make before she left, and she could hardly wait to get off the phone. Ann had just gotten married for the fifth time, and who gave a damn anymore? Tana was getting married! And to a justice on the court of appeals! And she said he was handsome too. Jean dithered around the house for the rest of the afternoon, in a total state, and she had to go into the city to Saks the following day. She needed a dress . . . no . . . maybe a suit . . . she couldn't believe it had happened finally. And that night she whispered silent prayers.

Chapter 18

The wedding was absolutely beautiful. They had it at Russ's house, with a piano and two violins playing something delicate from Brahms as Tana came slowly down the stairs in a simple dress of off-white crepe de chine. She wore her blond hair long, covered by a wide-brimmed picture hat, with a faint hint of veil, and ivory satin shoes. There were roughly a hundred people there, and Jean stood in a corner and cried ecstatically for most of the day. She had bought a beautiful beige Givenchy suit, and she looked so proud it made Tana cry every time she looked at her.

"Happy, my love?" Russ looked at Tana in a way that made her heart fly. It seemed impossible that she could be lucky enough to find a man like him, and she had never dreamed of anything like what she shared with him. It was as though she had been born to be his, and she found herself thinking of Harry as she walked down the aisle. "Okay, asshole? Did I do good?" She smiled through her tears.

You did great! She knew that Harry would have been crazy about Russ, and it would have been mutual. And she felt Harry very much there with her. Harrison and

Averil sent a telegram. Russ's daughters were there too. They were both slender, attractive, pleasant girls, with husbands that Tana liked. They were an easy group to love, and they did everything to welcome her. Lee was particularly warm in her reception of her new step-mother, and they were only twelve years apart in age.

"Thank God he had the sense to wait until we grew up before marrying again." Lee laughed. "For one thing, the house is a hell of a lot quieter now, and for another thing, you don't have to put up with us. He's been single for so long, Beth and I are grateful as hell that you married him. I hate to think of him alone in this house." She was a little bit zany, and wonderfully dressed in her own designs. She was clearly crazy about Russ, nuts about her own husband, and Beth doted on her entire family. It was the ideal group, and as Jean looked at them, she was suddenly grateful that Tana hadn't been foolish enough to fall for Billy, in the years when she was pushing that. How sensible Tana had been to wait for this extraordinary man to come along. And what a life. The house was the most beautiful place she'd ever seen. And Tana felt totally at ease with the butler and the maid he'd had for years. She floated from room to room, entertaining his friends, as people said "Your Honor" to her, and somebody else cited a funny poem about a justice and a judge.

It was a wonderful afternoon, and they went back to Mexico for their honeymoon, returning via La Jolla and Los Angeles. Tana had taken a month's leave from work, and when she returned she smiled to herself whenever she said her new name. Judge Carver . . . Tana Carver . . . Tana Roberts Carver. . . . She had added his name to everything, none of this women's lib crap for her. She had waited thirty-eight years for him, almost thirty-nine, and resisted marriage for almost four decades, and if she had taken the plunge now, she was going to enjoy all the benefits. She came home every night relaxed and happy to see him. So much so that he teased her about it one night.

"When are you going to start behaving like a real wife and nag me a little bit?"

"I forgot, I guess." He smiled at her, and they talked about her house again. She had been thinking about renting it. It was so pretty that she didn't want to sell it, yet she knew she would never live there again. "Maybe I should just sell it after all."

"What if I rent it from you for Beth and John when they come home?"

"That would be wonderful." She smiled at him. "Let's see . . . you can have it for two kisses and . . . a trip to Mexico. . . ." He laughed at her, and eventually they decided to keep the house and rent it out and Tana had never been happier in her life. It was one of those rare times when everything feels in total control, going just the way you want, when she ran full tilt into someone one day. She was hurrying from her courtroom to meet Russ for lunch, and suddenly found herself staring into Drew Lands' face. He looked as though someone had just struck oil on his front lawn when he saw who she was, and they stood chatting amiably for a minute or two. It was incredible to realize how much pain he had caused her once. As she looked at him, she could barely even imagine it. It was even more amazing to realize that Julie and Elizabeth were eighteen and twenty-two. "Good lord, is it as long ago as that?"

"It must be, Tan." His voice was smooth, and suddenly she was annoyed by him. She could see from his eyes that he was making assumptions that were no longer appropriate, and hadn't been for a long, long time. "Eileen and I have been divorced for six years now." How dare he tell her that . . . how dare he have gotten divorced after hurting Tan so much for her. . . .

"That's too bad." Her voice was cool, and she was losing interest in what he said. She didn't want to be late for Russ. She knew he was working on an important case.

"Gee . . . I wonder if . . . maybe we could see each other sometime. I'm living in San Francisco now. . . ."

She smiled at him. "We'd love to see you sometime. But my husband is just buried in a big case right now." She smiled almost evilly at him, waved her hand with a few garbled words, and was gone. And Russ could still see the victory in her eyes when he met her for lunch at the Hayes Street Grill. It was one of their favorite haunts, and she often met him there, to kiss at a corner table, and neck happily over lunch, while people smiled at them.

"What are you looking so pleased about?" He knew her very well.

"Nothing . . ." And then, she kept no secrets from him, she couldn't have anyway. "I just ran into Drew Lands for the first time in almost seven years. What a bastard he is. I guess he always was, the weak little shit."

"My, my, what did he do to deserve so many epithets?"

"He was the married man I told you about . . ."

"Ah!" Russ looked amused at the fire in her eyes. He knew he was in no danger of losing her to anyone, not because he was so sure of himself, but because he knew the kind of love they shared. It was one of those rare, rare things in life, and he was deeply grateful for it. He had never had a love like this before with anyone.

"And you know what? He finally divorced his wife.'

"Predictably." Russ smiled. "And now he wanted to take you out again. Right?"

She laughed at him. "I told him we'd love to see him sometime, and then I skibbled off."

"You're a little witch. But I love you anyway. How was court today?"

"Not bad. I have an interesting case coming up, an industrial injury. It's going to be messy but it brings up some very intriguing points and technicalities. How's your monster case coming along?"

He smiled at her. "I'm finally getting it back into its cage. And," he looked at her strangely for a minute, "I had a call from Lee."

"How is she?"

"Fine." He looked at his wife, and she looked at him. There was something odd in the air.

"Russ, what's wrong?" She was worried about him. He looked strange.

"It's happened. They've finally done it to me. I'm going to be a grandfather." He looked at once delighted and distressed and Tana laughed at him.

"Oh, no! How can she do a thing like that to you?"

"That's exactly what I said to her!" And then he smiled at Tana again. "Can you imagine that?"

"With difficulty. We'll have to buy you a white wig so you look the part. When is she having it?"

"January. For my birthday, apparently. Or New Year's Eve, something like that."

As it turned out, the baby was born on New Year's Day, and Russ and Tana decided it would be a lark to fly to New York and visit her. He wanted to see this first grandchild of his, another girl, like his own two. And he reserved a suite for them at the Sherry Netherland, and off they went. Lee was happily ensconced at New York Hospital's Lying-in, in the best room they had, and the baby was sweet and pink, and Russell made all the appropriate noises and when they went back to the hotel, he made passionate love to his wife. "At least I'm not totally over the hill yet. How does it feel to make love to a grandfather, my love?"

"Even better than it was before." But there was something odd in her eyes when she looked at him, and he saw it instantly. He grew very quiet and pulled her into his arms next to him, their naked flesh touching, and he loved to feel how velvety she was, but he was worried about her. Sometimes, when something mattered to her a lot, she burrowed deep inside herself and he could see her do it now.

"What's wrong, sweetheart?" He spoke in a whisper near her ear, and she turned toward him with a look of surprise.

"What makes you think something's wrong?"

"I know you better than that. You can't fool an old man like me. At least not one who loves you as much as I love you." She tried to deny it for a long time, and then much to his astonishment, she broke down and cried in his arms. There was something about seeing Lee and her baby that had filled her with the most awful pain . . .

an emptiness . . . a void more terrible than any she had
ever known before. He sat looking at her, amazed at the
emotions pouring out of her, and she was even more startled than he. She had never realized she felt that way
before.

"Do you want a baby, Tan?"

"I don't know . . . I've never felt this way before
. . . and I'm almost forty years old . . . I'm too old for
that . . ." But suddenly she wanted that more than anything, and she was suddenly haunted by Harry's words
again.

"Why don't you think about it, and we'll talk
again." And for the next month, the sight of Lee and her
baby haunted her. And suddenly, after they went home,
she began seeing pregnant women everywhere, and babies
in strollers on every street corner; it was as though everyone had a baby except her . . . and there was an envy
and a loneliness she couldn't even begin to describe. Russell saw it on her face, but he didn't mention it again until
their anniversary, and then she was sharp with him,
which was rare for her. It was almost as though it hurt
too much to talk about.

"You said you were too old for that. And so am I."

"Not if it matters to you. It might seem a little foolish to me at first, but I could live with it. Other men have
second families at my age, older in fact . . . a lot older,"
he smiled. And he himself had been surprised by how
touched he was by Lee's baby in her arms, and then his
own. He wouldn't have minded that at all. And Tana's
child would have meant the world to him. But she got
more and more sensitive about it, until finally he no
longer mentioned it to her. In March, they went to Mex-

o again, and had a fabulous holiday. They swam and
shed, and lay on the beach. Tana barely got *turista* that
me, although she didn't feel well when she got back.

"I think you've been working too hard." She had
ad the flu on and off for almost three weeks and he was
sisting on her going to see the doctor finally.

"I don't have time for that." But she was so tired
id draggy and so frequently sick to her stomach that
ne finally went, and she got the shock of her life. It was
hat she had wanted so desperately, but now, suddenly it
as there. And it terrified her. She didn't have time for
at. She had an important job. She would look ridicu-
us . . . she had never wanted that. . . . Russ would
e upset with her . . . she stewed so terribly that she
idn't even go home until seven o'clock that night and
uss knew there was something terribly wrong the min-
te he laid eyes on her. But he let her unwind for a while,
ced her a drink, opened a bottle of Château Latour with
eir dinner, but she didn't drink a drop of it, and she
as still tense when they went upstairs that night and
ere was an odd look in her eyes. He was actually get-
ng very worried about her, and as soon as she sat down,
e pulled a chair up next to her.

"All right, now tell me what happened to you today.
ou either lost your job or your best friend died."

She smiled sheepishly and visibly relaxed as he took
er hand. "You know me too well."

"Then do me the favor of taking me into your confi-
ence."

"I can't." She had already made up her mind. She
asn't keeping it. But Russ was not going to fool around.
is voice rose ominously, the famous frown appeared,

and her knees would have shaken if she didn't know hi
as well as she did. Instead she laughed at him. "Yc
know, you're very scary when you look like that."

He laughed exasperatedly at her. "That's the who
point. Now talk to me, dammit. What the hell is going c
with you?"

She stared at him for a long, long time, lowered h
eyes, and then raised them to his again. "You're not g
ing to believe this, sweetheart."

"You want a divorce."

"No, of course not." She smiled at him. Somehow k
always made things less terrible. She had been hysteric
all day, and now he had her laughing again.

"You're having an affair?"

"Wrong again."

"You were kicked off the bench."

"Worse than that. . . ." She was beginning to loc
serious again, because in her mind what had happene
meant the same thing. How could she keep her job wi
that? And then suddenly there were tears in her eyes ar
she was looking at him. "I'm pregnant, Russ . . ." For
moment everything around them stopped and then sud
denly he swept her into his arms and he was laughing ar
smiling, and acting as though it were cause for celebra
tion and not suicide.

"Oh, sweetheart . . . I'm so glad." He absolute
beamed at her and she stared at him.

"You are? I thought you didn't want any children
She was stunned. "We agreed. . . ."

"Never mind. Our baby is going to be so beautif
. . . a little girl that looks just like you . . ." He ha
never looked happier and he held her close as sh

rowned unhappily. She had wanted this, but now that it
ad happened, she couldn't imagine it, except in the
worst light.

"But it'll ruin everything. . . ." She was on the
erge of tears again, and he was anxious to comfort her.

"Like what?"

"Like my job. How can I be a judge with a baby at
ny breast?"

He laughed at the image she had in mind. "Be prac-
ical. You work right up till the last day before it's born,
nd then you take six months off. We get a good nurse,
nd you go back to work."

"As easy as that?" She looked shocked.

"It can be as easy as you want, my love. But there's
o reason why you can't have a career and a family. It
nay take a little juggling sometimes, but it can be done
with a little resourcefulness." He smiled at her, and a
ong, slow smile began to dawn in her eyes. There was the
ossibility that he was right about that, and if he was
. . if he was . . . it was what she had wanted more
han anything, and she wanted both. For years she had
hought she could only have one. . . . But she wanted
nore than just her work . . . she wanted Russ . . . she
vanted his child . . . she wanted everything . . . and
uddenly the void she had been feeling for months, that
ache, the terrible emptiness, was gone again. . . . "I'm
o proud of you, sweetheart." She looked at him, and the
ears slowly overflowed as she smiled at him. "Every-
hing is going to be just fine, you know . . . and you're
oing to look just wonderful."

"Ha!" She laughed at him. "I've already gained si
pounds. . . ."

"Where?" Tickling and teasing her, he began to loo
for them, and Tana lay in his arms and laughed.

Chapter 19

The judge walked ponderously to the bench
d sat down carefully, rapped the gavel smartly twice,
d went on with the morning's calendar. Her bailiff
ought her a cup of tea, at ten o'clock, and when she
od up at the noon recess, she could barely walk back
her chambers again. The baby was, by then, exactly
ne days late. She had planned to stop working two
eks before, but she had everything so well organized at
me that she had decided to work until the bitter end.
er husband picked her up right outside City Hall that
ght, opening the door smiling at her.

"How'd it go today?" The pride he felt showed eas-
in his eyes and she smiled back at him. It had been a
autiful time for them, even these extra days. She en-
yed the opportunity to spend these last days alone with
m, although she had to admit that she was getting terri-
y uncomfortable. Her ankles looked like lamp posts by
ur o'clock in the afternoon, and she had trouble sitting
r that long, but she didn't have anything else to do.

She sighed. "Well, the verdict is in. I think I might
ve it up at the end of this week, whether the baby shows
or not. What do you think?"

He smiled at her as he drove her home in the
Jaguar he had just bought. "I think that's a pretty g
idea, Tan. You could sit around for a couple of days,
know."

"Fancy that."

But she never got time for that. Her water brok
eight o'clock that night, and she suddenly turned to R
terrified. She knew it was going to happen eventually,
suddenly it was *now,* and she had the overwhelming u
to run away, and there was no place to run. Her b
would follow her everywhere. But Russ saw easily w
she felt, and tried to comfort her.

"Everything's going to be just fine."

"How do you know that?" She snapped at h
"What if I need a Caesarean? Christ, I'm a hundred y
old, for chrissake." Actually, she was forty years old
four months. She suddenly looked at Russell and be
to cry. She was terrified, and the contractions started
most as soon as her water broke.

"Do you want to lie down here for a while, Tan
do you want to go to the hospital?"

"I want to stay here." He called the doctor for
brought her a glass of ginger ale, flipped on the televis
across from their bed, and smiled to himself. It was g
to be a big night for them, and he also hoped that ev
thing would go well. He was confident that it would,
he was particularly excited. She had insisted on their
ing Lamaze training together, and although he had
been present at the birth of his girls so many years bef
he was going to be with Tana for the birth of their ch
He had promised her, and he could hardly wait. She
had the amniocentesis five months before, but they

ted not to know the sex of the child. And Russ could
el a mounting feeling of excitement now for both of
em. By midnight, Tana had had a short nap, and she
as in control again. She smiled up at him, and he timed
r pains, and at two o'clock he called the doctor again,
d this time they were told to come to the hospital. He
cked her bag up from the hall closet where it had sat
the last three weeks, helped her into the car, and out
ain at the hospital, and helped her to walk inside. She
uld hardly walk now, and the contractions took all her
ncentration and his help, just to get her through them,
t they were nothing like the pains she felt once she
ent into transition three hours after that. She was writh-
g in pain on the bed in the labor room, and she was
atching at his arm, as he felt his own panic begin to
e. He hadn't expected it to be quite like this, she was in
ch agony, and by eight o'clock the baby still hadn't
me. The sun was up, and she lay there panting horri-
y, her hair damp, eyes wild, looking at him as though
could do something for her. And all he could do was
eathe with her and hold her hand and tell her how
oud he was of her, and then suddenly at nine o'clock
eryone began to run around. They wheeled her into the
livery room, strapped her legs up, and she cried as the
ins came now. It was the worst pain she had ever
own in her entire life, and she felt as though she were
owning as she clutched at him, and the doctor urged
r on, and Russell cried, and Tana knew she couldn't
nd it anymore. She wanted to die . . . to die . . .
. . .

"I can see the head . . . oh, God . . . sweetheart
. it's here. . . ." And suddenly a tiny red face

popped out, as Russell cried, and Tana looked at him a
gave another ferocious push which forced the baby fr
her womb, and the doctor held him in his hands as
baby began to wail. They cut the cord, tied it, a
cleaned him rapidly, suctioned his nose, wrapped him
a warm blanket, and handed him to Russ.

"Your son, Russ. . , ." The doctor smiled at th
both. They had worked so hard and so long, and T;
looked at him victoriously now.

"You were wonderful, sweethcart." Her voice
hoarse and her face was gray, as he kissed her tende

"*I* was wonderful?" He was deeply impressed
what he had just seen her do. It was the greatest mira
he had ever seen. And at forty years of age, she had it
now. She looked at him. Everything she had ever wan
. . . everything . . . her eyes filled with tears as
reached out to him, and Russ gently put the baby in
arms, as he had once put it in her womb.

"Oh, he's so beautiful. . . ."

"No." Russell smiled at her through his tears. "
are, Tan. You're the most beautiful woman in the worl
And then he looked at his son. "But he's pretty cute to
Harrison Winslow Carver. They had long since agreed
that. He came into the world blessed in name, and
and love.

They wheeled her back to her room a little bef
noon, and she knew she would never want to do it ag;
but she was glad she had this once. Russell stayed w
her until she drifted off to sleep, the baby slept in
little bed they had left there for him, and Tana, all cl
again and sleepy now and so much in love with him.
opened her eyes once, drifting from the shot they'd gi

her for the pain afterwards. "I love you so much, Russ.
. . ."

He nodded, smiling again, his heart forever hers after tonight. "Shhh . . . sleep now . . . I love you too.
. . ."

Chapter 20

When baby Harry was six months old, Tana looked at her calendar with despair. She had to go back to work the following week. She had promised she would, and she knew it was almost time, but he was so sweet, and she loved spending the afternoons with him. They went on long walks, and she laughed when he smiled. They even dropped in on Russ at his office once in a while. It was a leisurely way of life she had never known, and she hated to give it up, but she was not yet ready to give up her career.

And once she was back on the bench, she was glad she hadn't given it up for good. It felt good to be back again. The cases, the verdicts, the juries, the decisions, the routine. It was incredible how fast the days flew by, and how anxious she was to come home at night, to Harry and Russ. Sometimes she would find Russ already at home with him, crawling around on the rug, and playing games with him. He delighted them both, and he was like the first child born on earth to them. Lee teased them about it when she came out to visit with Francesca, her little girl, and she was already expecting another one.

"And what about you, Tan?"

"Listen, at my age, Harry is enough of a miracle. Let's not push my luck, thanks." And even though the pregnancy had been a breeze, the delivery had been more painful than she thought. Though, with time, even that didn't seem quite as awful as it once had. And they were both so happy with the baby. "If I were your age, I might, Lee, and even then . . . you can't have everything, a career and ten kids." Not that it frightened Lee, though. She still had her job, and even now with the second one on the way, she was planning to work right till the end, and come back afterwards. She had just won the Coty Award and she wasn't giving that up. She didn't see why she should. She could do both, so why not?

"How was your day, sweetheart?" She threw her briefcase on a chair and bent to kiss Russ as he scooped the baby into his arms, as she glanced at her watch. She was still nursing him three times a day. Morning, evening, and late at night, and she wondered when his last feeding had been. She loved the closeness it gave her to the child, the silent moments in the nursery at three A.M. when only she and Harry were up. She had a sense of providing for his well-being which satisfied her too, and then there were other benefits as well. She'd been told that she was unlikely to get pregnant again as long as she was still nursing him. "Do you think it would matter if I did it till he's twelve?" she had asked Russ one day and he had laughed at her. They had such a good life, the two of them. It had been worth waiting for, no matter how long it took. At least she said that now. She had just turned forty-one, and he was fifty-two.

"You know, you look tired, Tan." Russell was looking carefully at her. "Maybe the nursing is too much for you, now that you're back at work." She fought the idea, but her body voted with him, as slowly, in the next few weeks, her milk dried up. It was as though her body didn't want to be nursing Harry anymore. And when she went to the doctor for a checkup, he weighed her, felt her, checked her breasts, and then said he wanted to do a blood test on her.

"Something wrong?" She glanced at her watch. She had to be back in court by two.

"I just want to check something out. I'll call you this afternoon." On the whole, he had found her all right, and she didn't have time to worry about it. She rushed back to City Hall, and when her clerk signalled her at five o'clock, she had forgotten that she was expecting the doctor's call.

"He said he had to speak to you."

"Thanks." She took the phone, scratching some notes as she listened to him, and suddenly she stopped. That couldn't be. He had to be wrong. She had been nursing until the week before . . . hadn't she . . . she sat down hard in a chair, thanked him, and hung up. Shit. She was pregnant again. And Harry was wonderful, but she didn't want another one. She was too old for that . . . she had her career . . . this time, she had to get rid of it . . . it was impossible . . . she didn't know what to do. She had a choice, of course, but what would she say to Russ? Tell him she had aborted his child? She couldn't do that. She spent a sleepless night that night, resisting him when he asked her what was bothering her. She couldn't tell him this time. It was all wrong . . . she was too old . . . her career meant too much to her . . . but Lee was going to continue her career after her second child . . . or was it meaningless? Should she resign from the bench? Would the children mean more to her in the end? She felt torn ten thousand ways and she looked like a nightmare when she woke up. Russ looked at her over breakfast and didn't say anything to her at first. And then, just before he left, he turned to her.

"You busy for lunch today, Tan?"

"No . . . not that I know of . . ." But she didn't want to have lunch with him. She had to think. "There's some stuff I really should get off my desk." She avoided his eyes.

"You have to eat. I'll bring sandwiches."

"Fine." She felt like a traitor not telling him, and her heart felt like lead as she went to work. She had dozens of small matters in and out of her court, and at eleven o'clock she looked up to see a wild-eyed man, with a mane of frizzy gray hair springing out of his head like watchsprings gone wild. He had planted a bomb in front of a foreign consulate, and the matter had to be set for trial. She began to go through all of the motions, and then suddenly stared at his name and looked up with a grin. And for no reason anyone understood in court, she had to disqualify herself. The man's name was Yael Mc-Bee, the wild-eyed radical lover she'd had in her last year of law school at Boalt. The boy who had gone to jail for bombing the mayor's house. She saw from his records that he had been in prison twice since then. How odd life was. So long ago . . . it brought Harry instantly to mind . . . and the funny little house they'd shared . . . and Averil so young then. . . . and the wild hippie commune she had visited with Yael. She looked across the court at him. He had grown old. He was forty-six years

old now. A man. And still fighting for his causes in hi
unruly ways. How far they'd come, all of them . . . thi
man with his wild ideas. His documents said that he wa
a terrorist. A terrorist. And she was a judge. An endles
road . . . and Harry gone, and all their bright ideas
little dim, some of them forgotten, so many gone . .
Sharon . . . Harry . . . and new lives in their place
. . . her son, little Harry, named after her friend, an
now this new baby in her womb . . . it was amazin
how life went on, how far they came, all of them . .
She looked up and saw her husband, standing there, look
ing at her, and she smiled at him, and dismissed the mat
ter of Yael McBee from her court, called a recess fo
lunch, and walked into her chambers with him.

"Who was that?" Russ looked amused. Her day
were certainly livelier than his, and she began to laugh a
she sat down.

"His name is Yael McBee, if that means anything t
you. I knew him when I went to Boalt."

"A friend of yours?" Russ looked at her sardonicall
and she grinned.

"Believe it or not, he was."

"You've come a long way since then, my love."

"I was just thinking that." And then she remem
bered something else. She looked at him, hesitantly, won
dering how he would react. "I've got something to te
you."

He smiled gently at her. "You're pregnant again."

She stared at him as he laughed. "How do yo
know? Did the doctor call you too?"

"No. I'm smarter than that. I figured it out las
night, and I assumed you'd tell me eventually. Of cours

by now, you think your career is over, we'll have to give up the house, I'll lose my job, or we both will . . ." She laughed and tears came to her eyes as he smiled at her. "Am I right?"

"Perfectly."

"And has it dawned on you that if you can be a judge with one child, you can be a judge with two? And a good judge at that."

"That just occurred to me as you walked in."

"My, my." He leaned over to kiss her, and they exchanged a look that belonged only to them. "What do you know . . . ?" He kissed her and her clerk walked in and hastily backed out again, smiling to herself as Tana silently thanked her lucky stars for the road she'd come, the man she'd found . . . the decisions she had made . . . from a career and no man, no child, to having it all, the man, the career, and her son. She had added each one, like wildflowers to a bouquet, until now she stood with full hands, full heart, having come full circle in the end.